THE
ECONOMICS
OF
TECHNOLOGICAL
CHANGE

Other Works by Edwin Mansfield

Industrial Research and Technological Innovation
Managerial Economics and Operations Research (EDITOR)
Monopoly Power and Economic Performance, Revised (EDITOR)
Defense, Science, and Public Policy (EDITOR)

THE
ECONOMICS
OF
TECHNOLOGICAL
CHANGE

Edwin Mansfield

PROFESSOR OF ECONOMICS
WHARTON SCHOOL, UNIVERSITY OF PENNSYLVANIA

W · W · Norton & Company, Inc.

NEW YORK

TO
Sally S. Mansfield
Charity L. Mansfield
Edwin L. Mansfield (1875–1947)

Contents

Preface

One of the most noteworthy developments in economics in the past decade has been the intense interest in technological change. No single reason accounts for the attention this topic has received, a number of related factors all being important. First, there has been a growing awareness that our nation's rate of economic growth depends heavily on our rate of technological change. Second, continued international tensions have made it painfully obvious that our national security depends on the output of our military research and development effort, which now costs the Department of Defense alone about $7 billion per year. Third, economists and others are coming to realize the full importance of competition through new products and processes rather than direct price competition. Fourth, some observers have asserted that "automation" will lead to widespread unemployment and to the necessity to retrain large segments of the labor force. Fifth, there has been considerable concern over the adequacy and efficiency of our national policies toward science and technology.

We have a long way to go before a satisfactory understanding of the economics of technological change is achieved, but the situation is vastly improved over that which prevailed a decade or so ago, when the subject was almost totally unexplored. Because of the work carried out in recent years, our knowledge of the subject has progressed very substantially. This book presents an overview and interpretation of this new and rapidly growing field. Drawing on recent economic studies, as well as on relevant work in the other social sciences, management, and operations research, I have set out to describe and analyze the way in which new processes and products are created and assimilated, and to investigate the public and private policy issues involved. At present, no book of comparable scope exists, this being the only book that is concerned with both public and private policy issues, with both military and a wide range of civilian policy issues, with both analysis and policy, and with both what is customarily called economics and relevant parts of related disciplines. It is a companion to my *Industrial Research and Technological Innovation* (Norton, 1968), which describes in detail the econometric studies that I have carried out in this area. The two books are complementary, the other being confined to my own studies and being directed at an advanced professional audience, this one dealing with a much wider spectrum of topics but at a less technical level.

Much of the work underlying these books was done while I was a member of the faculties at Carnegie Institute of Technology, the Cowles Foundation for Research in Economics at Yale University, and Harvard University. I am indebted to each of these universities for assistance and encouragement. I am also indebted to the National Science Foundation and the Ford Foundation for generous financial support. The writing of this book has also benefited from experience I obtained while serving as a consultant to the RAND Corporation; the President's Office of Science and Technology; the National Commission on Technology, Automation, and Economic Progress; the U.S. Army Ballistics Research Laboratories; the Assistant Secretary of Commerce for Science and Technology; the White House Panel on Civilian Technology; the U.S. Interagency Energy Study; the Federal Power Commission; the Ohio Research and Development Foundation; the University of Maryland; the Denver Research Institute; and a number of industrial firms. It also benefited from insights I gained while serving on the Governor's Science Advisory Committee.

Finally, my thanks go to Lee Bach of Stanford University, who encouraged me some years ago to work in this area; to Albert Rees of Princeton University, F. M. Scherer of the University of Michigan, and Jacob Schmookler of the University of Minnesota, who read and commented on the entire manuscript; to Zvi Griliches of the University of Chicago and Edmund S. Phelps of the University of Pennsylvania, who commented on Chapter II; to Richard Brandenburg of Carnegie Institute of Technology and Richard Rosenbloom of Harvard University, who commented on Chapter III; to Joseph Rossman who commented on part of Chapter VII; to William Capron of the Brookings Institution and Kenneth Sanow of the National Science Foundation, who commented on Chapters VI and VII; and to my colleagues and students at the University of Pennsylvania's Wharton School, who provided me with assistance and encouragement.

THE
ECONOMICS
OF
TECHNOLOGICAL
CHANGE

CHAPTER I

INTRODUCTION

◇◇◇◇◇◇◇◇◇◇◇◇◇◇◇◇◇◇◇◇◇◇◇

1. TECHNOLOGICAL CHANGE AND THE ECONOMY

Without question, technological change is one of the most important determinants of the shape and evolution of the American economy. Technological change has improved working conditions, permitted the reduction of working hours, provided an increased flow of products, old and new, and added many new dimensions to our way of life. The newspapers testify each day to the widespread and profound influence of technological change. Production facilities are automated, educational processes are aided by machines, space vehicles are developed, diseases are conquered, and countless other kinds of changes are made.

Unfortunately, there is also a more somber side to technological change. Advances in military technology have made possible the destruction of mankind on an unprecedented scale, modern technology has resulted in air and water pollution, the closing of plants made obsolete by technological change has thrown whole communities into distress, and the technological revolution in agriculture has contributed to serious problems, both urban and rural. Although most people would agree that, on balance, technological change has been beneficial, no one would claim it has been costless.

This introductory chapter describes briefly some of the principal ways in which the economy is affected by technological change—the advance in knowledge relative to the industrial arts which permits, and is often embodied in, new methods of production, new designs for existing products, and entirely new products and services.[1] We begin by investigating the relationship between technological change and the rate of economic growth. Then we look at the role of technological change in the activities of the Federal government and the effect of technological change on unemployment. Finally, we discuss the importance of technological change in the competition among firms for markets and profits.

2. TECHNOLOGICAL CHANGE AND ECONOMIC GROWTH

Technological change is an important, if not the most important, factor responsible for economic growth. The significance of maintaining a high rate of economic growth is widely accepted; target growth rates have been established by the governments of countries with such diverse economies as France, Japan, Sweden, India, Yugoslavia, and the Soviet Union. Even the United States and the United Kingdom, dissatisfied with their past growth records, have set such goals. Economic growth is also an important objective at the international level, the Organization for Economic Cooperation and Development having set as a goal a 50 percent increase in the collective gross product of the Atlantic Community during the sixties.[2]

Attempts have been made in recent years to measure the effect of a nation's rate of technological change on its rate of economic growth. Several influential studies carried out in the fifties concluded that about 90 percent of the long-term increase in output per capita in the United States was attributable to technological change, increased educational levels, and other factors not directly associated with increases in the quantity of labor and capital.[3] A more recent, and more exhaustive, study concludes that the "advance of knowledge" contributed about 40 percent of the total increase

[1] A more precise definition of technological change is given in Chapter II, section 1. "Change in technology" and "technological change" are used interchangeably in this book. There is still considerable variation among authors in definitions of terms. For a good discussion, see J. Schmookler, *Invention and Economic Growth*, Cambridge, Mass.: Harvard University Press, 1966, pp. 1–10.

[2] For a discussion of the arguments for a high rate of economic growth, see J. Tobin, "Economic Growth as an Objective of Government Policy," *American Economic Review*, May 1964. For a more skeptical view, see H. Stein and E. Denison, "High Employment and Growth in the American Economy," *Goals for Americans*, The American Assembly, 1960. Over the long run, our rate of economic growth has compared favorably with most other countries. However, during the early sixties, considerable dissatisfaction was expressed with our relative performance during the previous decade. See the 1962 and 1964 Reports of the Council of Economic Advisers.

[3] In particular, S. Fabricant, "Economic Progress and Economic Change," *34th Annual Report of the National Bureau of Economic Research*, New York, 1954; and R. Solow, "Technical Change and the Aggregate Production Function," *Review of Economics and Statistics*, August 1957.

in national income per person employed during 1929–1957.[4] Although these studies are useful, their results are extremely rough. Because of the complex interactions among the various factors that affect the economic development of a country, it is difficult to estimate from historical statistics the precise effect of a nation's rate of technological change on its rate of economic growth. All that can safely be said is that the effect has been substantial.[5]

3. TECHNOLOGICAL CHANGE
AND THE FEDERAL GOVERNMENT

Technological change plays a major role in the activities of the Federal government. Whereas the government's scientific and technical activities were formerly quite small, they now represent a vast enterprise which has important economic and social effects. In the mid-sixties, expenditures for research and development constituted about 15 percent of the Federal administrative budget, much of this research and development being connected with defense. Realizing that any nation which falls significantly behind in military technology will be at the mercy of a more progressive foe, the great powers have spent enormous amounts on military research and development, precipitating several revolutions in technology in the past twenty-five years. Most important have been the successful development and improvement of fission and fusion bombs, although significant achievements have also occurred in delivery vehicles, guidance techniques, radar, and other areas.[6]

The importance of the decisions made regarding military research and development is illustrated by the development of the hydrogen bomb. For a considerable period after World War II, development work on atomic weapons proceeded slowly. However, during the late summer of 1949, the situation changed radically when government scientists found evidence

---

[4] E. Denison, *The Sources of Economic Growth in the United States*, Committee for Economic Development, 1962.

[5] There are at least three problems in these estimates. First, the effects of technological change are measured entirely by the growth of output unexplained by other factors, the consequence being that they are mixed up with the effects of whatever inputs are not included. Second, the use of GNP as a measure of output has a number of important difficulties and misses some of the most important effects of technological change—on leisure and the spectrum of choice. In particular, there are problems in the valuation of entirely new products. Third, these studies fail to recognize the full interdependence of technological change, education, and growth in physical capital with the result that the estimated contribution of each may not be a good indication of the sensitivity of the growth rate to an extra investment in any one of them. See Chapter II, section 9.

[6] See C. Hitch and R. McKean, *The Economics of Defense in the Nuclear Age*, Cambridge, Mass.: Harvard University Press, 1960, pp. 243–244.

that the Russians had successfully tested an atomic weapon of their own. When the existence of the Russian bomb became known, some members of Congress asked that work be begun to develop a hydrogen fusion bomb, the possibility of which had been discussed extensively at the University of California during World War II. Although eminent scientists advised against a crash program on the ground that there was little point in going beyond the destructive power already available in the A-bomb, a special subcommittee of the National Security Council advised President Truman to inaugurate such a program, which he did early in 1950. From the point of view of national security, this turned out to be a very significant decision. The new bomb was much more powerful than the older one, and only nine months after it had been developed, the Soviet Union produced a similar weapon.[7]

In recent years, many observers have expressed concern over the adequacy of our national science policies. There has been considerable uneasiness regarding the heavy concentration of the nation's scientific resources on military and space work; some, like President Eisenhower, fearing that public policy may become the captive of a scientific elite allied with military and industrial power, others being concerned that other high-priority fields, like transportation and housing, are being deprived of research and development resources. Questions have been raised concerning the efficiency of various government research and development programs, the adequacy of the supply of scientific and engineering manpower, the effects of the patent system, and the effectiveness of the Federal decision-making process concerning research and development programs. National science policy is now a matter of widespread interest and considerable concern.

4. TECHNOLOGICAL CHANGE
AND UNEMPLOYMENT

Changes in techniques can result in the displacement of workers. This is another reason for public interest in technological change, particularly in periods like the late fifties and early sixties when the unemployment rate was relatively high. In 1962, President Kennedy stated that "The major domestic challenge of the sixties is to maintain full employment at a time when automation is replacing men." [8] There was a prominent debate over the extent to which the high unemployment rates that prevailed then were

---

[7] If attention is confined to the lithium 6 deuteride bomb, the Russians seem to have been first. See F. Scherer, "Was the Nuclear Arms Race Inevitable?," *Co-Existence*, 1966.

[8] Quoted in J. Dunlop, *Automation and Technological Change*, The American Assembly, 1962, p. 1.

due to changes in techniques, some economists arguing that technology was advancing more rapidly than in earlier years, that the advances being made were reducing the importance of blue-collar jobs and goods-producing industries relative to white-collar jobs and service-producing industries, and that consequently the unemployed were larger in numbers and out of work longer than in previous years. Other economists believed that the unemployment problem was due largely to an inadequacy of aggregate demand for goods and services. Although neither camp had a monopoly on the truth, statistical studies, as well as subsequent events, seemed to favor the latter position.[9]

Technological change occupies an important place in the economics of labor. The problem of labor displacement is not as prominent now as it was in the early sixties, but it has by no means vanished. Policy makers are still obliged to cope, as best they can, with the changes in the composition and distribution of the labor force induced by technological (and other) change. Collective bargaining is concerned continually with the problem of permitting changes in techniques while protecting worker security. Although unions and companies have experimented with various types of solutions to this problem, it seems likely, in the years immediately ahead, that successful adjustment to technological change will continue to require the best efforts of people on both sides of the bargaining table.

5. Technological Change and Industrial Competition

Technological change is a key element in the competitive struggle among firms. The extent and quality of a firm's research and development program can make it an industry leader or head it for bankruptcy. Technological change can transform an industry. For example, a spectacular case in the drug industry was the effect of American Cyanamid's Achromycin tetracycline, introduced in 1953, on sales of Aureomycin chlortetracycline, which had been marketed since late 1948. After an almost continuous upward trend in 1950–1953, Aureomycin sales dropped by nearly 40 percent during the first full year of the sale of Achromycin. This is hardly a typical case, but it illustrates the devastating effect a new product can have on an existing market. In most industries, new products account for a significant share of the market. For instance, in 1960, 10 percent of the sales of all

[9] See R. Solow, *The Nature and Sources of Unemployment in the United States,* Stockholm: Almqvist and Wiksell, 1964; C. Killingsworth, *Testimony before Senate Subcommittee on Employment and Manpower,* Fall, 1963; A. Rees, "Dimensions of the Employment Problem," Address to the American Bankers Association, February 1964; and the 1964 Annual Report of the Council of Economic Advisers. Also see Chapter V.

manufacturing firms were accounted for by products developed since 1956.[10]

Recognizing the importance of technological change, firms have increased their outlays on research and development at a rapid rate. This expansion of industrial research and development is one of the most remarkable economic developments of the postwar era. In 1941, industry performed less than $1 billion worth of research and development; in 1953, about $3.5 billion; and in 1963, about $13 billion. Moreover, this is not due entirely to the increased expenditures on research and development by the government; including only company-financed research and development, there has been a tremendous increase in recent years. Turning to the future, most economists seem to believe that spending on research and development will continue to rise, though at a reduced rate, during the rest of the sixties.[11]

This "new competition" through research and development has added fuel to the old argument regarding the evils and benefits from giant corporations. Some observers, following the lead of Joseph Schumpeter, have claimed that very large firms are needed to produce the technical achievements on which economic progress depends. For example, according to J. K. Galbraith, "technical development has long since become the preserve of the scientist and the engineer. Most of the cheap and simple inventions . . . have been made . . . [Development] can be carried on only by a firm that has the resources associated with considerable size." [12] Needless to say, this proposition has not gone unchallenged by those who feel that technological change (and the rapid acceptance of new techniques) can be achieved without encouraging industrial giantism. This question, as well as the others touched on in this introductory chapter, will be discussed in later sections of this book.

6. SUMMARY

Technological change—the advance in knowledge relative to the industrial arts—is an important, perhaps the most important factor responsible for

[10] Turning to individual manufacturing industries, sales of products not in existence in 1956 constituted the following percentage of all sales in 1960: aircraft, ships, and railroad equipment, 35 percent; electrical machinery, 12 percent; machinery, 14 percent; chemicals, 16 percent; motor vehicles and parts, 10 percent; fabricated metals and instruments, 17 percent; rubber, 2 percent; petroleum and coal products, 2 percent; nonferrous metals, 8 percent; paper, 9 percent; iron and steel, 5 percent; food and beverages, 6 percent; and textiles, 9 percent. See N. Terleckyj, *Research and Development*, National Industrial Conference Board, 1963. Of course, many of these "new" products may have been old products with rather minor variations.

[11] For example, see A. Stanley and K. White, *Organizing the R and D Function*, American Management Association, 1965; and "Research Funds," *Industrial Research*, January 1965.

[12] J. K. Galbraith, *American Capitalism*, Boston: Houghton Mifflin Company, 1952, pp. 91–92.

economic growth. For example, a recent study concludes that the "advance of knowledge" contributed about 40 percent of the total increase in national income per person employed during 1929–1957. Of course, the roughness of such estimates should be emphasized. Technological change plays a central role in the activities of the Federal government. Expenditures for research and development, most of them connected with defense and the space race, constituted about 15 percent of the Federal administrative budget in the mid-sixties. In recent years, there has been considerable concern over the adequacy of our national policies toward science and technology.

Changes in techniques can result in the displacement of workers. The closing of plants made obsolete by technological (and other) change has thrown whole communities into distress, and the technological revolution in agriculture has contributed to serious problems, both urban and rural. Technological change significantly affects the competitive struggle among firms. Industry's research and development expenditures have grown at a rapid rate in the postwar period, and in many industries, the quality and extent of a firm's research and development program are of paramount importance. This "new competition" has added fuel to the old argument over the benefits and evils of giant corporations.

CHAPTER II

TECHNOLOGICAL CHANGE AND PRODUCTIVITY GROWTH

◇◇◇◇◇◇◇◇◇◇◇◇◇◇◇◇◇◇◇◇◇◇◇◇◇

1. TECHNOLOGICAL CHANGE, NEW TECHNIQUES, AND SCIENTIFIC ADVANCE

In this chapter, we are concerned with the nature, determinants, and measurement of technological change, as well as with the behavior of various indexes of productivity. We begin by defining more precisely what we mean by technological change. Technology is society's pool of knowledge regarding the industrial arts. It consists of knowledge used by industry regarding the principles of physical and social phenomena (such as the properties of fluids and the laws of motion), knowledge regarding the application of these principles to production (such as the application of genetic theory to the breeding of new plants), and knowledge regarding the day-to-day operations of production (such as the rules of thumb of the craftsman). Technological change is the advance of technology, such advance often taking the form of new methods of producing existing products, new designs which enable the production of products with important new characteristics, and new techniques of organization, marketing, and management.

It is important to distinguish between a technological change and a change in technique. A technique is a utilized method of production. Thus, whereas a technological change is an advance in knowledge, a change in technique is an alteration of the character of the equipment, products, and organization which are actually being used. For a technological change to be used, much more is required than the existence of the information. The proper people must possess the information and must be part of an organization which can make effective use of the information. In addition, it is useful to distinguish between technological change and the diffusion of existing information. A new piece of knowledge is a technological change when it is first discovered; but it is not counted as a technological change when it subsequently is passed from one person to another.

It is also important to distinguish between technological change and scientific advance. Pure science is directed toward understanding, whereas technology is directed toward use. Although the distinction between science and technology is imprecise, it should not be ignored.[1] Technological change often occurs as a result of inventions that do not rely on new scientific principles. Indeed, according to historians, little practical use was made of scientific knowledge until the middle of the nineteenth century, when research methods were first used in a systematic way to develop new products in the field of chemistry. The inventions that provided the basis for the industrial revolution were invented by practical men and based upon observation, art, and common sense. The factory, with its machines and its employment of unskilled or semiskilled labor doing simple repetitive operations, and the utilization of materials like iron, coal, and copper are samples of this inventiveness. Turning to the present, it is still true that many changes in technology require no new scientific principles. For example, the zipper and the safety pin required none; neither did the continuous wide strip mill in the steel industry.

Even when changes in technology have been intimately connected with previous scientific breakthroughs, they have not necessarily followed these breakthroughs in any simple and direct way. For example, consider the case of the radio. During the nineteenth century, the developing scientific knowledge of electricity was exploited in a number of areas, the observations of Gilbert, Henry, and Maxwell being seized upon by the inventors of the electric motor, the electric generator, and the telegraph. However, although Maxwell announced his theory of electromagnetism in the 1860's

---

[1] There are differences of opinion regarding the objectives and methods of science, but these differences need not concern us here. See J. Conant, *Science and Common Sense*, New Haven, Conn.: Yale University Press, 1951, and the literature cited there.

and Hertz's first practical laboratory demonstrations of the production and detection of wireless waves took place in the 1880's, it was not until Marconi formed his company in 1897 that an appreciable amount of applied work began on the radio. [2]

It should be clear, therefore, that changes in technology are quite distinct from scientific advances. Two other points must be added. First, although it is often impossible to connect particular changes in technology with previous scientific advances in any simple way, this does not mean that the character and direction of the advance of science has not affected the rate and direction of technological change. On the contrary, the nature of scientific advance has had a very great influence on the kinds of technological changes we have been able to make. In many important cases, earlier scientific advances have been essential. For example, the discoveries of Faraday, Franklin, and Henry led to the creation of the electrical industry, and those of Chadwick, Fermi, Hahn, Meitner, and Strassmann led to the creation of nuclear technology.

Second, technological change now seems to be more closely related to scientific advance than in the past. The growth of the engineering profession has made a considerable difference in the speed with which new scientific discoveries are translated into changes in technology. (Germany pioneered in engineering education; in the United States engineering schools began to expand rapidly after the Civil War, but they were behind their German counterparts until the twentieth century.) Another factor promoting a closer relationship between science and technology is the growth of industrial and government research laboratories. It is becoming increasingly common for firms and government agencies to sponsor research in fields where improved knowledge is judged likely to open up important areas for development. Much more will be said about the growth of organized research and development in subsequent chapters. [3]

2. TECHNOLOGICAL CHANGE AND THE PRODUCTION FUNCTION

The technology existing at a given point in time sets limits on how much can be produced with a given amount of inputs. Given the level of technology, there is generally a wide range of possible methods of producing a particular good or service. Some require little capital and much labor, some

[2] See W. MacLaurin, "The Process of Technological Innovation," *American Economic Review*, March 1950; H. Bode, "Reflections on the Relation Between Science and Technology," *Basic Research and National Goals*, National Academy of Sciences, 1965; and National Academy of Sciences, *Applied Science and Technological Progress*, House Committee on Science and Astronautics, 1967.

[3] See Chapters III and VI in particular.

require much capital and little labor; some are cheap, some are expensive; some old, some new. Moreover, the range is wider than a simple choice among methods that can be taken off the shelf. Other techniques frequently have been explored and could be brought to perfection with only a small amount of development work. Each possible method requires certain inputs—labor, materials, equipment, land—to produce the good or service in question. Given a certain amount of these inputs, it is possible to determine which method results in the maximum output and what the maximum output is.

The production function shows, for a given level of technology, the maximum output rate which can be obtained from given amounts of inputs. For example, if there were only two inputs, capital and labor, Figure 2.1 might show the production function for a particular product at a particular point in time. [4] Each of the curves pertains to a certain level of output, and shows the various combinations of capital and labor that will produce this output. (For example, an output rate of 50 units per year can be achieved

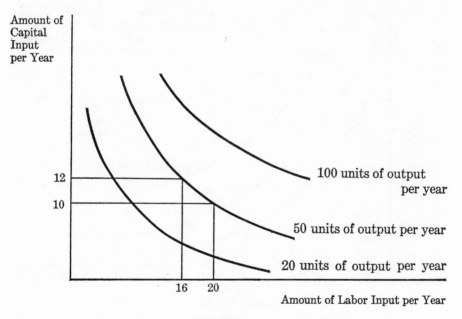

Amount of Capital Input per Year

12

10

100 units of output per year

50 units of output per year

20 units of output per year

16   20

Amount of Labor Input per Year

FIGURE 2.1

Hypothetical Production Function [a]

[a] See note 4.

[4] Of course, Figure 2.1 shows only part of the production function. There are curves for output levels other than 20, 50, 100; but for simplicity they are omitted from the diagram. An example of a production function is $Y = AL^{\alpha}K^{1-\alpha}$, where Y is the output rate, L is the rate of labor input, and K is the rate of capital input.

by using 20 units of labor and 10 units of capital per year or by using 16 units of labor and 12 units of capital per year.) Of course, the curve does not show all combinations that can produce a given output. Methods that are technically inefficient—in the sense that, to produce the given quantity of output, they use more of one input and at least as much of another input as some other method—are omitted.

Technological change results in a change in the production function. If the production function were readily observable, a comparison of the production function at two points in time would provide the economist with a simple measure of the effect of technological change during the intervening period. If there were constant returns to scale, the characteristics of the production function at a given date could be captured fully by a single curve that would show the various combinations of labor and capital inputs per unit of output that are technically efficient. [5] Under these circumstances, one could simply look at the changing position of this curve. For example, if this curve shifted from position 1 to position 2 in Figure

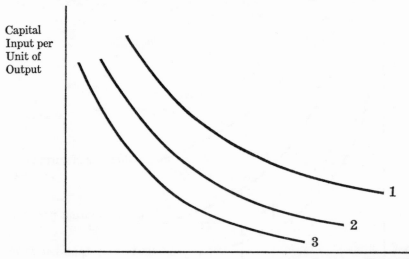

FIGURE 2.2

Technically Efficient Combinations of Labor and Capital Inputs per Unit of Output at Three Levels of Technology [a]

[a] Note that this diagram assumes constant returns to scale. See note 5.

[5] If there are constant returns to scale, an x percent increase in all inputs results in an x percent increase in output. Under these conditions, it is clear that the efficient combinations of labor and capital inputs per unit of output fall along a single curve, regardless of the level of output.

2.2 during a given period of time, technological change had less impact during this period than if the curve shifted to position 3. As we shall see in subsequent sections, it is sometimes possible to estimate the average rate of movement of the production function by a single number, and economists often use this number to measure the rate of technological change. Of course, it is only an indirect measure, but there is no way to measure the rate of technological change directly. [6]

Technological change also results in the availability of new products. In many cases, the availability of new products can be regarded as a change in the production function, since they are merely more efficient ways of meeting old wants, if these wants are defined with proper breadth. This is particularly true in the case of new intermediate goods, which may result in little or no change in the final product. In other cases, however, the availability of new products cannot realistically be viewed as a change in the production function, since they entail an important difference in kind.[7]

The variety of ways in which technological change can influence the production functions in various industries is evident in the development of the electronic computer—a device that incorporates some of the most important technological advances of the twentieth century. Although mechanical tabulating and calculating machines have been in existence for over fifty years, the electronic computer permits information to be processed many times faster and more accurately than any previous method. In the United States, work on the first electronic computer, ENIAC, began at the University of Pennsylvania in 1942 and was completed in 1946. It received financial support from the Army and was mainly designed to calculate trajectories of shells and bombs. After the war, rapid progress was made in solving problems of logic design, memory storage systems, and programming techniques. Eventually, the computer became not only technically but economically feasible for a wide range of scientific and business applications.

[6] The production function shows the best that can be achieved in an industry; it does not show what the average firm—or an inefficient or ill-informed firm—can achieve. Thus, changes in the production function indicate the rate at which the technological frontier for the industry moves forward. It is also important to study the rate at which knowledge is applied and new techniques and products are accepted throughout an industry. These topics are discussed below, particularly in Chapter IV.

[7] For a suggested treatment of new products, see K. Lancaster, "Change and Innovation in the Technology of Consumption," *American Economic Review*, May 1966.

It is sometimes asserted that, since firms report that only about 13 percent of their expenditures on research and development go for pure process improvement, it is unrealistic to emphasize cost-reducing technological change. But this is wrong because much of the research and development concerning new products and product improvements is devoted to new and improved intermediate goods and capital goods. In civilian industry, perhaps 80 percent of the reported research and development goes for new processes, new intermediate goods, and new capital goods.

The development of the computer has resulted in important changes in the production function for many goods and services. For example, in the chemical, petroleum, and steel industries, digital computers are the latest step in the evolution of control techniques. Computers help to determine and enforce the best conditions for process operation, as well as act as data loggers. In addition, they can be programmed to help carry out the complex sequence of operations required to start up or shut down a plant. Use of digital computers for process control began about 1958–59 and has grown rapidly, about 300 systems having been installed or ordered in the United States at the end of 1964. They have resulted in increased production, decreased waste, better control of quality, and reduced chance of damage to equipment.

Banking is another quite different industry where the computer has resulted in an important change in the production function. Two of the most important new devices in banking are reader-sorters—which read and sort documents (particularly checks), sending data via a computer to be recorded on tape—and the computer itself, which processes the information it receives from the reader-sorter. These devices often eliminate the conventional machines and processes for sorting checks, balancing accounts, and computing service charges. They greatly facilitate the handling of checks, high-speed sorters being able to process more than 1500 checks per minute. In addition, electronic bookkeeping machines have taken the place of many of the conventional posting machines; one large bank has reported that its posting errors have decreased two-thirds as a result.

Computers have also resulted in an important change in the production function in scientific research and education. Present machines are ten million times faster than a human being in performing many mathematical calculations and, consequently, make possible scientific studies that formerly were beyond reach. According to current forecasts, computers are likely to become important in other areas in education as well—as tools of research into the learning process, as devices to take over much of the clerical work and information-handling in education, and as ways to increase the student's productivity by permitting individualized instruction. Of course, some areas of instruction (like drill-and-practice systems) are more readily adapted to the computer than others (like tutorial systems), and much more work and experimentation will be required before these forecasts become a reality.[8]

[8] See P. Armer, "Computer Aspects of Technological Change, Automation, and Economic Progress"; M. Flood, "Commercial Information Processing Networks"; T. Stout, "Manpower Implications of Process Control Computers in the Process Industries"; J. Newhouse, "Technological Change in Banking"; D. Bushnell, R. de Mille, and J. Purl, "The Application of Computer Technology to the Improvement of Instruction and Learning"; and J. Finn, "The Emerging Technology of Education," all in *The Report to the President of the National Commission on Technology, Automation, and Economic Progress*, February 1966.

3. DETERMINANTS OF THE RATE OF TECHNOLOGICAL CHANGE

What determines the rate of technological change in an industry? Existing theory is still in a relatively primitive state, for it is only recently that economists have begun to give this question the attention it deserves. On a priori grounds, one would expect an industry's rate of technological change to depend to a large extent on the amount of resources devoted by firms, by independent inventors, and by government to the improvement of the industry's technology. The amount of resources devoted by the government depends on how closely the industry is related to the defense, public health, and other social needs for which the government assumes major responsibility; on the extent of the external economies [9] generated by the relevant research and development; [10] and on more purely political factors. The amount of resources devoted by industry and independent inventors depends heavily on the profitability of their use. Econometric studies indicate that the total amount a firm spends on research and development is influenced by the expected profitability of the research and development projects under consideration and that the probability of its accepting a particular research and development project depends on the project's expected returns. Case studies of particular inventions and studies of patent statistics seem to support this view.[11]

If we accept the proposition that the amount invested by private sources in improving an industry's technology is influenced by the anticipated profitability of the investment, it follows that the rate of technological change in a particular area is influenced by the same kinds of factors that determine the output of any good or service. [12] On the one hand, there are demand factors which influence the rewards from particular kinds of technological change. For example, if a prospective change in technology

[9] External economies and diseconomies are benefits and costs which accrue to bodies other than the one sponsoring the economic activity in question—which in this case is the firm or agency financing the research and development.

[10] For a precise definition of what we mean by "research" and "development," see Chapter III.

[11] For example, see M. Peck, "Inventions in the Postwar American Aluminum Industry"; T. Marschak, "Strategy and Organization in a System Development Project"; and R. Nelson, "The Link Between Science and Invention: The Case of the Transistor," all in *The Rate and Direction of Inventive Activity*, Princeton, N.J.: Princeton University Press, 1962. The econometric studies are described in Chapter III.

[12] Needless to say, these factors are not the only ones that influence the rate of technological change. As emphasized in subsequent chapters, there is considerable uncertainty in the research and inventive processes, and laboratories, scientists, and inventors are motivated by many factors other than profit. Nonetheless, the factors discussed in this section seem very important. For further discussion of other factors, see Chapters III and IV.

reduces the cost of a particular product, increases in the demand for the product are likely to increase the returns from effecting this technological change. Similarly, a growing shortage and a rising price of the inputs saved by the technological change are likely to increase the returns from effecting it. As an illustration, consider the history of English textile inventions. During the eighteenth century, there was an increase in the demand for yarn, due to decreases in the price of cloth and increased cloth output. This increase in demand, as well as shortages of spinners and increases in their wages, raised the returns to inventions that increased productivity in the spinning processes and directly stimulated the work leading to such major inventions as the water frame, the spinning jenny, and the spinning mule. [13]

On the other hand, there are also supply factors which influence the cost of making particular kinds of technological change. Obviously, whether people try to solve a given problem depends on whether they think it can be solved, and on how costly they think it will be, as well as on the expected payoff if they are successful. The cost of making science-based technological changes depends on the number of scientists and engineers in relevant fields and on advances in basic science; for example, advances in physics clearly reduced the cost of effecting changes in technology in the field of atomic energy. In addition, the rate of technological change depends on the amount of effort devoted to making modest improvements that lean heavily on practical experience. Although there is often a tendency to focus attention on the major, spectacular inventions, it is by no means certain that technological change in many industries is due chiefly to these inventions, rather than to a succession of minor improvements; for example, Gilfillan has shown that technological change in ship-building has been largely the result of gradual evolution. In industries where this is a dominant source of technological change and where technological change is only loosely connected with scientific advance, one would expect the rate of technological change to depend on the number of people working in the industry and in a position to make improvements of this sort. [14]

Besides being influenced by the quantity of resources an industry devotes to improving its own technology, an industry's rate of technological change depends on the quantity of resources devoted by other industries

[13] It is easy to see why an increase in product demand raises the expected returns from an investment in improving the industry's technology. It raises the total, absolute returns from a given percentage cost reduction, and tends to increase the total returns from a given product improvement. For a discussion of the effects of relative factor costs, see section 4.

[14] See S. Gilfillan, *Inventing the Ship*, New York: Follett Publishing Company, 1935; S. Hollander, *The Sources of Increased Efficiency*, Boston: M.I.T. Press, 1965; and K. Arrow, "The Economic Implications of Learning by Doing," *Review of Economic Studies*, June 1962. Of course, there are problems in defining "major" and "minor" inventions and in allocating credit among them.

to the improvement of the capital goods and other inputs it uses. Technological change in an industry that supplies components, materials, and machinery often prompts technological change among its customers. Consider the case of aluminum. For about thirty years after the development of processes to separate aluminum from the ore, aluminum technology remained dormant because of the lack of low-cost electrical power. Technological change in electric power generation, due to Thomas Edison and others, was an important stimulus to the commercial production of aluminum and to further technological change in the aluminum industry. In addition, there is another kind of interdependence among industries. Considerable "spillover" occurs, techniques invented for one industry turning out to be useful for others as well. For example, continuous casting was introduced successfully in the aluminum industry before it was adapted for use in the steel industry. The inventor, Siegfried Junghans, turned his attention to steel after inventing a process for non-ferrous metals, which were easier to cast because of their lower melting points. Similarly, when shell molding was first introduced, its value was thought to be limited to molding non-ferrous items, but recent work indicates that it can be used for ferrous items too. [15]

Other factors which influence an industry's rate of technological change are the industry's market structure, the legal arrangements under which it operates, the attitudes toward technological change of management, workers, and the public, the way in which the firms in the industry organize and manage their research and development, the way in which the scientific and technological activities of relevant government agencies are organized and managed, and the amount and character of the research and development carried out in the universities and in other countries. All of these factors are important—and all will be discussed in subsequent chapters. We describe in sections 7, 8, and 10 the results of several studies that have tried to quantify the effects of some of the factors discussed in this section.[16]

4. LABOR-SAVING AND CAPITAL-SAVING TECHNOLOGICAL CHANGE

It is customary for economists to distinguish among neutral, labor-saving, and capital-saving technological change. Suppose that the output rate for

[15] J. Jewkes, D. Sawers, and R. Stillerman, *The Sources of Invention*, New York: St. Martin's Press, Inc., 1959.

[16] Of course, the factors cited in this and the previous paragraph in the text can be encompassed within the supply-and-demand apparatus discussed above. For a very good description of the factors influencing the rate of technological change, see R. Nelson, M. Peck, and E. Kalachek, *Technology, Economic Growth, and Public Policy*, Washington, D.C.: The Brookings Institution, 1967.

a given product, as well as the relative prices of capital and labor, are held constant. If technological change results in a greater percentage reduction in capital input than labor input, it is capital-saving; if it results in a greater percentage reduction in labor input than capital input, it is labor-saving; if it results in an equal percentage reduction in capital and labor inputs, it is neutral. To determine whether or not a technological change is labor-saving, it is not enough to know that labor requirements per unit of output have decreased. For example, although the assembly line principle is sometimes considered labor-saving for this reason, this does not prove the point, because the assembly line principle also reduced capital requirements per unit of output by saving floor space and inventories. The important question is whether labor requirements decreased by a greater percentage than capital requirements.[17]

What determines whether technological change is labor-saving, capital-saving, or neutral? Obviously, a firm that attempts to improve technology in a particular area cannot determine very precisely the kind of technological change, if any, that will result from many of its efforts. But to the extent that the firm can influence the results, what determines whether it aims for labor-saving, capital-saving, or neutral technological change? This question has received considerable attention, but the proposed answers suffer from important limitations. In recent discussions of this subject, it is generally assumed that there is a reasonably well defined set of technological changes that can be obtained from a given research and development budget, that the trade-offs between various types of technological change are known and constant over time, and that the elasticity of substitution is less than one.[18] Under these circumstances, if an attempt is made

[17] Using a diagram ilke Figure 2.2, one can illustrate the effects of a labor-saving, capital-saving, or neutral technological change on the production function. For example, if the combination of inputs used currently is represented by point A and if

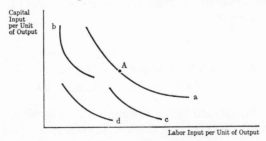

technological change results in a movement from position a to position b, it is labor-saving; if it results in a movement from position a to position c, it is capital-saving; if it results in a movement from position a to position d, it is neutral. For some relevant discussion, see M. Blaug, "A Summary of the Theory of Process Innovation," *Economica*, February 1963.

[18] The elasticity of substitution is defined for a given output as the percentage change in the relative amount of the inputs employed divided by the proportionate change in their marginal products (defined in note 26) or relative prices.

to achieve the greatest possible reduction in the total unit cost of production of the product in question, the choice will depend on the percentage of total costs represented by labor costs and on the relative costs of making various types of technological change. In particular, as the ratio of labor costs to total costs increases, the more labor-saving will be the sought-after changes in technology; as the ratio decreases, the more capital-saving they will be. An increase in the cost of making labor-saving changes in technology (relative to the cost of making capital-saving changes in technology) causes the firm to seek more capital-saving changes in technology; a decrease in this relative cost causes it to seek more labor-saving changes.[19]

The United States has experienced for some time an increase in the wage rate relative to the cost of new machinery. According to many economists and economic historians, this should induce labor-saving technological change. This view accords, I suspect, with what most laymen would guess to be the case. However, it is surprising how little evidence there is to support this view. Of course, one complication is that the definition of a labor-saving technological change must be altered when we consider the economy as a whole, since input prices can no longer be taken as given.[20] But this is only part of the problem. (Note that it is not possible to conclude that technological change is labor-saving because new techniques are intricate and round-about or because big, heavy equipment is used.) Many economists have the feeling that technological change has been quite labor-saving, but they generally acknowledge that the evidence is indirect and too weak to permit a clear-cut judgment.

[19] The costs of making various types of technological change are reflected in Kennedy's postulated transformation function between improvements in input requirements. However, the existence and realism of this function are questionable. See P. Samuelson, "Notes on Weisäcker-Kennedy Theories of Innovation," *Review of Economics and Statistics*, November 1965; W. Salter, *op. cit.*; W. Fellner, "Does the Market Direct the Relative Factor-Saving Effects of Technological Progress?," and E. Mansfield, "Comment," both in *The Rate and Direction of Inventive Activity*, Princeton, N.J.: Princeton University Press, 1961; M. Blaug, *ibid.*; C. Kennedy, "Samuelson on Induced Innovation," and P. Samuelson, "Rejoinder," both in *Review of Economics and Statistics*, November 1966. In recent work, it is frequently assumed that technological change is factor augmenting. For example, see Samuelson's paper cited earlier in this note.

[20] Whether or not technological change is labor-saving or capital-saving depends in this case on whether it tends to lower or raise the relative share of output going to labor. The difference between Hicks's and Harrod's definitions need not concern us here. See J. Hicks, *The Theory of Wages*, London, 1932; J. Robinson, "The Classification of Inventions," *Review of Economic Studies*, 1937–1938; R. Harrod, *Towards a Dynamic Economics*, London, 1948; and the papers cited in note 19. Both in this and the preceding paragraphs in the text, we are hampered by the unsatisfactory state of existing knowledge regarding the elasticity of substitution.

5. PRODUCTIVITY GROWTH

Since the days of Adam Smith, economists and policy makers have been interested in productivity—the ratio of output to input. The oldest and most commonly-studied measure of productivity is labor productivity, that is, output per man-hour of labor.[21] Obviously, changes in labor productivity are of importance, since they are intimately related to, though by no means synonymous with, changes in a nation's standard of living. One determinant of the rate of growth of labor productivity is the rate of technological change. In a particular industry or in the entire economy, a rapid rate of technological change is likely to result, all other things being equal, in a high rate of growth of labor productivity. However, since the rate of technological change is not the only determinant of the rate of growth of labor productivity, the latter is a very incomplete, though frequently used, measure of the rate of technological change.

Another important factor influencing the rate of growth of labor productivity is the extent to which capital is substituted for labor in response to changes in relative input prices; obviously, increases in the amount of capital per worker will increase labor productivity. Also, increases in labor productivity may arise because of economies of scale or increases in the extent to which productive capacity is used. In addition, since there is often a considerable gap between labor productivity with best-practice techniques and labor productivity with the existing mix of techniques, the rate of growth of labor productivity depends on the rate of diffusion of the best practices. Finally, the rate of growth of labor productivity depends on the nature, as well as on the rate, of technological change, labor-saving technological change resulting in greater increases in labor productivity than capital-saving or neutral technological change.

Despite its inadequacies as a measure of the rate of technological change, it is worthwhile giving a brief account of the behavior of labor productivity in the United States. During 1889–1957, the nation's real output per man-hour increased at an average rate of about 2 percent per year. The productivity gains were widely diffused, real hourly earnings growing about as rapidly, on the average, as output per man-hour. These gains were also used to promote increased leisure, working hours being cut by 20 or 30 percent, on the average, since the turn of the century. In the private economy, output per man-hour grew at an average rate of about 2.4 percent, which is somewhat higher than the rate of growth in the economy

[21] Needless to say, there is no necessary implication in the term "labor productivity" that all, or any particular part of it, stems from greater effort on the part of workers. This should be obvious from the ensuing discussion in the text. The empirical results in this section are based largely on J. Kendrick, *Productivity Trends in the United States*, Princeton, N.J.: Princeton University Press, 1961, which is a very valuable and comprehensive study of productivity statistics in this country.

as a whole. The relatively low rate of growth of productivity in government may be due to the fact that our measures of government output are extremely poor. For this reason, most economists have more faith in the figures for the private economy than for the economy as a whole.[22]

After World War I, there was an increase in the rate of increase of output per man-hour. During 1889–1919 output per man-hour rose at an average rate of 1.6 percent per year; during 1920–1957, it grew at an average rate of 2.3 percent per year. The reasons for this increase are by no means clear. It may have been due to the spread of the scientific management movement, the expansion of college and graduate work in business administration, the spread of organized research and development, and the change in immigration policy. There has also been a tendency for output per man-hour to rise more rapidly during some phases of the business cycle than during others. Average year-to-year increases in labor productivity were greater when business was expanding (2.4 percent per year) than when it was contracting (1.3 percent per year); the rate of increase was poorest in the first phases of contraction and highest toward the end of the contraction and the beginning of the expansion. In part, these cyclical changes reflect indivisibilities which cause output to decline more than employment even though employees may be fully occupied. In part, such changes reflect the fact that because of their investment in the employees, firms, expecting that business will improve, retain some of their work force even though they are not fully employed.

There were considerable differences among industries in the rate of increase of output per man-hour, as shown in Table 2.1. However, it is important to note that these figures are less reliable than the national figures—due partly to errors that tend to cancel out in the more aggregative measures and partly to the fact that the output figures for individual industries are gross, not net, of supplies from other industries. Thus, changes over time in the extent to which an industry manufactures its own supplies can influence the labor productivity index. Finally, a relatively great increase in labor productivity in an industry generally meant lower relative costs, lower relative prices, and a better-than-average increase in the volume of production. Better-than-average increases in the volume of production were generally accompanied by better-than-average increases in the level of employment, despite the relatively great increase in output per man-hour. Correspondingly, relatively low increases in labor productivity were usually accompanied by less-than-average increases in output and employment.

---

[22] There are also very great difficulties in measuring productivity in the service industries. It is generally believed that productivity in services has not (and perhaps cannot) grow as rapidly as in goods-producing industries, but the data are poor. See V. Fuchs and J. Wilburn, *Productivity Differences Within the Service Sector*, National Bureau of Economic Research, 1967.

TABLE 2.1

Average Annual Rates of Change of Output per Unit of Labor Input,
Various Sectors of the U.S. Private Domestic Economy, 1899–1953

Sector	Estimate (percent)	Sector	Estimate (percent)
Farming	1.7	Manufacturing	2.2
Mining	2.5	Foods	1.8
Metals	2.6	Beverages	1.6
Anthracite coal	0.7	Tobacco	5.1
Bituminous coal	1.7	Textiles	2.5
Oil and gas	3.4	Apparel	1.9
Nonmetals	2.9	Lumber	1.2
Transportation	3.4	Furniture	1.3
Railroads	2.8	Paper	2.6
Local transit	2.4	Printing	2.7
Residual transport	4.1	Chemicals	3.5
Communications and		Petroleum	3.8
public utilities	3.8	Rubber	4.3
Telephone	2.0	Leather	1.3
Telegraph	1.6	Glass	2.7
Electric utilities	6.2	Primary metals	2.3
Manufactured gas	4.7	Fabricated metals	2.7
Natural gas	3.0	Machinery, nonelectric	1.8
Residual sector	1.4	Machinery, electric	2.4
		Transportation equipment	3.7

Source: J. Kendrick, op. cit.

6. Interplant Differences in Productivity and the Coexistence of Old and New Techniques

At a given point in time, there often are large differences in labor productivity among plants in a particular industry. For example, Table 2.2 shows that, during the first quarter of this century, output per man-hour in blast furnaces using the most up-to-date techniques was generally at least twice as large as the industry average. In addition, the difference between best-practice and average labor productivity often varies considerably among the operations included in an industry. For example, Table 2.3 shows that, in the postwar cotton yarn and cloth industry, the difference was small for some operations (like card tending and loom fixing) and large for others (like spinning and weaving).

TABLE 2.2

Best-Practice and Average Labor Productivity, U.S. Blast Furnace
Industry, 1911–1926

| | GROSS TONS OF PIG-IRON PRODUCED PER MAN-HOUR | |
YEAR	BEST-PRACTICE PLANTS	INDUSTRY AVERAGE
1911	0.313	0.140
1917	0.326	0.150
1919	0.328	0.140
1921	0.428	0.178
1923	0.462	0.213
1925	0.512	0.285
1926	0.573	0.296

Source: U.S. Bureau of Labor Statistics, *The Productivity of Labor in Merchant Blast Furnaces,* 1928.

In part, the interplant differences in productivity are due to the co-existence of a variety of techniques in a particular industry. Petroleum refining provides one illustration. The first commercial process for cracking heavy petroleum fractions to yield gasoline was introduced in 1913 by William Burton of Standard Oil (Indiana). The Burton process was supplanted by the Dubbs and Tube-and-Tank processes, both introduced

TABLE 2.3

Best-Practice and Average Labor Productivity, U.S. Cotton Yarn
and Cloth Industry, 1946

| | POUNDS OF COTTON PROCESSED PER MAN-HOUR | |
OPERATION	BEST-PRACTICE PLANTS	INDUSTRY AVERAGE
Picking	985	575
Card tending	296	272
Drawing frame	493	461
Spinning	86	53
Doffing	141	115
Slashing	979	545
Weaving	89	56
Loom fixing	151	143

Source: A. Grosse, "The Technological Structure of the Cotton Industry," in W. Leontief and others, *Studies in the Structure of the American Economy,* Oxford University Press, 1953.

in the early twenties. Yet for almost a decade after their introduction, the Burton process accounted for at least 10 percent of the total U.S. output of cracked gasoline. The Dubbs, Tube-and-Tank, and other thermal processes were supplanted in turn by the Houdry, Fluid, and other catalytic processes. Yet for about fifteen years after the introduction of the first catalytic processes, the thermal processes continued to account for most of the industry's capacity.[23]

The mixture of techniques in use at any point in time is the result of a complex combination of technological and economic forces. Technological change results in a new product or in a change in the production function, that is, in the list of technically feasible alternative ways to produce an existing product. Whether a change in technology is applied depends on whether, given the prices of the inputs and outputs, it is economically, as well as technically, attractive to producers. Unless its application seems profitable, it will remain only a potentiality, awaiting the day when altered economic circumstances make it profitable. According to Brozen, the "Detroit Automation" of the fifties was a case of this sort. The use of transfer equipment to move work from one automatic machine tool to another and interlocking these tools to get higher utilization, was first considered in 1927 but was not profitable at the time. Only when wage rates had risen and machine tools had become more expensive did it become economically attractive.[24]

Because of technological change, changes in input prices, changes in demand for the product, or other changes, a new method may become profitable for some firms and consequently it may be adopted by them. But this does not mean that all firms in the industry will immediately switch over to the new technique. Because of their investment in existing equipment and because the economic conditions they face may be different from those faced by the users of the new technique, it may not be economical for some firms to adopt the new technique. Moreover, in the absence of strong economic pressures on them, some firms may be slow to appreciate the new opportunities and to adjust to them. In Chapter 4, we shall see

[23] J. Enos, *Petroleum Progress and Profits*, Boston: M.I.T. Press, 1962.
[24] See Y. Brozen, "The Economics of Automation," *American Economic Review*, May 1957. Changes in techniques are due to changes in factor prices, as well as to changes in the production function due to technological change. A diagram like Figure 2.2 can be useful in analyzing the effects of each type of change. To determine the minimum-cost method, lines can be drawn which represent the combinations of quantities of labor and capital that can be purchased for a certain amount. The minimum-cost method corresponds to the point where one of these lines is tangent to the curve in Figure 2.2. Given a change in the curve (due to technological change) or a change in the slope of the lines (due to a change in factor prices), one can determine the change in the minimum-cost method. For example, see E. Mansfield, "Technological Change: Measurement, Determinants, and Diffusion," *Report to the President by the National Commission on Technology, Automation, and Economic Progress*, February 1966.

that the diffusion of new techniques often takes a considerable period of time.

7. TOTAL PRODUCTIVITY INDEXES

The total productivity index relates changes in output to changes in both labor and capital inputs, not changes in labor inputs alone. Specifically, this index equals $q/(zl + vk)$, where q is output (as a percent of output in some base period), l is labor input (as a percent of labor input in some base period), k is capital input (as a percent of capital input in some base period), z is labor's share of the value of output in the base period, and v is capital's share of the value of the output in the base period. Substituting values of q, l, and k over a given period into this formula, one can easily compute the value of the index for that period.[25] As a measure of technological change, this index has important advantages over labor productivity, the most important being that it takes account of the changes over time in the amount of capital inputs. However, it has the disadvantage of assuming that the marginal products[26] of the inputs are altered only by technological change and that their ratios remain constant and independent of the ratios of the quantities of the inputs.[27]

This formula, or variants of it, has been used to estimate the rate of increase of total productivity in the United States for the period 1899–1957, with these results: First, total productivity for the private domestic economy increased by about 1.7 percent per year over the whole period. Second, there seems to have been an increase in the rate of productivity growth to about 2.1 percent per year in the period following World War I. Third, the rate of productivity increase seems to have been higher in communications and transportation than in mining, manufacturing, and farming (Table 2.4). Fourth, within manufacturing it seems to have been highest in rubber, transportation equipment, tobacco, chemicals, printing, glass, fabricated metals, textiles, and petroleum (Table 2.4).[28]

Another study of the rate of productivity advance presents results for the United States, United Kingdom, Germany, Japan, and Canada during the period since World War II.[29] The findings, presented in Table 2.5,

[25] This formula comes from E. Domar, "On Total Productivity and All That," *Journal of Political Economy*, December 1962. This article is a valuable commentary on Kendrick, *op. cit.* For an alternative definition of the "total productivity" index, see Domar's eq. (3).

[26] Using the notation in note 4, the marginal product of labor is $\delta Y/\delta L$ and the marginal product of capital is $\delta Y/\delta K$.

[27] See Domar, *op. cit.*

[28] Kendrick, *op. cit.*

[29] E. Domar, S. Eddie, B. Herrick, P. Hohenberg, M. Intrilligator, and I. Miyamoto, "Economic Growth and Productivity in the United States, Canada, United Kingdom, Germany, and Japan in the Postwar Period," *Review of Economics and Statistics*, February 1964.

TABLE 2.4

Estimates of Annual Rate of Increase of Total Productivity in
Various Sectors of the U.S. Private Domestic Economy, 1899–1953

Sector	Estimate (percent per year)	Sector	Estimate (percent per year)
Farming	1.1	Manufacturing	2.0
Mining	2.2	Foods	1.7
Metals	2.2	Beverages	1.6
Anthracite coal	0.7	Tobacco	3.5
Bituminous coal	1.6	Textiles	2.4
Oil and gas	3.0	Apparel	1.7
Nonmetals	2.6	Lumber	1.0
Transportation	3.2	Furniture	1.4
Railroads	2.6	Paper	2.3
Local transit	2.5	Printing	2.6
Residual transport	4.0	Chemicals	2.9
Communications and		Petroleum	2.4
public utilities	3.6	Rubber	4.1
Telephone	2.0	Leather	1.2
Telegraph	1.8	Glass	2.6
Electrical utilities	5.5	Primary metals	1.9
Manufactured gas	4.7	Fabricated metals	2.6
Natural gas	2.0	Machinery, nonelectric	1.7
Residual sector	1.3	Machinery, electric	2.2
		Transportation equipment	3.5

Source: J. Kendrick, op. cit.

indicate that the rate of increase of total productivity was higher in Germany and Japan than in the United States and Canada, and higher in the United States and Canada than in the United Kingdom. However, if capital inputs had been adjusted for under-utilization, the United States, United Kingdom, and Canada might have turned in a better performance. Examination of the results by sector indicates that in Canada and the United Kingdom agriculture and public utilities had the highest rates of productivity increase; in Germany, agriculture; in Japan and the United States, public utilities, transportation, and communication.

Finally, what factors seem to influence the rate of growth of total productivity in an industry? Apparently, an industry's rate of growth of total productivity is related in a statistically significant way to (1) its ratio of research and development expenditures to sales, (2) its rate of change of output level, and (3) the amplitude of its cyclical fluctuation. Specifically, the rate of growth of total productivity increases (on the average) by 0.5 percent for each tenfold increase in the ratio of research and develop-

TABLE 2.5

Estimates of Annual Rate of Increase of Total Productivity in
United States, Canada, United Kingdom, Germany, and Japan

Sector	United States 1948–1960	Canada 1949–1960	United Kingdom 1949–1959	Germany 1950–1959	Japan 1951–1959
	(PERCENT PER YEAR)				
Economy	n.a.	1.2	0.6	3.6	3.7
Private economy	1.4	n.a.	0.7	n.a.	3.8
Private nonfarm economy	n.a.	n.a.	n.a.	n.a.	3.9
Agriculture	2.6	2.0	} 2.0 a	} 4.3	} 1.2
Forestry, fishing, trapping	n.a.	0.7			
Mining, quarrying, wells	n.a.	0.9	0.3		−0.6
Manufacturing	2.6	1.4	0.7 a	} 3.4	4.1
Construction	n.a.	0.6	0.2 b		2.2
Public utilities	} 3.4	2.0	1.9 c		} 4.5
Transportation and communication		1.5	1.8	} 1.5	
Wholesale and retail trade	n.a.	−0.6	−1.0 b		−0.5
Finance, insurance, real estate	} n.a.	0.6	} 0.6	} 1.4	} 4.1
Other services		} −0.8			
Government	n.a.		−2.8		6.7

Source: E. Domar *et al., op. cit.*
a 1950–1959.
b 1953–1959.
c 1950–1958.
n.a. Not available.

ment expenditures to sales and by 1 percent for every 3 percent increase in the industry's growth rate.[30] These empirical results seem to be consistent with the theories in section 3. However, they are somewhat ambiguous; for example, the observed relationship between the rate of productivity growth and the industry's growth rate could be due partly to an effect of the former on the latter. Correlation does not prove causation.

[30] N. Terleckyj, *Sources of Productivity Advance*, Ph.D. Thesis, Columbia University, 1960.

8. OTHER MEASURES
OF TECHNOLOGICAL CHANGE

Economists have tried to devise better measures of the rate of movement of the production function than the total productivity index. These measures rest on somewhat different assumptions about the shape of the production function, the Cobb-Douglas and CES production functions sometimes, but not always, being used.[31] For example, in an important paper published in 1957, Robert Solow provided an estimate of the rate of technological change for the nonfarm economy during 1909–1949.[32] The results suggest that, for the entire period, the average rate of technological change was about 1.5 percent per year. That is, the quantity of output derivable from a fixed amount of inputs increased at about 1.5 percent per year. In addition, Solow found evidence that the average rate of technological change was smaller during 1909–1929 than during 1930–1949. Benton Massell carried out a similar analysis for United States manufacturing, his estimate of the annual rate of technological change during 1919–1955 being about 3 percent.[33] In contrast with Solow, his results show little or no evidence of a higher rate of technological change during the thirties and forties than in previous decades.[34]

The studies by Solow and Massell assume implicitly that technological change is disembodied—that is, that all technological change consists of better methods and organization that improve the efficiency of both old capital and new. Examples of such improvements are various advances in industrial engineering (for example, the development of time and motion studies) and operations research (for example, the development of linear programming). Although technological change of this sort has undoubtedly

[31] The Cobb-Douglas production function is shown in note 4. For a description of the CES production function, see the first reference in note 34.

[32] R. Solow, "Technical Change and the Aggregate Production Function," *Review of Economics and Statistics*, 1957. Solow assumed that there were constant returns to scale, that capital and labor were paid their marginal products, and that technological change was neutral.

[33] B. Massell, "Capital Formation and Technical Change in U.S. Manufacturing," *Review of Economics and Statistics*, May 1960.

[34] Arrow, Chenery, Minhas, and Solow obtained an estimate of the rate of technological change in the non-farm economy, based on Solow's figures for 1909–1949, and somewhat different assumptions about the shape of the curves in Figure 2.2. The result was 1.8 percent, as compared with Solow's estimate of 1.5 percent. See their "Capital-Labor Substitution and Economic Efficiency," *Review of Economics and Statistics*, August 1961.

Another approach to the measurement of technological change entails the comparison of input-output tables. A comparison for 1947–1958 indicates that technological change during that period tended to reduce the differences in input structure distinguishing the major groups of industries. See A. Carter, "The Economics of Technological Change," *Scientific American*, April 1966.

been of importance," many changes in technology must be embodied in new equipment if they are to be utilized. For example, the introduction of the continuous wide strip mill in the steel industry and the diesel locomotive in railroads required new investment in plant and equipment. No one has attempted to measure fully the extent to which technological change in recent years has been capital-embodied, as this kind of technological change is called. But the available evidence clearly indicates that a great deal of capital-embodied technological change has taken place.

If technological change is assumed to be capital-embodied, not disembodied, somewhat different methods must be used to estimate the rate of technological change. What do the results look like? Solow has estimated that the rate of technological change in the private economy during 1919–1953 was 2.5 percent per year.[35] This estimate is higher than his earlier estimate based on the assumption that technological change was disembodied. Turning to individual firms, estimates have been provided for ten large chemical and petroleum firms in the postwar period, one set of estimates assuming that technological change was disembodied, the other assuming that it was capital-embodied. The results are shown in Table 2.6.[36] At the industry level, estimates for ten manufacturing industries suggest that the rate of capital-embodied technological change during 1946–1962 was highest in motor vehicles and instruments, next highest in food, chemicals, electrical equipment, paper, and apparel; and lowest in machinery, furniture, and glass (Table 2.7).[37] Outside manufacturing, the rate of capital-embodied technological change in the railroad industry during 1917–1959 has been estimated at 3 percent per year.[38]

What factors seem to influence the rate of technological change, as measured by the estimated change in the production function? My results, based on data regarding ten large chemical and petroleum firms and ten manufacturing industries in the postwar period, indicate that, both for firms and for industries, the rate of technological change is directly related to the

[35] R. Solow, "Investment and Technical Change," *Mathematical Models in the Social Sciences,* ed. by Arrow, Karlin, and Suppes, Stanford, Calif.: Stanford University Press, 1959. It is important to note that the two rates of technological change are not entirely comparable, the capital-embodied rate of technological change generally being the larger. See E. Phelps, "The New View of Investment," *Quarterly Journal of Economics,* November 1962; and R. Solow, "Capital, Labor and Income in Manufacturing," *The Behavior of Income Shares,* Princeton, N.J.: Princeton University Press, 1964.

[36] E. Mansfield, *Industrial Research and Technological Innovation,* New York: W. W. Norton & Company, Inc., 1968, Chapter IV. Of course, when we speak about the rate of technological change in a firm, we mean the rate at which its production function, not the industry's, shifts over time. See note 6.

[37] *Ibid.*

[38] E. Mansfield, "Innovation and Technical Change in the Railroad Industry," *Transportation Economics,* National Bureau of Economic Research, 1965. For some other studies of individual industries, see T. Liu and J. Hildebrand, *Manufacturing Production Functions in the United States,* Ithaca, N.Y.: Cornell University Press, 1965.

TABLE 2.6

Estimates of the Rate of Technological Change, Disembodied and
Capital-Embodied, Ten Chemical and Petroleum Firms, 1946–1962

FIRM [1]	DISEMBODIED	CAPITAL-EMBODIED
	(PERCENT PER YEAR)	
C1	0.4	0.5
C2	2.4	6.2
C3	2.6	2.0
C4	1.4	3.5
C5	[2]	5.3
P1	0.3	2.1
P2	1.9	5.9
P3	3.2	6.6
P4	1.1	9.5
P5	1.8	8.8

Source: E. Mansfield, Industrial Research and Technological Innovation, Norton,
1968, Chapter IV.
[1] The basic data were obtained from the firms with the understanding that their
names would not be divulged. Thus, C1 stands for the first chemical firm, P1 stands
for the first petroleum firm, etc.
[2] Less than zero.

TABLE 2.7

Estimates of Rate of Capital-Embodied Technological Change, Ten
Two-Digit Manufacturing Industries, 1946–1962

INDUSTRY	ESTIMATE (PERCENT PER YEAR)
Chemicals	3.7
Machinery	[1]
Food	4.7
Paper	3.4
Instruments	8.3
Electrical equipment	3.6
Stone, clay, and glass	1.5
Apparel	3.0
Motor vehicles	8.6
Furniture	1.9

Source: E. Mansfield, Industrial Research and Technological Innovation, Norton,
1968, Chapter IV.
[1] Less than zero.

rate of growth of cumulated research and development expenditures made by the firm or industry. If technological change is disembodied, the average effect of a 1 percent increase in the rate of growth of cumulated research and development expenditures is a .1 percent increase in the rate of technological change. If technological change is capital-embodied, it is a .7 percent increase in the rate of technological change.[39] These results are quite compatible with the theories in section 3. Needless to say, however, they are tentative, since they are based on a relatively small amount of data and since, as noted before, correlation does not prove causation.

9. PROBLEMS OF MEASUREMENT

It is important that we point out some of the problems in the measures discussed in the previous section. First, these measures of the rate of technological change are indirect measures that look only at the effects of technological change; and since they equate the effects of technological change with whatever increase in output is unexplained by other factors, they do not isolate the effects of technological change alone. In addition, they contain the effects of whatever factors are excluded—which, depending on the particular study, are increases in education, betterment of worker health and nutrition, economies of scale, changes in project mix, or improved allocation of resources. For this reason, they are sometimes called "residuals." So far, economists have been unable to sort out the effects of "pure" technological change, except perhaps when dealing with individual processes.[40]

Second, there are difficulties in measuring inputs, the measurement of aggregate capital being a particularly nettlesome problem. In addition, it is difficult to adjust for quality changes in inputs; and there are problems in choosing among price deflators.[41] Third, the customary measures often assume that there are no economies of scale and that technological change is neutral. The restrictiveness of these assumptions is obvious.[42] Fourth, it

---

[39] E. Mansfield, *Industrial Research and Technological Innovation, op. cit.,* Chapter IV.

[40] See Domar, *op. cit.* There are also considerable difficulties in taking proper account of new products in existing measures. Further, the available measures generally reflect both technological change and the diffusion of new techniques, since they do not pertain only to conditions on the technological frontier.

[41] For example, see J. Robinson, "Some Problems of Definition and Measurement of Capital," *Oxford Economic Papers,* June 1959. According to D. Jorgensen and Z. Griliches, there are many measurement errors and errors of aggregation in the measures that are ordinarily used; and these errors inflate the residual. See "The Explanation of Productivity Change," *Review of Economic Studies,* July 1967. One can always "explain" changes in output by changes in input (appropriately measured), but many of these changes in input must themselves be attributed to technological change. It is true, however, that technological change is due in some part at least to inputs invested to advance technology.

[42] See G. Stigler, "Economic Problems in Measuring Changes in Productivity," *Output, Input, and Productivity Measurement,* Princeton, N.J.: Princeton University

often is impossible to distinguish capital-embodied from disembodied technological change on the basis of available data. For this and other reasons, there has been some reaction recently against the usefulness of the capital-embodied–technological–change hypothesis, as generally put forth.[43] Fifth, when one compares a number of studies, there is considerable variation in the estimated rates of technological change in particular industries. Apparently the results are quite sensitive to the detailed assumptions that are made and the data that are used.[44]

The moral of this section is clear. Because the available measures are beset by many important problems, they should be used only as very rough guides. We are a long way from having precise measurements of the rate of technological change.

10. PATENTS AND TECHNOLOGICAL CHANGE

The number of patents is sometimes used as a crude index of the rate of technological change, or some important component thereof, in a given field at a certain point in time. Used in this way, patent statistics have important disadvantages. For one thing, the average importance and cost of the patents granted at one time and place may differ from those granted at another time and place. For another, the proportion of the total inventions that are patented may vary considerably. Nonetheless, it is of interest to see what the patent statistics suggest, since they are the basis for some major investigations in this area.[45]

According to a series of studies by Jacob Schmookler, there is a high correlation between the patent rate on capital-goods inventions in an in-

---

Press, 1961; J. Hicks, "Thoughts on the Theory of Capital—The Corfu Conference," *Oxford Economic Papers,* June 1960; and E. Mansfield, "The Economics of Research and Development," *Patents and Progress,* ed. by Alderson, Terpstra, and Shapiro, Irwin, 1965.

[43] See D. Jorgensen, "The Embodiment Hypothesis," *Journal of Political Economy,* February 1966; M. Nerlove, "Statistical Production Functions: A Selective Review," and Z. Griliches, "Production Functions in Manufacturing: Some Preliminary Results," both in M. Brown (ed.), *The Theory and Empirical Analysis of Production,* National Bureau of Economic Research, 1967.

[44] See E. Mansfield, "Comment," *The Theory and Empirical Analysis of Production, ibid.*

[45] For some discussion of the limitations of patent statistics, see S. Kuznets, "Inventive Activity: Problems of Definition and Measurement," *The Rate and Direction of Inventive Activity,* Princeton, N.J.: Princeton University Press, 1961; R. MacLaurin, "The Sequence from Invention to Innovation," Conference on the Quantitative Description of Technological Change, 1951; B. Sanders, "Some Difficulties in Measuring Inventive Activity," and J. Schmookler's "Comment," both in *The Rate and Direction of Inventive Activity,* Princeton, N.J.: Princeton University Press, 1961.

dustry and the lagged value of the industry's investment or value-added.[46] That is, a high patent rate on capital-goods inventions is associated with a high previous level of investment or value-added. Turning from comparisons over time to comparisons among industries at a given point in time, there seems to be a tendency for the number of patents on capital-goods inventions to be directly related to the level of investment or value-added in an industry. That is, industries with high investment or value-added account for more patents than those with low investment or value-added. Moreover, this relationship persists when the effects of industry size are taken into account.[47]

What are the implications of these findings? In the past, some, though by no means all, economists assumed that the rate of technological change was determined outside the economic system and was independent of economic variables. To the extent that the patent rate is a useful index of the rate of technological change, or some important component thereof, Schmookler's results seem to contradict this assumption. Going a step further, he concludes that the distribution of inventions according to function, that is, according to the industry expected to use them, is largely determined by demand factors of the sort discussed in section 3. The supply factors, reflecting, for example, advances in basic science, enter in as determinants of the form—mechanical, chemical, electrical, and so on—in which the inventions occur. Put differently, demand conditions determine which industries or consumer activities inventions are made for; supply conditions determine which industries or branches of science and technology inventions are made by. This is an interesting hypothesis, which

[46] An industry's value-added is its dollar sales minus its purchases of intermediate products from other firms or industries. Griliches and Schmookler found that 84 percent of the variation in the patent rate on process inventions could be explained by the industry's value-added three years before. See their "Inventing and Maximizing," *American Economic Review*, September 1963. For results based on investment data, see J. Schmookler, *Invention and Economic Growth*, Cambridge, Mass.: Harvard University Press, 1966, as well as his paper with Griliches. Also, Schmookler found that a significant correlation exists between patent applications and variable production inputs, both expressed as deviations from trend. Earlier, Graue found considerable correlation, after removing trends from both series, between the level of industrial production and the number of mechanical patents issued. See E. Graue, "Inventions and Production," *Review of Economics and Statistics*, November 1943; and J. Schmookler, "The Level of Inventive Activity," *Review of Economics and Statistics*, May 1954.

[47] J. Schmookler and O. Brownlee, using data for eighteen manufacturing industries, show that this relationship is quite strong, particularly when the patent data are lagged several years behind the value-added data. The coefficient of correlation, which is higher in more recent years, exceeded .9 in 1947. See their "Determinants of Inventive Activity," *American Economic Review*, May 1962. For results based on investment data, see J. Schmookler, *Invention and Economic Growth*, *op. cit.* However, if a firm's patent rate, including both process and product inventions, is correlated with its sales, the correlation coefficient is only about .6. See F. Scherer, "Firm Size, Market Structure, Opportunity, and the Output of Patented Inventions," *American Economic Review*, December 1965. Also, see Griliches and Schmookler, *op. cit.*

undoubtedly will be subjected to further tests using other bodies of data.[48]

As an industry grows older, there seems to be a tendency for the rate of patenting to rise first at an increasing rate, then at a decreasing rate, and finally to decline. This pattern has occurred in a wide variety of industries, the ultimate decline in the patent rate being explained in two quite different ways. According to one hypothesis, the technology in any field rather quickly approaches perfection, with the result that fewer important inventions can be made in it and inventors leave the field. According to the other hypothesis, the decrease in the patent rate occurs because of a decrease in the rewards to be gained from technological change in this industry, these rewards being associated with the growth and profitability of the industry. The decline in the patent rate may be due partly to both hypotheses, but the available evidence, though not entirely unambiguous, seems to indicate that the latter hypothesis is more important.[49]

11. Productivity Growth and Technological Change: A New Era?

Is there any evidence that productivity has been increasing more rapidly now than in the past? It is easy to find statements by economists and others asserting that the rate of growth of productivity in the postwar period is much more rapid than that before the war. It is also possible to find statements asserting the opposite. For example, John Diebold has stated that "the aggregate productivity figures would not reveal any abnormally high productive influence in the postwar economy," [50] and Lee DuBridge, president of California Institute of Technology, has asserted that "the recent introduction of automation has produced no radical change in trend." [51]

What do the facts suggest? According to the National Automation Commission, the average rate of increase of output per man-hour in the total private economy during 1947–1965 was 3.2 percent, whereas the 1910–1945 average was 2 percent. If agriculture is omitted, the difference is

---

[48] See J. Schmookler, *Invention and Economic Growth, op. cit.,* a valuable study which brings together and extends the author's previous work.

[49] See S. Kuznets, *Secular Movements in Production and Prices,* Boston: Houghton Mifflin Company, 1930; R. Merton, "The Rate of Industrial Invention," *Quarterly Journal of Economics,* May 1935; A. Stafford, *Trends in Invention in Material Culture,* Ph.D. Thesis, University of Chicago, 1950; W. Salter, *Productivity and Technical Change,* Cambridge University, 1960; and J. Schmookler, *ibid.*

[50] J. Diebold, *Testimony Submitted to the Subcommittee on Automation and Energy Resources,* 86th Congress, Second Session, as quoted in M. Philipson, *Automation,* New York: Random House, Inc., 1962.

[51] L. DuBridge, "Educational and Social Consequences," *Automation and Technological Change,* American Assembly, 1962, p. 31.

smaller, the average being 2 percent before the war and 2.5 percent after.[52] According to the Council of Economic Advisers, the average rate of increase during 1947–1963 was 3.2 percent, as contrasted with 2.2 percent during 1919–1947.[53] Thus, regardless of which study one cites, the rate of increase of output per man-hour in the postwar period seems higher than that before the war.

In addition, there have been studies to determine whether the relatively high rates of increase in output per man-hour during 1961–1963 can be explained by cyclical and transitory factors affecting productivity. The Council of Economic Advisers[54] carried out several statistical analyses of the nonfarm productivity gains of 1949–1960 to estimate the effects on productivity of the average age of equipment, the rate of growth of output, and the degree of capacity utilization. The findings were then used to estimate the increases in productivity that might have been expected in 1961–1963 if the past relationship held. The results suggest that the increases in 1961–1963 were either about equal to the expectation or in excess of it by amounts ranging up to 1 percentage point.[55]

Using the measures described in sections 7 and 8, is there any evidence that the aggregate production function has shifted more rapidly in the postwar period than in earlier years? This is an important question which bears on a number of major policy issues discussed in subsequent chapters. According to one study,[56] the average annual rate of increase of total productivity in the private domestic economy during 1948–1960 was 2.14 percent, as contrasted with 2.08 percent during 1919–1960. According to another study,[57] the estimated rate of disembodied technological change averaged 1.9 percent in 1929–1947, 2.9 percent in 1947–1954, and 2.1 percent in 1954–1960. If technological change was capital-embodied and if changes in labor quality are taken roughly into account, it averaged 4.4 percent in 1929–1947, 6 percent in 1947–1954, and 3.6 percent in 1954–1960. Thus, there is some evidence that the rate of technological change may have been higher since World War II, but the difference, if it exists, is considerably smaller than is indicated by the behavior of output per man-hour.

[52] *Report to the President by the National Commission on Technology, Automation, and Economic Progress, op. cit.*, pp. 2–3.
[53] See the 1964 *Annual Report* of the President's Council of Economic Advisers.
[54] *Ibid.*
[55] Part of the difference was revised out of existence by the Bureau of Labor Statistics. See R. Solow, *The Nature and Sources of Unemployment in the United States*, Stockholm: Almqvist and Wiksell, 1964, p. 49.
[56] J. Kendrick and R. Sato, "Factor Prices, Productivity, and Growth," *American Economic Review*, December 1963.
[57] R. Nelson, "Aggregate Production Functions and Medium Range Growth Projections," *American Economic Review*, September 1964.

12. TECHNOLOGICAL FORECASTING

Technological forecasting is an attempt to anticipate the rate and direction of technological change and the nature, rate of diffusion, and effect of the new processes and products that are used in a particular field. Examples of technological forecasts are: "A means of traveling on the ground from Boston to Washington in two hours will be achieved by 1975." "We will land a man on the moon by 1970." "A fuel cell cost-performance ratio of $18 per watt of capacity will be achieved by 1975." Despite the obvious difficulties in forecasting the nature and extent of technological change in a particular area, it is a necessary part of decision-making by firms and government agencies. There is no way to avoid it, since, whether or not an explicit forecast is made, a forecast is implicit in each such decision.

With regard to public policy, technological forecasting has received considerable attention in connection with manpower and defense problems.[58] In the manpower field, there is a need for forecasts leading to more complete and reliable information regarding future occupational and skill requirements, as well as future trends in the total number of workers required, in particular areas and industries. An example of such forecasts is shown in Table 5.2, which contains a Bureau of Labor Statistics projection of the 1975 industrial composition of the labor force.[59] With regard to industrial decision making, the very survival of a firm may depend on its ability to forecast the direction future technology will take. New processes and products can transform an industry, as illustrated by the case of the early plastics, which were brittle and highly inflammable, had low resistance to heat, and were subject to early discoloration. Because of competition from new products, virtually none is presently on the market.

Technological forecasts generally fall into three categories. The first type is based primarily on expert opinion. A group of technical or scientific experts are brought together and asked to gaze into their crystal balls.

[58] See D. Schon, "The Role of the Federal Government in Technological Forecasting," *Report to the President by the National Commission on Technology, Automation and Economic Progress*, February 1966; and E. Jantsch, *Technological Forecasting in Perspective*, Organization for Economic Cooperation and Development, 1966. The latter is concerned with forecasting by firms as well as government agencies. Also, see R. Isenson, "Technological Forecasting in Perspective," *Management Science*, October, 1966; F. Pardee, "State-of-the-Art Projection and Long-Range Planning of Applied Research" in M. Yovits, D. Gilford, R. Wilcox, E. Staveley, and H. Lerner, *Research Program Effectiveness*, New York: Gordon and Breach, Science Publishers, 1966; and J. B. Quinn, "Technological Forecasting," *Harvard Business Review*, March 1967.

[59] Of course, the kind of forecast contained in Table 5.2 is only one of many sorts of technological forecasting. For example, it is quite different from the hypothetical illustrations in the first paragraph of this section. For a discussion of various kinds of forecasts, see I. Siegel, "Technological Change and Long Run Forecasting," *Journal of Business*, July 1953.

Unfortunately, even when based on the opinion of distinguished experts, the results are subject to large errors. Vannevar Bush, Director of the Office of Scientific Research and Development, predicted in 1945 that a 3,000 mile rocket was impossible "and will be impossible for many years." [60] Earnest Rutherford, the Nobel Prize winner who was the father of experimental nuclear science, believed that the large-scale use of nuclear energy was unlikely; and Robert A. Millikan, another Nobel Prize winner, said in 1930 that "There is no appreciable energy available to man through atomic disintegration." [61] Apparently, the experts are more likely to be right when they say something is possible than when they say it is not.

The second type of forecast is based on extrapolation of statistical trends. For example, if some measure of the rate of improvement of the performance of a process or product has remained approximately constant in the recent past, it is sometimes assumed that it will continue to remain constant in the future.[62] The dangers involved in such an assumption are obvious. Thus, the development of smokeless powder, TNT, and RDX explosives prior to 1940 pointed to moderate increases in the intensity of military explosives during the forties. This was a poor forecast in anyone's book. In general, the accuracy of this type of forecast, like the others, is likely to be inversely related to how far one attempts to peer into the future.

Finally, the third type of forecast is based on somewhat more sophisticated models of the process by which new techniques arise and become accepted. These models, some of which are described in subsequent chapters, attempt to relate in a systematic way various aspects of this process to a set of measurable explanatory variables. Models of this sort are still in their infancy, and it is difficult to predict their ultimate usefulness. At present, they seem better suited to forecasting the diffusion of new processes and products that are already in existence rather than the occurrence of future inventions. However, this limitation may be less important than it seems, since the inventions that have already occurred are sometimes all that really matter in the short—and intermediate run.

Many companies are experimenting with technological forecasting techniques. For example, Westinghouse Electric Corporation has charted likely developments in about twenty technological fields out to the year 2000. The engineering analysis group has prepared a network product plan something like a PERT chart (see Chapter 3) for each promising intersection

[60] V. Bush, "Testimony before the Special Senate Committee on Atomic Energy," December 1945, cited in *Inquiry into Satellite and Missile Programs*, Part I, *Preparedness Investigating Subcommittee on Armed Services*, 85th Congress, November 1957–January 1958.

[61] See J. Jewkes, D. Sawers, and R. Stillerman, *op. cit.*

[62] Of course, in making forecasts of this sort, it is not necessary to assume an exponential trend. Other kinds of mathematical functions can be used instead. See J. Bright, *Research, Development, and Technological Innovation*, Homewood, Ill.: Richard D. Irwin, Inc., 1964, p. 759.

of technology and function. TRW, Inc. has compiled a long list of technological achievements that it thinks will occur in the next two decades. TRW's technique is a variant of the RAND Corporation's Delphi method, which relies on a consensus of experts in a field to forecast technological advances. Individual forecasts are obtained on anonymous questionnaires and circulated for written criticism until a consensus on development and timing is reached. Although some of the work in this area will undoubtedly prove valuable, existing techniques are crude. Technological forecasting is a young and relatively undeveloped art.[63]

13. SUMMARY

Technology is society's pool of knowledge regarding the industrial arts. Technological change is the advance of technology, such advance often taking the form of new methods of producing existing products, new designs which enable the production of products with important new characteristics, and new techniques of organization and management. It is important to distinguish between a technological change and a change in technique. Whereas a technological change is an advance in knowledge, a change in technique is an alteration of the character of the equipment, products, and organization which are actually being used. Technological change must also be distinguished from scientific advance, many changes in technology occurring as a result of inventions that do not rely on new scientific principles. Although technological change and scientific advance are by no means the same thing, the nature of scientific advance has had a very great influence on the kinds of technological change we have been able to effect, and technological change is much more closely related to scientific advance now than in the past.

Technological change results in a change in the production function or in the availability of new products. Since there is no satisfactory way to measure the rate of technological change directly, economists often measure it by its effects, the average rate of movement of the production function being used for this purpose. The rate of technological change in an industry depends to a large extent on the amount of resources devoted by firms, by independent inventors, and by government to the improvement of the industry's technology. The amount of resources devoted by the government depends on how closely the industry is related to the defense, public health, and other social needs for which the government assumes major responsibility, on the extent of the external economies generated by the relevant research and development, and on more purely political factors. Since the amount of resources devoted by industry and independent inventors de-

[63] For further description of the Delphi technique, see T. Gordon and O. Helmer, *Report on a Long-Range Forecasting Study*, RAND Corporation Report P-2982, September 1964.

pends heavily on the anticipated profitability of their use, the rate of technological change depends on factors which influence the rewards from particular kinds of technological change and on factors which influence their costs. Among the reward-determining factors are the nature of product demand and the configuration of input prices; among the cost-determining factors are advances in basic science.

Besides being influenced by the quantity of resources an industry devotes to improving its own technology, an industry's rate of technological change depends on the quantity of resources devoted by other industries to the improvement of the capital goods and other inputs it uses. In addition, there is another kind of interdependence among industries, technology meant for one industry turning out to be useful for others as well. An industry's rate of technological change also depends on its market structure, the legal arrangements under which it operates, the attitudes toward technological change of management, workers, and the public, and the organization and management of its research and development. Attempts have been made to study the quantitative effect of various factors on the estimated rate of technological change experienced by an industry or firm. The results seem to indicate that the rate of technological change is correlated with previous expenditures on research and development. Interesting attempts have also been made to analyze patent statistics in various industries and to see the extent to which technological change has been labor-saving or capital-saving.

Economists and policy makers have long been interested in productivity —the ratio of output to input. The oldest and most commonly-studied measure of productivity is output per man-hour. During the past seventy-five years, output per man-hour has increased at an average annual rate of about 2 percent in the economy as a whole. The productivity gains were widely diffused, real hourly earnings growing about as rapidly, on the average, as output per man-hour. At a given point in time, there often are large differences in output per man-hour among plants in a particular industry, due in part to the coexistence of a variety of techniques. Whether a firm uses a particular technique depends, of course, on the prevailing configuration of product and input prices, as well as on purely technical factors.

For a variety of reasons, changes in output per man-hour are a very inadequate measure of the rate of technological change. A better measure is the total productivity index, which relates changes in output to changes in both labor and capital inputs. The rate of growth of total productivity seems to have varied considerably among industries and nations. Over the long run, it seems to have been higher in communications and transportation than in mining, manufacturing, and farming. Comparing the United States with Germany, Japan, Canada, and the United Kingdom during the postwar period, our rate of productivity growth seems lower than that of

Germany and Japan, but at least equal to that of Canada and the United Kingdom. The total productivity index is not the only measure of the rate of technological change. On the basis of various simplifying assumptions regarding the nature of the production function and the way it shifts over time, economists have devised somewhat more sophisticated measures; some assume that technological change is disembodied, others that it is capital-embodied. These measures suffer from very important limitations, but used with proper caution, they are useful guides.

The rate of growth of labor productivity in the United States seems to have varied appreciably over time. There is considerable evidence that it increased after World War I and that it increased again after World War II. However, in the period after World War II, the available evidence suggests that, although the rate of technological change may have been somewhat higher than in prewar days, the difference, if it exists, is smaller than is indicated by the behavior of labor productivity. Attempts are constantly being made by firms and government agencies to forecast the rate and direction of technological change. Technological forecasts are generally based on expert opinion, extrapolation of statistical trends, or mathematical models of the process by which new processes and products are created and adopted. The use of reasonably sophisticated models in this area is still in its infancy. At present, they seem better suited to forecasting the diffusion of new methods that are already beginning to be used, rather than the occurrence and impact of future inventions.

CHAPTER III

INDUSTRIAL RESEARCH
AND DEVELOPMENT

1. SCIENCE, TECHNOLOGY, AND INDUSTRIAL LABORATORIES

In the previous chapter, it was pointed out that the rate and direction of technological change depends on the extent and nature of the research and development [1] (R and D) carried out by private industry, government, and universities. This chapter is concerned with industrial research and development. We look at the nature of industrial research and development, the size and composition of industry's R and D expenditures, the organization and management of industrial R and D, and the role of various types of firms and independent inventors in the process by which new technology is created.

The first thing to note is that the organized application of science to

---

[1] According to the National Science Foundation definitions, which are used throughout this book, research and development "includes basic and applied research in the sciences (including medicine) and in engineering, and design and development of prototypes and processes. It does not include quality control, routine product testing, market research, sales promotion, sales service, research in the social sciences or psychology, or other nontechnological activities or technical services." K. Sanow, "Development of Statistics Relating to Research and Development Activities in Private Industry," *Methodology of Statistics on Research and Development*, National Science Foundation, 1959, p. 124. Also see notes 4, 5, and 7 below.

advance technology is a relatively new thing. Until the middle of the nineteenth century, the connection between science and technology was very loose. The periods when science flourished did not coincide with those when technology was moving ahead most rapidly. When they did flourish together, it was not necessarily at the same place. On balance, science was far more indebted to technology than technology was to science. For example, magnetism was known as an empirical fact, and had been used to construct compasses for centuries before the physicists began studying the subject in the eighteenth and nineteenth centuries. During the second half of the last century, science and technology began to draw somewhat closer together, and science began to take the lead in some areas. The beginnings of the synthetic drug and dye industries were related to previous discoveries in chemistry. The application of the dynamo was an outgrowth of Faraday's pioneering work that had taken place about forty years before. The telegraph cable was related to scientific work during the first half of the century. Nonetheless, the relation between science and technology during this period was on the whole quite remote.[2]

Toward the end of the nineteenth century, as the connection between science and technology gradually became closer, commercial research laboratories began to appear. The first organized research laboratory in the United States was established by Thomas Edison in 1876. In 1886, Arthur D. Little, an applied scientist and a missionary of applied science to industry, started his firm. Eastman Kodak (1893), B. F. Goodrich (1895), General Electric (1900), and DuPont (1902) were some of the earliest manufacturing firms to establish laboratories; the Bell Telephone System (1907) was among the first utilities to do so. These companies recognized the potential profitability of in-house research activities. For example, in the case of General Electric, the company was impressed by its debt to Faraday, Maxwell, and other European scientists and hoped to establish corresponding lines of inquiry in the United States.

The industrial laboratory constituted a significant departure from previous days when invention was mainly the work of independent inventors like Eli Whitney (cotton gin), Robert Fulton (steamboat), Samuel Morse (telegraph), Charles Goodyear (vulcanization of rubber), and Cyrus McCormick (reaper). These men were responsible for an extremely rich crop of inventions, some of which established whole new industries. As we shall

---

[2] See H. Bode, "Reflections on the Relation Between Science and Technology," *Basic Research and National Goals*, National Academy of Sciences, 1965; J. Conant, *Science and Common Sense*, New Haven, Conn.: Yale University Press, 1951; D. de Solla Price, *Little Science, Big Science*, New York: Columbia University Press, 1963; T. Kuhn, *The Structure of Scientific Revolutions*, Chicago: Chicago University Press, 1962; the latter's "Comment" in *The Rate and Direction of Inventive Activity*, National Bureau of Economic Research, 1962; and National Academy of Sciences, *Applied Science and Technological Progress*, House Committee on Science and Astronautics, 1967.

see in subsequent sections, the advent of the industrial laboratory did not result in the total displacement of the independent inventor. On the contrary, independent inventors continue to produce a significant share of the important inventions, although their relative importance seems to have declined.

During the twentieth century, the number of industrial laboratories grew by leaps and bounds. By World War I, there were perhaps 100 industrial research laboratories in the United States, most of them being in the new fields of electricity and chemistry. The number tripled during the war, and with confidence in organized research increased by wartime successes, most of the new laboratories remained in existence during peacetime. The number increased again during World War II, and by 1960 there were more than 5,400 industrial research laboratories.[3]

2. THE NATURE OF INDUSTRIAL RESEARCH AND DEVELOPMENT

Research and development encompasses work of many kinds, and it is important that we identify the various types. First, there is basic research,[4] which is aimed purely at the creation of new knowledge. Its purpose is to permit changes in ways of looking at phenomena and activities, to identify and measure new phenomena, and to create new devices and methods for testing various theories. For example, the biologist who tries to understand how and why certain cells proliferate, without having any particular application in mind, is carrying out basic research. Industrial laboratories carry out some basic research, but it is a very small proportion of their efforts. The principal bastions of basic research in our society are the universities. Second, there is applied research,[5] which is research expected to have a practical pay-off. Projects of this sort might be directed at ways of making steel resist stresses at particular temperatures, ways of inhibiting

[3] See L. Silk, *The Research Revolution,* New York: McGraw-Hill, Inc., 1960.

[4] According to the National Science Foundation, basic research includes "research projects which represent original investigation for the advancement of scientific knowledge and which do not have specific commercial objectives, although they may be in fields of present or potential interest to the reporting company." See K. Sanow, *op. cit.,* p. 124. The definition for government agencies and universities is somewhat different. "Basic research is that type of research which is directed toward increase of knowledge in science. It is research where the primary aim of the investigator is a fuller knowledge or understanding of the subject under study, rather than, as in the case with applied research, a practical application thereof." *Ibid,* p. 75.

[5] Applied research includes "research projects which represent investigation directed to discovery of new scientific knowledge and which have specific commercial objectives with respect to either products or processes. Note that this definition of applied research differs from the definition of basic research chiefly in terms of the objective of the reporting company." *Ibid,* p. 124. Note 4 contains the definition for government agencies and universities.

the growth of streptococci, or ways of obtaining the energy from atomic fission directly as electricity. The distinction between basic and applied research is fuzzy. Essentially, the distinction is based on the motivation of the researcher, basic research being aimed at new knowledge for its own sake, applied research being aimed at practical and commercial advances. In many cases both motives are present, and it is difficult to classify a particular project in this way.

The nature of industrial research projects can be illustrated by the history of the transistor, which was the result of a research project started in 1946 at the Bell Telephone Laboratories. Before and during World War II, Bell and a number of other laboratories supported extensive research on semiconductors. During 1945, William Shockley persuaded the Bell management to intensify its work in this area. A research group composed of physicists, chemists, and metallurgists was formed, the general scientific aim of the program being to obtain as complete an understanding as possible of semiconductor phenomena on the basis of atomic theory. Shockley was particularly interested in the prospects for a solid-state amplifier, and experiments were devised to see if such a gadget worked as theory said it should. When it did not, new theories were proposed and new experiments were performed, one of these experiments providing the first indication of the transistor effect.[6]

The transistor is by no means the only research achievement of fundamental importance that has emerged from industrial laboratories. The discovery of electron diffraction and the wave properties of electrons by Davisson and Germer of the Bell Telephone Laboratories brought Davisson the 1937 Nobel Prize in physics. Irving Langmuir of General Electric received the 1932 Nobel Prize in chemistry. Many other achievements could be noted. Nonetheless, it would be a serious mistake to think that most industrial research is concerned with such fundamental and major goals as these projects. On the contrary, much of it is, as one would expect, rather limited in scope and focused closely on particular applications.

Third, there is development,[7] which is aimed at the reduction of research findings to practice. Development projects are of many kinds. The more advanced development projects aim at the construction of entirely new

[6] In the summer of 1948, the Bell Telephone Laboratories announced the invention of the point contact transistor, and in 1951, the junction transistor. See R. Nelson, "The Link Between Sciences and Invention: The Case of the Transistor," *The Rate and Direction of Inventive Activity*, National Bureau of Economic Research, 1962.

[7] Development includes "technical activity concerned with non-routine problems which are encountered in translating research findings or other general scientific knowledge into products or processes. It does not include routine technical services to customers or other items excluded from definition of research and development above." Sanow, *op. cit.* The definition for government and universities is "the systematic use of scientific knowledge directed toward the production of useful materials, devices, systems, or methods, including design and development of prototypes and processes. It excludes quality control or routine product testing." *Ibid*, p. 75.

types of products and processes; the more routine development projects, which often constitute the bulk of the total, aim only at relatively minor modification of products already brought into being by previous research and development. By the time a project reaches the development stage, much of the uncertainty regarding its technical feasibility has been removed, but there usually is considerable uncertainty regarding the cost of development, time to completion, and utility of the outcome. The development phase of a project is generally more expensive than the research phase. There is a long road from a preliminary sketch, showing schematically how an invention should work, to the blueprints and specifications for the construction of the productive facilities. The tasks that are carried out depend, of course, on the nature and purpose of the development project. In some cases, various types of experiments must be made, and prototypes must be designed and developed. Frequently, pilot plants are built and the experience with the pilot plant is studied before large-scale production is attempted. The construction of adequate materials and the design of new ways to work with these new materials are sometimes of crucial importance: In the development of the transistor, particularly the silicon transistor, it was important to find materials in a very pure form; and in the development of the jet engine, it was important to find metals which would withstand abnormal stresses and strains.

An instructive example of development can be found in the history of penicillin. In 1928 Alexander Fleming, Professor of Bacteriology at the University of London, discovered that penicillin destroyed bacteria. Professors Raistrick and Florey took up the tasks of extracting penicillin from the growing mold, making it stable, and increasing its yield. The beginning of the development stage can perhaps be regarded as 1941, when Florey encouraged American drug manufacturers to produce penicillin on a large scale. The problem of producing a mold on an industrial scale under absolutely sterile conditions was an extremely difficult one. A laboratory of the Department of Agriculture suggested deep culture fermentation, which was one of the important steps toward final success. A number of drug firms built plants for large-scale production, but there were serious problems of bacterial contamination, sterile zones had to be created in the factories, and techniques were needed to sterilize large volumes of air to prevent bacteria from reaching the culture fluid. Gradually, however, the problems were solved and the new processes became routinized.[8]

Development projects often proceed along the following lines. First, a technical objective is provided or identified. After using scientific knowledge of various sorts to identify problems and after designing and analyzing critical experiments to make sure that the desired result is physically possible, the developer generates one or more design concepts that theo-

[8] J. Jewkes, D. Sawers, and R. Stillerman, *The Sources of Invention*, New York: St. Martin's Press, Inc., 1958, pp. 23–25.

retically will attain the objective. Second, the design concepts are analyzed to specify the characteristics of the subsystems, components, and materials. The basic design concept is qualitative and schematic, and it is necessary to proceed by concept, analysis, and test through the various areas of uncertainty until at least one apparent solution is found for each problem. At this stage, considerable attention is devoted to the probable cost and performance of the item under development and the time required for development. A preliminary design emerges, which together with the related analysis and experimentation allows a working prototype to be designed in detail. Third, there is the process of detailed design, during which instructions are formulated for the purchase of materials, for the construction of components, and for the assembly of the prototype. Detailed design is sometimes started in parallel with preliminary design, but this means the work is subject to constant correction as the preliminary design evolves. After the design is frozen, proposed improvements tend to be rejected if they cause delay. Fourth, the prototype is tested, altered to eliminate defects, and tested again. Hopefully, it eventually reaches an acceptable level of performance.[9]

The distinction between research and development is often rather hazy. The differences between them relate primarily to the orientation of the work, the degree of uncertainty inherent in a given problem, and the length of time work can be expected to proceed without demonstrable pay-off. Research tends to be oriented more toward the search for new knowledge (rather than toward the capacity to produce a particular product), to involve greater uncertainty of outcome, and to require more time for maturity than development. Nonetheless, although research and development are not the same things, in a particular project, a hard-and-fast distinction between research and development may be very difficult to make.[10]

3. NYLON: A CASE STUDY OF INDUSTRIAL RESEARCH AND DEVELOPMENT

A further illustration of the nature of industrial research and development is provided by nylon, one of the most significant inventions in the twentieth century. The story begins in 1927 when DuPont decided to support a pro-

---

[9] These steps are described as a straightforward sequence, but in reality there is a feedback from later steps to earlier ones to refine concepts and assumptions. See M. O'Brien, "Technological Planning and Misplanning," *Technological Planning on the Corporate Level*, edited by J. Bright, Cambridge, Mass.: Harvard University Press, 1961.

[10] For further discussion of the nature of research and development, see D. Novick, "What Do We Mean by Research and Development?," *California Management Review*, 1959; and his testimony before the Senate Subcommittee on Antitrust and Monopoly, May 27, 1965.

gram of fundamental research. In accord with the primary aim of this program, which was to discover scientific knowledge regardless of immediate commercial value, the company set aside about $250,000 per year for a number of research projects in chemistry. Wallace H. Carothers, a 32-year-old chemist who had taught at Harvard and Illinois, was offered the direction of the group and joined the firm in 1928. At DuPont, Carothers continued work he had started at Harvard on condensation polymers, and his early work at DuPont yielded considerable fundamental knowledge of polymerization. At first this information was purely of academic value, but something occurred in 1930 during an experiment with a polyester made from ethylene glycol and sebacic acid which was destined to be of great practical value. While cleaning out a reaction vessel in which he had been making one of these polymers, one of Carothers' associates discovered in pulling a stirring rod out of the reaction vessel that he pulled out a fiber. Moreover, he noted its unusual flexibility and strength, as well as its remarkable ability to cold draw. Although fibers of this original superpolymer were not of practical use because they were easily softened by hot water, they suggested that some related compound might possess characteristics suitable for making commercial fibers.

Additional investigation was undertaken. Numerous superpolymers were synthesized, but each was deficient in some important respect. Discouraged, Carothers gave up the project in 1930 and DuPont seriously considered dropping the work. But the director of the Chemical Department urged Carothers to review his findings and continue the work. Carothers turned his attention to the polyamides and found that several polyamides, when extruded through a spinneret improvised from a hypodermic needle, produced filaments from which fibers could be made. These new polyamides seemed extremely promising. After further experimentation, Carothers and his associates developed a polyamide from which strong, tough, elastic, water-resistant fiber could be made. This polymer, which they called "66" polymer, is made by the reaction between hexamethylene diamine and adipic acid. Textile experts chose this polymer for commercial development, and although many other polyamides have been evaluated since, it is still the type most commonly used for textile purposes. The resulting fiber was called nylon.

During the next two years DuPont scientists and engineers tackled "the development on a laboratory scale of the manufacturing processes for the intermediates, the polymer and nylon yarn, and the development on a semi-works scale of the chemical engineering data for the erection and operation of a large-scale plant." [11] After many trial runs, yarn for an experimental batch of stockings was available in April 1937. In July 1938, a pilot plant was completed. In October 1938, DuPont announced its inten-

[11] E. Bolton, "Development of Nylon," *Industrial and Engineering Chemistry*, January 1942, p. 6.

tion of building a commercial plant with an annual capacity of three million pounds, but before the plant was completed, its capacity was increased to eight million pounds. The R and D leading to nylon was very expensive and time consuming. Eleven years elapsed from the beginning of research on superpolymers to the production of nylon on the first commercial unit. Although there is some disagreement over the size of the R and D expenditures, even the lowest estimate is about $2 million. According to a representative from Imperial Chemical Industries, about $800,000 was spent prior to the construction of the pilot plant, about $400,000 was spent on the pilot plant, and about $800,000 was spent on sales development. Other estimates of the costs are much higher.

Nylon provides an interesting illustration of the uncertainties involved in research and development. The original fiber was discovered quite by accident, and the project was almost dropped prior to completion. Also, this case illustrates the large investment that is sometimes required to carry an R and D project to completion. It should be recognized, however, that not all projects are as far-reaching as this. Most industrial R and D is directed at much more modest goals.[12]

4. THE PROCESS OF INVENTION

"Invention" has been defined in many ways. According to one definition, an invention is a prescription for a new product or process that was not obvious to one skilled in the relevant art at the time the idea was generated. Other definitions add the requirement that the product or process must have prospective utility as well as novelty. This raises difficult questions as to how one is to find out whether a particular new product or process is prospectively useful, but it has the advantage of eliminating tinkering of an economically irrelevant sort. Thus, we include prospective utility as part of the definition.

Inventions can occur in either the research phase or the development phase of organized R and D activity. Generally, according to officials of the National Science Foundation, the central ideas come from research, and inventions in patentable form arise in the course of development. In addition, of course, many inventions occur through the efforts of independent inventors. How do inventions come about? According to one school of thought, they are due to the inspirations of genius, these inspirations not being susceptible to analysis. According to another school of thought, invention proceeds under the stress of necessity. If the great in-

---

[12] For further discussion of the research and development leading to nylon, see Jewkes, Sawers, and Stillerman, *op. cit.*; Bolton, *ibid.*; and W. Mueller, "The Origin of the Basic Inventions Underlying DuPont's Major Product and Process Innovations, 1920 to 1950," *The Rate and Direction of Inventive Activity*, National Bureau of Economic Research, 1962.

ventive geniuses had never lived, the same inventions would have been made by others without serious delay. When the time is ripe they are inevitable. Neither of these views is taken very seriously at the present time. The first is useless because the emergence of inventions is regarded as inexplicable. The second minimizes the significance of individual effort, ignores chance elements, and is too mechanistic.

Most economists view the situation differently. To them, invention is an activity characterized by great uncertainty, but one which nonetheless shares most of the characteristics of other economic activities. In particular, they hypothesize that the amount of resources devoted to inventing in a particular field is dependent both on the social demand for inventions of this type and on the prospective costs of making the invention, the latter being related to the state of scientific knowledge. This, of course, is a variant of the conventional theories of expected profit or utility maximization. However, there is no intention of characterizing the inventor as an "economic man." It is recognized that, besides having economic motives, inventors invent for fun, fame, and the service of mankind, and perhaps to express the "instinct of workmanship" or the "instinct of contrivance." [13]

It is also recognized that invention is inherently a very difficult process to analyze, map out, organize, and direct. Contrary to popular impression, this process frequently moves from the observation of a phenomenon to exploration of a use for it, not from a clearly defined goal to the discovery of technical means to achieve this goal. The process "does not usually move in a straight line, according to plan, but takes unexpected twists and turns."[14] Need and technique interact with one another, and it is not always apparent ahead of time from what disciplines or technologies answers will come. For example, a process for drawing brass rod arose from an adaptation of candle-making technology. Moreover, in trying to solve one problem, an answer to quite a different problem may result. Thus, Avicel, the non-nutritive food, was invented by an American Viscose Company chemist in the course of attempting to produce stronger rayon tire cord.

Turning to the psychological aspects of the process, some, like Abbot Usher,[15] postulate the existence of four steps leading to a successful invention. First, a problem of some kind is perceived. Second, the elements or data necessary for solving the problem are assembled through some particular set of events or train of thought, one of the elements being an indi-

[13] See J. Schmookler, *Invention and Economic Growth*, Cambridge, Mass.: Harvard University Press, 1966; F. Taussig, *Inventors and Money Makers*, New York: The Macmillan Company, 1915; and T. Veblen, *The Instinct of Workmanship and the State of the Industrial Arts*, New York: The Macmillan Company, 1914.

[14] See D. Schon, *Technology and Change*, New York: Delacorte Press, 1967, Chapter I.

[15] A. Usher, *A History of Mechanical Inventions*, Cambridge, Mass.: Harvard University Press, 1954.

vidual with the required skill in manipulating the other elements. Third, an act of insight occurs, in which the solution of the problem is found. Fourth, there is a period of critical revision in which the solution becomes more fully understood and is worked into a broader context. To illustrate what Usher means by an act of insight, consider James Watt's most fundamental invention in the field of steam engine technology—the separate condenser. In 1763, a small model of the Newcomen steam engine was brought for repairs to Watt, a twenty-eight-year-old mathematical instrument maker at the University of Glasgow. Watt was perplexed by several aspects of the model's operation. After some experimentation, he recognized a deficiency in the engine's concept. Then while strolling on the green of Glasgow "on a fine Sabbath afternoon" early in 1765, "the idea came into my mind that as steam was an elastic body it would rush into a vacuum, and if a connection were made between the cylinder and an exhausting vessel it would rush into it and might there be condensed without cooling the cylinder . . . I had not walked farther than the golf house, when the whole thing was arranged in my mind." [16]

Finally, a few words should be added regarding the characteristics of successful inventors. A study [17] based on a random sample of about 100 persons granted patents in 1953 indicates that about 50 percent were college graduates and that about 60 percent were technologists—engineers, chemists, metallurgists, and directors of research and development. Another study [18] investigates the age of inventors when they made "very important" inventions. In proportion to the number of inventors alive at various ages, very significant inventions were made at the highest average rate when inventors were not more than thirty to thirty-four years old. Moreover, the mean age of the inventors of 554 great inventions was about thirty-seven years. Thus the most significant inventions seem to be largely the product of relatively young men.

[16] Quoted in *ibid.*, p. 71.
[17] J. Schmookler, "Inventors Past and Present," *Review of Economics and Statistics*, August 1957. Also, see J. Rossman, *The Psychology of the Inventor*, Inventors Publishing Company, 1931.
[18] H. Lehman, *Age and Achievement*, Princeton, N.J.: Princeton University Press, 1953. It is also interesting to consider some of the recent studies of creativity by psychologists. Unfortunately, however, these studies are hampered by the extreme difficulty of measuring creativity. As crude measures, psychologists use a variety of devices, e.g., the ratings or judgments of experts in a field, or tests requiring individuals "to state defects or deficiencies in common implements or institutions; to produce words containing a specified letter or combination of letters; to produce in a limited time as many synonyms as they can for a stimulus word; to produce phrases or sentences; to name objects with certain properties . . .; or to give various uses for a common object." S. Golann, "Psychological Studies of Creativity," *Psychological Bulletin*, November 1963. Using crude measures of this sort, there have been numerous studies of the relationship of various factors with creativity. For example, controlling education and opportunity, there is evidence that creativity is positively correlated with I.Q. score. However, beyond an I.Q. of about 120, measured intelligence seems to be unrelated to creativity. For further discussion, see section 16.

5. EXPENDITURES ON RESEARCH AND DEVELOPMENT: GROWTH AND FLOW OF FUNDS

At this point, we should provide a brief description of the basic statistics regarding R and D expenditures in the United States. Recent decades have witnessed a tremendous growth in the amount spent on research and development. In 1945, industry performed about $1.3 billion worth of R and D; by 1963, this figure had increased to about $12.7 billion. In 1945, about $400 million of R and D was performed by government; by 1963, it performed about $2.4 billion of R and D. In 1945, the universities and other non-profit organizations performed about $200 million of R and D; by 1963 they performed about $2.2 billion.[19] Table 3.1 shows the enormous

[19] Extensive and detailed data on R and D expenditures have a relatively short history. After World War II, Vannevar Bush and the Research and Development Board of the Department of Defense prepared time series of total expenditures on R and D going back to 1920. In addition, the Harvard Business School conducted two surveys for 1951 and 1952, the purpose being to determine the volume and character of R and D performed and/or financed by firms of various kinds. See V. Bush, *Science, the Endless Frontier,* Government Printing Office, 1945; U.S. Department of Defense, *The Growth of Scientific Research and Development,* Washington, D.C., 1953; and D. Dearborn, R. Kreznek, and R. Anthony, *Spending for Industrial Research,* 1951–1952, Cambridge, Mass.: Harvard University Press, 1953.

In 1954, the National Science Foundation began to carry out its surveys of R and D expenditures. These surveys were much more detailed and complete than their predecessors, and they have become the foremost source of statistics on R and D in this country. Nonetheless, they are subject to a number of limitations. First, there are problems concerned with the definitions of R and D. In recent years, firms may have tended to inflate their estimate of the amount of R and D financed because of tax advantages and because of the favorable attitude of investors and others towards R and D. In addition, firms have had difficulties in separating development from production, applied research from development, and basic research from applied research. The problem of separating development from production and procurement is particularly difficult and important in the case of the Department of Defense. Depending on how one classifies expenditures on prototypes, the expenditures on R and D of the Department of Defense can vary a great deal. See W. Shapley, "Problems of Definition, Concept and Interpretation of Research and Development Statistics," *Methodology of Statistics on Research and Development,* National Science Foundation, 1959.

Second, these figures do not take account of changes over time in the value of the R and D dollar. Also, there are problems due to the fact that accounting records in many firms are not designed to yield data of this sort. Firms sometimes have difficulties in separating routine testing, quality control, and so forth, from R and D; they sometimes can report on the R and D performed in a central laboratory but not on that performed in individual operating divisions; they sometimes cannot separate costs of R and D from costs of production; and they sometimes (particularly in the aircraft industry) include R and D performed by firms to which they have subcontracted work, thus resulting in double counting. Finally, there are problems associated with the exclusion of geological and geophysical exploration and industrial social science research. See E. Johnson and H. Milton, "A Proposed Cost-of-Research Index," *IRE Transactions on Engineering Management,* December 1961; S. Kuznets, "Inventive Activity: Problems of Definition and Measurement," and H. Leibling,

increase in total R and D expenditures in the United States during the forties and fifties.[20] Paralleling this increase in R and D expenditures, there has been a great increase in the number of engineers and scientists engaged in research and development. In 1941, there were less than 90,000; in 1961, there were almost 400,000 (Table 3.1). Although the number of engineers

TABLE 3.1

Total R and D Expenditures and Number of Research Scientists and Engineers, United States, 1941–1962

YEAR	TOTAL R AND D EXPENDITURES (MILLIONS OF DOLLARS)	NUMBER OF RESEARCH SCIENTISTS AND ENGINEERS (THOUSANDS)
1941	900	87
1943	1,210	97
1945	1,520	119
1947	2,260	125
1949	2,610	144
1951	3,360	158
1953	5,160	223 [b]
1955	6,200	n.a.
1957	9,810	327 [c]
1959	12,430	n.a.
1961	14,380	387
1963 [a]	17,350	n.a.

Source: The Growth of Scientific Research and Development, U.S. Department of Defense, 1953, pp. 10 and 12; National Science Foundation Review of Data on Research and Development, No. 33, April 1962; and National Science Foundation Reviews of Data on Science Resources, Vol. I, No. 4, May 1965.

[a] Preliminary.
[b] 1954 figure.
[c] 1958 figure.
n.a. Not available.

"Comment on Kuznets and Sanders," both in the Rate and Direction of Inventive Activity, Princeton, N.J.: Princeton University Press, 1962; and H. Milton, "Cost-of-Research Index, 1920–65," Operations Research, November 1966.

[20] The 1945 figures in the text come from D. Keezer, D. Greenwald, and R. Ulin, "The Outlook for Expenditures on Research and Development During the Next Decade," American Economic Review, May 1960. They are not entirely comparable with the figures in the tables below.

Of course, part of the increase in R and D expenditures is undoubtedly due to inflation and shifting definitions of R and D, but it is generally agreed that if these factors could be taken into account, there still would be a tremendous growth in R and D expenditures.

Note too that, although R and D performance in manufacturing increased considerably during the sixties, the ratio of R and D expenditures to sales of R and D performers increased only from 4.2 percent in 1960 to 4.4 percent in 1964. See "Basic Research, Applied Research, and Development in American Industry, 1964," Review of Data on Science Resources, National Science Foundation, January 1966. Also, the increase in the Federal R and D budget seems to be slowing down. See Chapter VI.

and scientists engaged in R and D has increased at an impressive rate, it has not increased as rapidly as R and D expenditures. This is because the increases in demand for research personnel have resulted in higher salaries, and because less skilled labor and equipment seem to have been substituted where possible for the time of engineers and scientists.

It is also important to note that much of the R and D *performed* by one sector is *financed* by another sector. Table 3.2 shows that a large and

TABLE 3.2

Sources of R and D Funds and Performers of R and D, by Sector,
United States, 1953 and 1963

SOURCES OF R AND D FUNDS (SECTOR)	R AND D PERFORMANCE, BY SECTOR				
	FEDERAL GOVERN-MENT	INDUSTRY	COLLEGES AND UNIVER-SITIES	OTHER NON-PROFIT ORGANIZA-TIONS	TOTAL
	1953 TRANSFER OF FUNDS (MILLIONS OF DOLLARS)				
Federal government	1,010	1,430	260	60	2,760
Industry		2,200	20	20	2,240
Colleges and universities			120	—	120
Other nonprofit organizations			20	20	40
Total	1,010	3,630	420	100	5,160
	1963 TRANSFER OF FUNDS[a] (MILLIONS OF DOLLARS)				
Federal government	2,400	7,340	1,300	300	11,340
Industry		5,380	65	120	5,565
Colleges and universities			260	—	260
Other nonprofit organizations			75	110	185
Total	2,400	12,720	1,700	530	17,350

Source: National Science Foundation Reviews of Data on Science Resources, Vol. I, No. 4, May 1965.
[a] Preliminary figures.

increasing percentage of the R and D performed in the industrial sector is financed by the Federal government. In 1953, about 40 percent was financed in this way; in 1963, it had risen to about 60 percent. The situation is similar in the university sector. In 1953, about 60 percent of the R and D performed by the universities was financed by the government; in 1963, it had risen to about 75 percent. In addition, the Federal government financed a large and relatively stable (about 60 percent) portion of the R and D carried out by nonprofit organizations other than universities. Besides this massive outflow of funds from the Federal government to support R and D performed in other sectors, there were other flows of funds that are note-worthy, although much smaller. In recent years, industry financed about 4 percent of the R and D carried out by universities and about 20 percent of the R and D carried out by nonprofit organizations other than univer-sities. Nonprofit organizations, such as the private foundations, financed about 4 percent of the R and D performed by colleges and universities.

6. INTERINDUSTRY DIFFERENCES IN EXPENDITURES

Which industries spend most on R and D? Which spend least? How much goes for basic research? Applied research? Development? How much goes for new products? Product improvements? New processess? These ques-

TABLE 3.3

Performance of Industrial Research and Development, by Industry, 1927–1961

INDUSTRY	1927	1937	1951	1957[a]	1961[a]
			(PERCENT OF SALES)		
Aircraft and parts	n.a.	n.a.	11.9	18.9	24.2
Instruments	n.a.	n.a.	3.0	7.3	7.3
Electrical equipment	0.54	1.5	3.6	11.0	10.4
Chemicals	0.42	1.1	1.5	3.5	4.6
Rubber	0.36	0.96	0.5	n.a.	2.2
Machinery	0.19	0.43	0.5	4.2	4.4
Stone, clay, and glass	0.13	0.43	0.4	n.a.	1.8
Motor vehicles	0.07	0.4	0.5 ⎫	2.9 ⎫	2.9
Other transportation equipment	0.07	0.07	0.3 ⎭		
Primary metals and products	0.07	0.17	n.a.	n.a.	n.a.
Fabricated metal	n.a.	n.a.	0.3	1.5	1.3
Primary metal	n.a.	n.a.	0.2	0.5	0.8
Petroleum	0.09	0.45	0.7	0.8	1.0
Paper	0.06	0.17	0.3	0.7	0.7
Food	0.02	0.04	0.10	0.3	0.3
Forest products	0.01	0.04	0.03	n.a.	0.5
Leather	0.01	0.02	0.03	n.a.	n.a.
Textiles and apparel	0.01	0.02	0.07	n.a.	0.6

Source: Y. Brozen, "Trends in Industrial Research and Development," *Journal of Business*, July 1960, Table 3, and *Research and Development in Industry, 1961*, National Science Foundation, 1964.

[a] The 1957 and 1961 figures are not entirely comparable with the earlier ones. See the *Source*.

n.a. Not available.

tions are obviously basic ones. Fortunately, the National Science Foundation's annual surveys of American industry help to answer many of them.

In the sixties, R and D performance as a percentage of sales has been highest in the aircraft, electrical equipment, instrument, and chemical industries (Table 3.3). Of course, this is due in considerable part to the fact that these industries carry out a great deal of R and D for the Federal

TABLE 3.4

Research and Development Performance and Amount Financed by Federal Government, by Industry, 1964

INDUSTRY	R AND D PERFORMANCE	AMOUNT FINANCED BY FEDERAL GOVERNMENT
	(MILLIONS OF DOLLARS)	
Food and kindred products	135	n.a.
Paper and allied products	73	——
Chemicals and allied products	1,284	230
Industrial chemicals	856	172
Drugs and medicines	235	11
Other chemicals	193	47
Petroleum refining and extraction	337	27
Rubber products	150	26
Stone, clay, and glass products	133	10
Primary metals	191	8
Primary ferrous products	113	2
Nonferrous and other metal products	78	6
Fabricated metal products	152	18
Machinery	1,028	258
Electrical equipment and communication	2,635	1,628
Communication equipment and electronic components	1,480	973
Other electronic equipment	1,154	655
Motor vehicles and other transportation equipment	1,189	324
Aircraft and missiles	5,097	4,607
Professional and scientific instruments	483	208
Scientific and mechanical measuring instruments	210	120
Optical, surgical, photographic, and other instruments	273	88
Textiles	32	2
Lumber	11	n.a.

Source: National Science Foundation Reviews of Data on Science Resources, No. 7, January 1966.
n.a. Not available.

government. In 1964, the Federal government financed about 90 percent of the R and D in the aircraft industry, 60 percent of the R and D in the electrical equipment industry, and 40 percent of the R and D in the instruments industry. The situation in all industries in 1964 is shown in Table 3.4.

TABLE 3.5

Percent Distribution of Funds for the Performance of Basic Research, Applied Research, and Development, by Industry, 1964

INDUSTRY	BASIC RESEARCH	APPLIED RESEARCH	DEVEL- OPMENT	TOTAL
	(PERCENT)			
Food and kindred products	9	47	44	100
Paper and allied products	3	36	62	100
Chemicals and allied products	13	n.a.	n.a.	100
Industrial chemicals	13	n.a.	n.a.	100
Drugs and medicines	16	49	35	100
Other chemicals	n.a.	23	68	100
Petroleum refining and extraction	15	45	39	100
Rubber products	7	20	73	100
Stone, clay, and glass products	5	35	59	100
Primary metals	6	37	57	100
Primary ferrous products	7	n.a.	n.a.	100
Nonferrous and other metal products	4	43	53	100
Fabricated metal products	3	23	75	100
Machinery	2	14	84	100
Electrical equipment and communication	5	14	81	100
Communication equipment and electronic components	8	16	76	100
Other electrical equipment	2	12	86	100
Motor vehicles and other transportation equipment	3	n.a.	n.a.	100
Aircraft and missiles	1	16	83	100
Professional and scientific instruments	n.a.	n.a.	77	100
Scientific and mechanical measuring instruments	3	11	86	100
Optical, surgical, photographic, other instruments	n.a.	n.a.	n.a.	100
Textiles	3	50	47	100

Source: National Science Foundation Reviews of Data on Science Resources, No. 7, January 1966.
n.a. Not available.

When company-financed R and D rather than R and D performance is considered, the differences among industries are reduced, but the industries remain in much the same rank order—instruments, electrical equipment, chemicals, and machinery being highest. The amount of basic research, applied research, and development performed by each industry is shown in Table 3.5. Basic research constitutes the largest percentage of total R and D performance in the chemical and petroleum industries, but in no case does it exceed 20 percent of the total. Development is a particularly large percentage of the total in the aircraft, electrical equipment, and machinery industries. For all industries combined, about 4 percent of the total is basic research, 20 percent applied research, and 76 percent development. Thus, the bulk of the funds goes for development, not research.

A survey of business plans for new plant and equipment provides further information regarding the character of the R and D being carried out by industry. In all manufacturing industries combined, about 47 percent of the firms reported in 1962 that their main purpose was to develop new products, 40 percent reported that it was to improve existing products, and 13 percent reported that it was to develop new processes. Development of new products seemed to be particularly important in the electrical equipment, chemical, and fabricated metal industries. Improvement of existing products seemed to be particularly important in the transportation equipment, machinery, auto, steel, and textile industries. Development of new processes was particularly important in the petroleum and rubber industries.[21] Finally, Table 3.6 shows that a considerable amount of the applied research and development performed in one industry is directed at products in another industry. In large part this is because firms classified in one industry are often in other industries as well. For example, many large petroleum refiners are chemical producers. In addition, it is because firms look somewhat beyond their own product lines for profitable R and D projects. An important moral of Table 3.6 is that one should not assume that all—or almost all—of the R and D performed in an industry is directed at its own products.

We must look more closely at the large interindustry differences in the ratio of company-financed R and D expenditures to sales and investigate the reasons why these differences exist.[22] At least three factors seem to be important. First, industries differ considerably in the value their customers place on increased performance. Being second best in product performance in some fields is not a great handicap because consumers do not care very much about the difference in performance; in other industries, a second-best product has relatively little value. For example, improvements in drugs

[21] These figures pertain to 1962, but it seems doubtful that there has been much of a change since then.

[22] Chapter VI discusses the factors influencing the level and allocation of government R and D expenditures.

TABLE 3.6

Funds for Applied Research and Development Performance, by Industry and Product Field, Selected Industries, 1962

Product Field	Industry (Millions of Dollars)								
	Chemicals[a]	Petroleum	Primary Metals	Fabricated Metals	Machinery	Electrical Equipment[b]	Motor Vehicles[c]	Aircraft[d]	Instruments
Aircraft	n.s.a.	n.s.a.	n.s.a.	1	30	144	41	925	6
Atomic Energy	91	n.s.a.	2	24	12	280	3	116	2
Chemicals	561	68	n.s.a.	n.s.a.	9	18	9	n.s.a.	11
Drugs	182	n.s.a.	n.s.a.	—	n.s.a.	173	n.s.a.	—	n.s.a.
Electrical equipment	n.s.a.	—	3	4	n.s.a.	n.s.a.	45	11	19
Communication equipment	3	n.s.a.	2	8	139	1,207	166	497	100
Fabricated metals	8	—	13	40	16	14	20	6	6
Food	18	n.s.a.	n.s.a.	3	n.s.a.	n.s.a.	n.s.a.	n.s.a.	n.s.a.
Missiles	11	—	5	1	106	191	68	2,176	70
Machinery	n.s.a.	n.s.a.	n.s.a.	n.s.a.	504	n.s.a.	62	n.s.a.	n.s.a.
Motor vehicles	n.s.a.	—	4	1	21	4	530	25	6
Petroleum	9	167	n.s.a.	1	1	n.s.a.	n.s.a.	n.s.a.	n.s.a.
Primary metals	9	n.s.a.	103	4	3	8	8	2	n.s.a.
Instruments	4	9	1	4	3	54	2	19	137
Rubber	6	n.s.a.	1	1	1	1	n.s.a.	n.s.a.	1
Stone, clay, and glass	3	n.s.a.	2	3	n.s.a.	4	n.s.a.	1	n.s.a.
Other	n.s.a.	n.s.a.	9	n.s.a.	39	65	29	257	46
Total	1,053	258	168	145	895	2,289	987	4,085	434

Source: Basic Research, Applied Research, and Development in Industry, 1962, National Science Foundation, 1965.
[a] Includes drugs.
[b] Includes communication.
[c] Includes other transportation equipment.
[d] Includes missiles.
n.s.a. Not separately available but included in total.

seem to have great importance for consumers in the sense that they are willing to pay more for a more effective medicine. In industries where this is the case, it is not surprising that the ratio of R and D expenditures to sales tends to be high. Second, industries seem to differ considerably in the ease with which research and development can bring about significant inventions. Although an industry's "science base" is a very slippery concept, it is difficult to deny that some industries, like electronics and chemicals, lie closer to well-developed basic sciences than others and that for this reason the effectiveness of a given amount of research and development may be greater than in other industries.[23] Third, industries differ in market structure. Industries composed of many very small firms are unlikely to spend as much on R and D as somewhat less fragmented industries do. More will be said on this score in section 22.

Of course, the fact that some industries spend much more than others on R and D does not mean that the latter are spending too little. As we noted in Chapter II, an industry's rate of technological change depends on the nature and extent of the research and development carried out by other industries, as well as its own. Many industries, particularly those producing consumer goods, rely on their suppliers and equipment producers to carry out research and development. In effect, they buy R and D, incorporated in new products, from their suppliers. Other industries, like agriculture, medicine, and aviation, rely in an important way on research and development carried out by government laboratories. There are advantages in certain industries specializing more than others in research and development. Whether this specialization has gone too far is hard to say; the issues are discussed at some length in Chapter VII.

7. The Firm's Research and Development Budget

We turn now to the decision-making process within the individual firm. Ideas and proposals for R and D projects arise from many sources. Customers often point out, and press for, improvements in the firm's product. The sales and production divisions of the firm sometimes make suggestions. New developments in science or innovations made by competitors often stimulate new projects. According to one study of over 100 large companies, 60 percent of the topics originated within the research department, 17 percent came from the sales department, 9 percent came from manage-

[23] See Y. Brozen, "R and D Differences Among Industries"; F. Scherer, "Comment on Brozen and Merrill"; and E. Ames, "Comment on Merrill and Brozen"; all in R. Tybout, *The Economics of Research and Development*, Columbus, Ohio: Ohio State University Press, 1965. Also, see W. Comanor "Research and Competitive Product Differentiation in the Pharmaceutical Industry in the United States," *Economica*, November 1964.

ment, and 4 percent came from customers. The R and D department was a more important source of ideas in the chemical, pharmaceutical, and food industries than in the others; the sales department was a particularly important source in the metallurgical industries; and the government was a particularly important source in the electronics and aerospace industries.[24]

What determines how much a firm spends on research and development? In the short run, there often is a tendency for firms to maintain a fairly constant ratio between R and D expenditures and sales, some executives using such ratios as rules of thumb.[25] In the longer run, firms obviously change their desired ratio of R and D expenditures to sales, particularly in response to changes in the prospective profitability of research and development. Although the profitability of R and D is very difficult to measure and firms can make only crude attempts to do so, there is considerable evidence that their estimates of this variable play an important role in determining the size of their R and D expenditures.[26] The size of a firm's R and D budget is also influenced by a kind of "bandwagon effect." Research by one segment of an industry tends to bring forth research in other segments of the same and other industries, both because it creates competitive pressures and makes additional research profitable, and because firms, like people, tend to follow the leader. Still another factor is the emphasis firms seem to place on the stability of their R and D programs; they try to avoid an expansion of their program which may soon have to be cut back.[27] Moreover, because of the costs involved in rapid expansion, they try to build up to a desired level over a period of years.

These factors have been incorporated into a single econometric model.[28] According to this model, a firm sets its expenditures so as to move part way from the previous year's level toward a desired level that depends on the firm's expectation regarding the average profitability of the R and D projects at hand, the profitability of alternative uses of its funds, and its size. The firm's speed of adjustment toward the desired level depends on the extent to which the desired level differs from the previous year's level and on the percent of its profits spent during the previous year on R and D.

[24] R. Seiler, *Improving the Effectiveness of Research and Development*, New York: McGraw-Hill Company, 1965, p. 133. Also see C. Carter and B. Williams, *Industry and Technical Progress*, New York: Oxford University Press, 1957. The roughness of these figures need not be labored.

[25] E. Mansfield, "Comment," *The Rate and Direction of Inventive Activity*, Princeton, N.J.: Princeton University Press, 1962; and N. Seeber, "Decision-Making on Research and Development in the Business Firm," *NSF Reviews of Data on Research and Development*, February 1964.

[26] E. Mansfield, *Industrial Research and Technological Innovation*, New York: W. W. Norton & Company, 1968, Chapter II.

[27] National Science Foundation, *Science and Engineering in American Industry*, Final Report on a 1953–1954 Survey, Washington, D.C., 1956.

[28] E. Mansfield, *op. cit.* An econometric model consists of one or more equations that give empirical content to economic theories designed to explain the phenomenon in question.

This model was formulated in part on the basis of interviews with research directors and other executives of a number of firms in the chemical and petroleum industries. For eight firms where the necessary data could be obtained, this model, in more specific and operational form, could fit historical data regarding these firms' expenditures quite well. Moreover, when supplemented with additional assumptions, it could fit the 1945–1958 data for thirty-five firms in five industries (petroleum, chemicals, drugs, glass, and steel) quite well, and it could do a reasonably good job of "forecasting" their 1959 expenditures. Of course, the model is a more apt description of decision making regarding applied research and development than basic research, but, as Table 3.5 points out, industry does relatively little basic research. Nonetheless, because of the small number of observations and the roughness of the basic data, the results are tentative.

8. PROJECT SELECTION

How does a firm decide which R and D projects to accept and which to reject? Perhaps the best way to begin answering this question is to describe briefly the procedure that is used in the central research laboratory of one of the nation's largest firms, a major equipment producer. This procedure is used for applied research and development, but not basic research. It is necessary here to consider only the projects proposed by the operating divisions, since the procedure for the others, excluding basic research, is much the same. Take the case in 1963. In the summer of 1962, the laboratory asked the divisions for proposals for 1963. For each research proposal, a division was requested to estimate (1) the probability of commercial success of the project (if technically successful), (2) the extra profit to the firm if the project were commercially successful, and (3) the investment required to put the research results into practice.

These proposals were then sent to the managers of the relevant laboratory departments, who made preliminary estimates of the cost of doing the R and D and the corresponding chance of technical success. On the basis of the information provided by the division and the department manager, the laboratory's project evaluation group, a small group of project analysts that report to the laboratory management, computed a "figure of merit" for each proposal and rated it "A," "B," or "C." [29] Given these ratings the division requests were returned to the department managers who then drew up their respective proposed R and D programs. It was recommended that the "A" proposals be given top priority and that the "C" proposals be

[29] The figure of merit was computed by multiplying the total estimated profit to the firm if the project was successful by the estimated probability of success and dividing by the sum of the estimated R and D costs and the investment required to put the research results into practice.

avoided. The department managers then formulated a number of research projects, each of which was aimed at satisfying one or more of the proposals. The laboratory management evaluated each proposal, decided whether to accept it or reject it, and suggested a level of expenditures on each project that it accepted. Finally, the resulting list of projects went to corporate management for approval.

A detailed study [30] of project selection in this laboratory suggests that expected profit maximization is of use in explaining the allocation of funds. The size of the budget proposed for a project can be explained fairly well by a model which assumes that proposed spending is increased to the point where the increase in the probability of success is no longer worth its cost. The alterations made by the laboratory management in the proposed budget also can be explained fairly well by a similar model. Note, however, that this model is rough, that the data are limited in both quantity and quality, and that about half of the variation in the allocation of funds remains unexplained. Four factors seem to account for much of this unexplained variation: (1) Holding expected profit constant, safe projects are preferred over risky ones; (2) Some attempt is made to satisfy scientific as well as commercial objectives, the consequence being that some projects are justified more on the basis of scientific interest than expected profit; (3) Intra-firm politics are important. For example, projects differ considerably in the amount of pressure applied by operating executives to have them carried out; (4) Some scientists and department managers are much more effective than others in arguing for their proposals and in mobilizing support for them.

To evaluate projects, most large firms seem to use quantitative criteria similar to the figure of merit used by this laboratory. Although the precise nature of these formulas varies from firm to firm, they tend to be relatively simple extensions of the criteria—like the pay-out period and the rate of return—used in capital budgeting. An important difficulty in these techniques is the fact that firms cannot estimate the factors that enter these formulas with much accuracy. For example, in this laboratory, a comparison of the estimate of the probability of a project's technical success (made prior to the beginning of the project) with the outcome of the project indicates that such estimates have some predictive value—but not much. Using these estimates as best one can, a correct prediction can be made in only about two thirds of the cases. And, according to a survey of research managements, the probability of technical success is among the easiest factors to estimate.[31]

[30] E. Mansfield, op. cit., Chapter III.

[31] E. Mansfield, op. cit. and R. Seiler, op. cit. For further discussion of allocation techniques, see N. Baker and W. Pound, "R and D Project Selection: Where We Stand," IEEE Transactions on Engineering Management, June 1964; C. Mottley and R. Newton, "The Selection of Projects for Industrial Research," Operations Research, November 1959; and J. Quinn, Yardsticks for Industrial Research, Ronald, 1959. Also see section 19.

As a new product or process moves from research toward the market, it is subjected to closer and closer scrutiny from both a technological and an economic viewpoint. When projects are first proposed, the screening may be relatively cursory and informal, since there is considerable uncertainty regarding the results and the costs are small. However, as projects go into development, costs increase and uncertainties decrease, the consequence being that detailed economic evaluation of the project becomes both more necessary and more feasible. Most of the projects that are accepted initially are scrapped before the development stage. For example, one study of twenty large firms reported that less than 2 percent of the initial proposals were forwarded for development. Many of the remaining proposals drop by the wayside as they travel the slippery path toward commercial introduction.[32]

9. MEASURING THE RETURNS FROM INDUSTRIAL RESEARCH AND DEVELOPMENT

Measuring the returns from research and development is as difficult as it is important. For some years, the McGraw-Hill Economics Department gathered data from firms regarding the *expected* profitability of their R and D programs. Table 3.7 shows for each industry, in 1958 and 1961, the distribution of firms classified by their expected pay-out period for research and development. Although the pay-out period is a very crude measure of profitability, it is all that is available on a widespread basis. According to McGraw-Hill economists, the 1958 expected returns on R and D were "significantly better than the typical return, or pay-off, on investment in new plant and equipment, . . . [which helps to] make it clear why many companies with a given amount of capital to reinvest found it profitable to increase the proportion going to research and development." [33] More recently, there is evidence that firms in many industries have become somewhat less optimistic concerning the prospective returns from additional research and development.

For a small group of firms and industries, some very tentative and experimental estimates have been made of the marginal rate of return from R and D expenditures, that is, the rate of return from an extra dollar spent on research and development.[34] If the production function is Cobb-Douglas,[35] if total past R and D expenditures as well as labor and capital are inputs, and if R and D expenditures have grown exponentially, one can

[32] Booz, Allen, and Hamilton, *Management of New Products,* New York, 1960.
[33] D. Keezer, D. Greenwald, and R. Ulin, *op. cit.,* p. 366.
[34] E. Mansfield, *op. cit.,* Chapter IV.
[35] The production function is Cobb-Douglas if $o = I_1^{\alpha 1} I_2^{\alpha 2} \ldots I_n^{\alpha n},$ where o is the output rate and $I_1 \ldots I_n$ are inputs. A special case is shown in note 4, Chapter II.

TABLE 3.7

Expected Average Pay-Out Periods from R and D Expenditures,
1958 and 1961

INDUSTRY	1958			1961		
	LESS THAN 3 YEARS	3 TO 5 YEARS	6 YEARS AND OVER	3 YEARS OR LESS	4 TO 5 YEARS	6 YEARS AND OVER
	(PERCENT OF COMPANIES ANSWERING)					
Iron and steel	50	50	0	38	50	12
Nonferrous metals	42	42	16	64	18	18
Machinery	49	45	6	51	39	10
Electrical machinery	23	69	8	61	32	7
Autos, trucks, and parts	40	60	0	54	40	6
Transportation equipment (Aircraft, ships, railroad equipment)	24	65	11	43	44	13
Fabricated metals and instruments	24	71	5	77	14	9
Chemicals	15	56	29	33	41	26
Paper and pulp	25	69	6	50	32	18
Rubber	50	17	33	38	38	24
Stone, clay, and glass	44	50	6	38	46	16
Petroleum and coal products	12	63	25	17	33	50
Food and beverages	37	54	9	54	43	3
Textiles	65	29	6	76	24	0
Miscellaneous manufacturing	66	31	3	71	25	4
All manufacturing	39	52	9	55	34	11

Source: McGraw-Hill Inc., *Business Plans for Expenditures on Plant and Equipment*, annual.

obtain relatively simple expressions for the marginal rate of return from research and development, whether technological change is capital-embodied or disembodied. If it is capital-embodied, the marginal rate of return is directly related to the elasticity of output with respect to total past R and D expenditures and the rate of investment, but inversely related to the amount spent in the past on R and D and the ratio of capital to output. If it is disembodied, the marginal rate of return is directly related to the elasticity of output with respect to total past R and D expenditures and inversely related to the ratio of total past R and D expenditures to present output.[36]

[36] The elasticity of output with respect to total past R and D expenditures is the percent increase in output that would result from a 1 percent increase in total past R and D expenditures. For a complete list of the factors that, under the assumed circumstances, influence the marginal rate of return, see E. Mansfield, *op. cit.*, Chapter IV.

Using these theoretical results, estimates of the marginal rates of return in 1960 were made for ten major chemical and petroleum firms and lower bounds for the marginal rates of return were estimated for ten manufacturing industries. Judging from the data for individual firms, the rate of return was very high in petroleum; in chemicals, it was high if technological change was capital-embodied but low if it was disembodied. The rate of return was directly related to a firm's size in chemicals, but inversely related to it in petroleum. Turning to the industry data, the rate of return seems to have been relatively high (15 percent or more) in the food, apparel, and furniture industries. These results are merely experimental and should be viewed with considerable caution. They are based on a number of highly simplified assumptions regarding the shape of the production function, and they contain substantial sampling errors. Moreover, they are incomplete estimates of the social rate of return, since they do not take account of the effects of increased R and D expenditures in one industry or firm on productivity in another industry or firm. (The social rates of return may be higher.) Finally, although it is easy to include lags in the effect of R and D expenditures on the production function, as well as a finite elasticity of supply [37] of R and D inputs to the firm, this was not done because of the lack of relevant data.

On the basis of the crude measurements that can be made, does it seem that a firm's output of significant inventions [38] is closely related to the amount it spends on R and D? Is there any evidence that the productivity of a firm's R and D activities increases with the amount spent on R and D? Is there any evidence that productivity is greater in large firms than in small ones? A study [39] has been made of the chemical, petroleum, and steel industries, using data regarding the number of significant inventions carried out by about ten large firms in each industry. Because of the roughness of the data, the results are crude and tentative. Nonetheless, they are of interest. Holding size of firm constant, the number of significant inventions carried out by a firm seems to be highly correlated with the size of its R and D expenditures. Thus, although the output from an individual R and D project is obviously very uncertain, it seems that there is a close relationship over the long run between the amount a firm spends on R and D and the total number of important inventions it produces.

The evidence from the study also suggests that increases in R and D expenditures in the relevant range (and holding size of firm constant) result in more than proportional increases in inventive output in chemicals. But in petroleum and steel, there is no real indication of either economies or diseconomies of scale within the relevant range. Thus, except for chem-

[37] The elasticity of supply is the percent increase in the amount supplied resulting from a 1 percent increase in the price.

[38] Note that an invention may be of great importance to the industry as a whole, but not particularly profitable to the firm responsible for the invention.

[39] E. Mansfield, *op. cit.*, Chapter II.

icals, the results do not indicate any marked advantage of very large-scale research activities over medium-sized and large ones. Finally, when a firm's expenditures on R and D are held constant, increases in size of firm seem to be associated in most industries with decreases in inventive output. Thus, the evidence suggests that the productivity of an R and D effort of given scale is lower in the largest firms than in the medium-sized and large ones.[40]

10. Uncertainty in Research and Development

Chance plays a crucial role in research and development, and a long string of failures often occurs before any sort of success is achieved. For example, a survey of 120 large companies doing a substantial amount of R and D indicates that, in half of these firms, at least 60 percent of the R and D projects never resulted in a commercially used product or process. (The smallest failure rate for any of these firms was 50 percent.) Moreover, even when a project resulted in a product or process that was used commercially, the profitability of its use was likely to be quite unpredictable.[41]

A study [42] carried out by the RAND Corporation goes further in describing the extent of the difficulties in predicting the results of military development projects. First, the RAND study showed that there were substantial errors in the estimates (made prior to development) of the costs of producing various types of military hardware. When adjusted for unanticipated changes in factor prices and production-lot sizes, the average ratio of the actual to estimated cost was 1.7 (fighters), 3.0 (bombers), 1.2 (cargoes and tankers), and 4.9 (missiles). Thus, the estimates made prior to the development of these types of equipment were, on the average, in error by several hundred percent—and almost always they understated the actual costs.

Second, the extent to which costs were understated was directly related to the extent of the technological advance. In cases where a "large" technological advance was required, the average ratio was 4.2; in cases where a "small" technological advance was required, the average ratio was 1.3. Moreover, when corrected for bias, there was much more variation in the ratio in cases where the required technological advance was large than in those where it was small. Of course, this is what one would expect.

[40] Note once again that these results are based on only a small amount of very rough data and that they pertain to only three industries. For some results based on the drug industry, see W. Comanor, "Research and Technical Change in the Pharmaceutical Industry," *Review of Economics and Statistics*, May 1965.

[41] *Chemical and Engineering News*, July 10, 1957. For estimates of the proportion of products emerging from research and development that fail at various stages see Chapter IV.

[42] A. Marshall and W. Meckling, "Predictability of the Costs, Time, and Success of Development," *The Rate and Direction of Inventive Activity*, Princeton, N.J.: Princeton University Press, 1962.

Third, there were very substantial errors in the estimated length of time it would take to complete a project. For ten weapons systems, the average error was two years, the maximum being five years. The average ratio of the actual to the expected length of time was 1.5, indicating once again that estimates tend to be overly optimistic. The results suggest too that the estimates are more accurate when "small" technological advances are required than when "large" technological advances must be made. Fourth, given the extent of the technological advance that had to be made, the estimates of costs and development time became more accurate as the project ran its course. For example, at the early stages of projects requiring advances of "medium" difficulty, the average ratio of the actual to expected cost was 2.15 and the standard deviation [43] was .57. At the middle stages of such projects, the average ratio was 1.32 and the standard deviation was .39. At the late stages of such projects, the average ratio was 1.06 and the standard deviation was .18.

These findings pertain entirely to military R and D. To some extent, they reflect the fact that defense contractors have had an incentive in the past to make optimistic estimates, the penalties for being over-optimistic often having been small and the possible rewards having been large. They also reflect the ambitious nature of development in the defense sphere. Nonetheless they are not an utterly undependable guide to the civilian economy. The errors in estimation in the civilian economy, although smaller than those presented above, are also quite large, particularly when large technological advances are attempted.[44]

11. LEARNING AND PARALLEL RESEARCH AND DEVELOPMENT EFFORTS

A research or development project can be regarded as a process of uncertainty reduction, or learning. Suppose, for example, that a firm, which is trying to fabricate a part, can use one of two alloys and that it is impossible to use standard sources to determine their characteristics. Suppose that strength is of paramount importance and that the firm's estimates of the strengths of the alloys—Alloy 1 and Alloy 2—are represented by the subjective probability distributions in Figure 3.1a. If the firm were forced to make a choice immediately, it would probably choose Alloy 1, since it believes there is better than a fifty-fifty chance that Alloy 1 will turn out to be stronger than Alloy 2. However, there is a good chance that this decision would turn out to be wrong, the consequence being that the part would be weaker than if Alloy 2 had been used. Thus, the firm may decide

---

[43] The standard deviation, a measure of dispersion, is the square root of the mean squared deviation of observations from their mean.

[44] E. Mansfield, *op. cit.*, Chapter III.

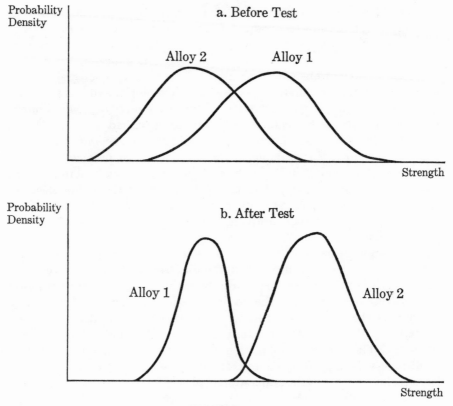

FIGURE 3.1

Subjective Probability Distributions of Strength of Alloys 1 and 2, before and after Test

to perform a test prior to making the selection. On the basis of the test results, the firm will formulate new estimates, represented by new probability distributions, such as those shown in Figure 3.1b. Because of the tests, uncertainty—as measured by the degree of overlap of the distributions—will be reduced.[45]

The process of uncertainty reduction lies at the heart of the development task. When a firm carries out a development project, it must answer four questions: What will be the approximate performance attributes for each of the components or subsystems comprising the desired system? How interrelated should the components be? How should the project's resources be distributed among various kinds of uncertainty-reducing activities—construction of mathematical models, review by specialists, testing of phys-

[45] This example is similar to one presented in T. Marschak, T. Glennan, and R. Summers, *Strategy for R and D*, New York, N.Y., Springer-Verlag, 1967. See any elementary textbook in statistics for a discussion of probability distributions.

ical models, prototype testing, and testing of production items? How many parallel approaches should be taken on each component? All of these questions, with the possible exception of the first, are concerned, at least in part, with the reduction of uncertainty.

Many development projects use parallel R and D efforts to help cope with uncertainty. For example, in the development of the atomic bomb, there were several methods of making fissionable materials, and no consensus existed among scientists as to which of these alternatives was most promising. To make sure that the best one was not discarded, all methods were pursued in parallel. The wisdom of this decision was borne out by the fact that the method that was first to produce appreciable quantities of fissionable material was one that had been considered relatively unpromising early in the development program.[46]

Under what conditions is it optimal to run parallel R and D efforts? What factors determine the optimal number of parallel efforts? Suppose that an R and D manager can select n approaches, spend M dollars on each one over a period of Θ months, pick the one that looks most promising at the end of the period, and follow it to completion, dropping the others. Suppose that the only relevant criterion is the extent of the development costs, the usefulness of the result and the development time being assumed to be the same regardless of what strategy is pursued. For further simplification, suppose that all approaches look equally promising and that the results of the approaches are independent.

Under these conditions, the optimal value of n—the number of parallel R and D efforts—is inversely related to M and directly related to the amount learned in the next Θ months. This result can be proved easily, but it requires some mathematics. Intuitively, it is eminently plausible. As the cost of running each effort increases, one would certainly expect the optimal number of parallel efforts to decrease. Moreover, as the prospective amount of learning increases, one would also expect the optimal number of parallel efforts to increase. This result is important because it puts in proper perspective some of the criticisms of "duplication" and "waste" in research and development. Contrary to popular belief, parallel efforts may produce results more quickly and more cheaply than attempting in advance to choose the optimal approach and concentrating all one's efforts on pursuing it. The fact that most of the parallel paths are ultimately rejected does not mean that they are a waste. On the contrary, given considerable uncertainty, this may be the cheapest way to proceed.[47]

[46] See J. Baxter, *Scientists Against Time*, Boston: Little, Brown & Company, 1947.
[47] See R. Nelson, "Uncertainty, Learning, and the Economics of Parallel Research and Development Efforts," *Review of Economics and Statistics*, 1961. Unfortunately, difficulties arise when one attempts to extend the solution to cases involving more than one decision point. See Marschak, Glennan, and Summers, *op. cit.* Also see F. Scherer, "Time-Cost Tradeoffs in Empirical Research Projects," *Naval Logistics Research Quarterly*, 1966.

12. DETERMINANTS OF DEVELOPMENT COSTS

What determines how much a particular development project will cost? First, there is the size and complexity of the product being developed. It takes more resources to redesign a big product with a large number of components, because there are more drawings to be made, more analyses to be done, and more tests to perform. Moreover, holding the number of components constant, the cost of developing a product tends to be directly related to the interdependence among these components. If there is considerable interdependence, a change in one part requires the redesign of other parts. Thus, the cost of making a major alteration tends to be high.

Second, there is the extent of the advance in performance that is sought. Larger advances generally mean higher costs because more components will need to be specially designed, more mistakes will be made, and more jobs will have to be redone. When larger advances are sought, there is generally more uncertainty surrounding the project; in extreme cases, it may even be difficult to tell which technological problems will be most important. Costs must be incurred to reduce the uncertainties; the project tends to be more expensive, if possible at all, than if it attempts a more modest advance in the state of the art.

Third, there is development time. Some economists have postulated that there exists a function—like that in Figure 3.2—which relates expected development time to the expected total quantity of resources employed in a development effort. Their principal point is that between N and R the time-cost function has a negative slope, indicating that time can be decreased only by increasing total cost. As the development schedule is shortened, more tasks must be carried out concurrently rather than sequentially, and since each task provides knowledge that is useful in carrying out the others, there are more false starts and wasted designs. Also, diminishing returns set in as more and more technical workers are assigned simultaneously to the development effort. It is argued that these factors offset the possibility that shorter development time eliminates unnecessary work and some overhead-type costs.[48]

Fourth, there is the stock of basic knowledge and of components and materials. The task of developing a particular product can be made much easier and cheaper by advances in basic knowledge which allow better

[48] See M. Peck and F. Scherer, *The Weapons Acquisition Process*, Cambridge, Mass.: Harvard University Press, 1962; F. Scherer, "Government Research and Development Programs," in *Measuring Benefits of Government Expenditure*, edited by R. Dorfman, Washington, D.C.: The Brookings Institution, 1965; and R. Kershner, "The Size of Research and Engineering Teams," *IRE Transactions on Engineering Management*, June 1958.

Development
Time

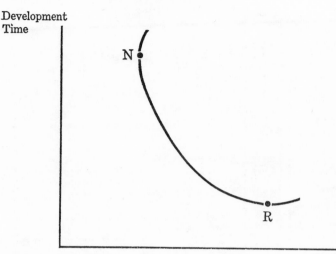

Total Development Cost

FIGURE 3.2

Development Possibility Curve

Source: F. M. Scherer, "Government Research and Development Programs," *Measuring Benefits of Government Expenditures,* edited by R. Dorfman, Washington, D.C.: The Brookings Institution, 1965.

prediction of relevant phenomena. Similar effects are produced by advances in the quality of test equipment (and such changes as the greater use of computers in design). Moreover, the development task is obviously made easier by improvements in components and materials, improvements in materials often being particularly important.[49]

Fifth, there is the development strategy that is used. Essentially, the development strategy is the set of decision rules employed to allocate resources during the course of the project. A great deal of attention has been devoted to development strategy, particularly with regard to the development of military aircraft. It is often argued that the proper strategy when trying to carry out a considerable advance in the state of the art is to stay flexible and search for significant new knowledge, rather than to try to force the development along a predetermined route.[50] More will be said on this score in Chapter VII.

Although these propositions may be true, there have been very few attempts to test them empirically. The little quantitative analysis that has

[49] H. Bode, *op. cit.,* p. 62.
[50] See B. Klein, "Policy Issues Involved in the Conduct of Military Development Programs," *The Economics of Research and Development,* edited by R. Tybout, Columbus, Ohio: Ohio State University Press, 1965; and "The Decision Making Problem in Development," *The Rate and Direction of Inventive Activity,* National Bureau of Economic Research, 1962.

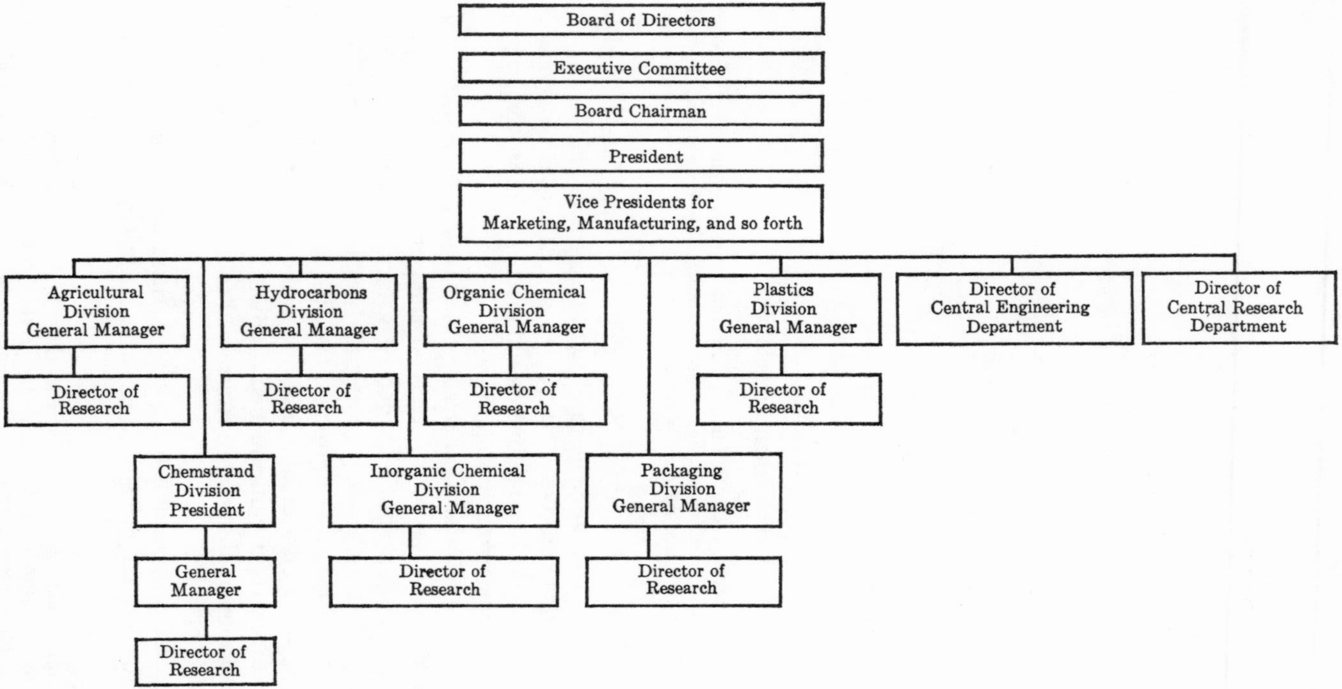

FIGURE 3.3

Corporate Organization, Monsanto Company

Source: A. Stanley and K. White, *Organizing the R a nd D Function,* American Management Association, 1965.

been carried out is largely the product of the RAND Corporation—and much of it is classified. RAND's unclassified results pertain to the development of thirteen military airframes—the F-84, F-86, F-86D, F-89, F-100, F-101, F-104, F-105, F-106, B-47, B-52, B-58, and F-4. In accord with our first proposition, they indicate that development cost is an increasing function of size and complexity. Also according to unpublished work by Glennan, there is some evidence that development costs are inversely related to development time. Unfortunately, the tests of the other propositions are inconclusive because of the difficulty of measuring the relevant factors and because of the smallness of the sample.[51]

13. Organization of Industrial Research and Development

Firms organize their R and D activities in quite different ways. In large, decentralized firms, there is frequently a central research laboratory, which emphasizes applied or basic research and separate R and D departments in each of the operating divisions, these departments doing product and process development of a more immediate nature. For example, Monsanto Chemical Corporation has a central research department as well as R and D departments in each of its seven operating divisions (Figure 3.3). There are advantages in separating the more basic work from the more applied, since the organization, style of leadership, and constraints that are appropriate for more applied work are often inappropriate for more basic work. However, it obviously is important that this separation does not result in too little communication between the advanced researchers and the people who are wrestling with problems of current design, manufacturing, and marketing. Otherwise, research findings may not be properly utilized, and research projects may not be chosen with proper reference to the firm's commercial needs.

Within a firm's central research laboratory, there is often a grouping of scientific personnel by academic disciplines or subjects. The subject areas, which often parallel the fields of learning at educational institutions, naturally depend on the problems predominant in the firm. Figure 3.4 shows the organization of the central research laboratories of Westinghouse Electric Corporation. This kind of organization makes it relatively easy for the researcher to keep in touch with others in the same subject field, it encourages him to keep up to date in his science, and it makes it easier to recruit outstanding scientists to the company. However, although it helps bring to one-science problems the best one-science expertise, it is likely to be less successful in dealing with complex multidisciplinary projects.

With regard to projects at the development end of the R and D spec-

[51] T. Glennan, "Methodological Problems in Evaluating the Effectiveness of Military Aircraft Development," RAND Corporation P-3357, May 1966.

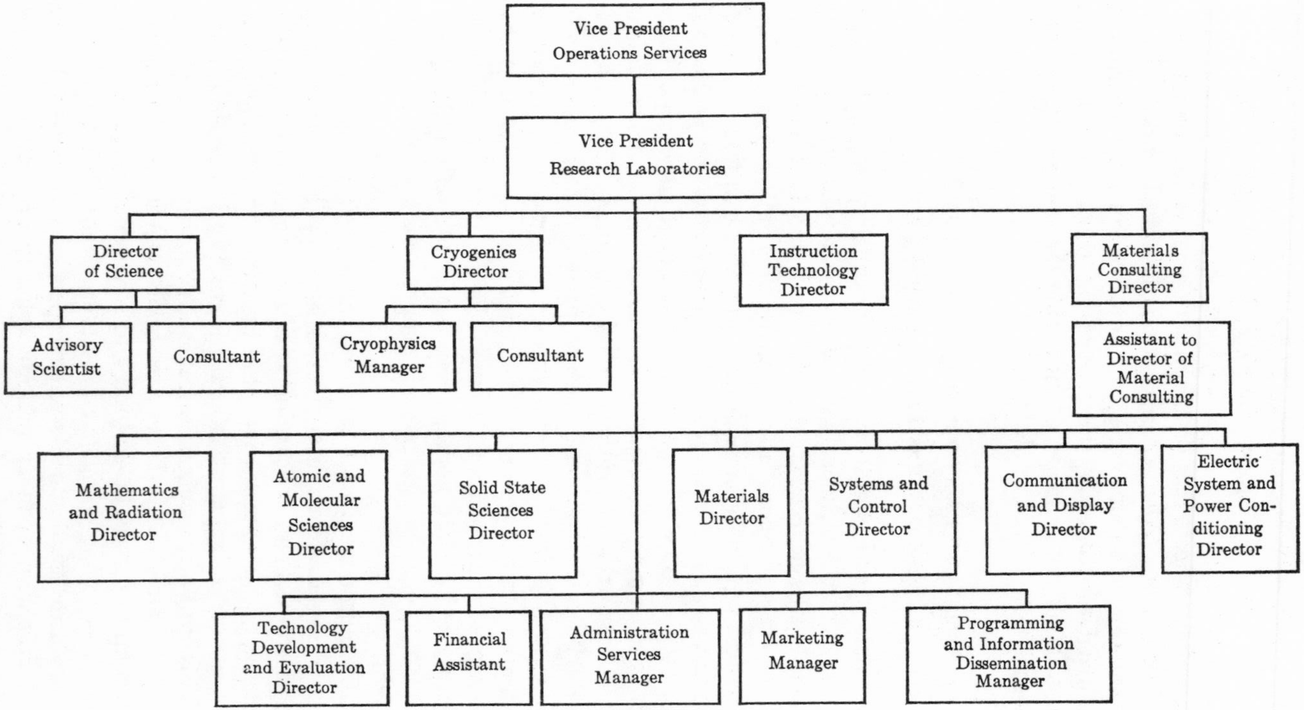

FIGURE 3.4

Organization of Central Research Laboratories,
Westinghouse Electric Corporation

Source: A. Stanley and K. White, *op. cit.*

trum, scientists and engineers are generally organized on a product basis, each group being composed of various disciplines needed to solve problems in the development, design, or manufacture of a particular set of products. In large, decentralized firms, the product-specialized R and D groups may be physically decentralized, each being attached to the relevant operating division. Typically, the divisional R and D manager reports to the general manager of his division, who has day-to-day control over the division's R and D staff and activities. The corporate R and D director reviews and coordinates the R and D programs of all the operating divisions, looking particularly at the technical quality and promise of the work. Organization of applied work on a product basis has a number of advantages, the most important being that it directs the work toward the realities of the market-place and shortens the communication links between the people in R and D and the design groups who can use their findings in the divisions. One disadvantage is that group members seem to be somewhat less concerned in keeping up to date in their scientific fields.

In handling multidisciplinary problems, both basic and applied, special project teams are often formed. For example, members of various departments of the central research laboratory may be combined with a development group for a limited period of time to accomplish a particular task. Organization by project results in numerous benefits. Since the objective is clear and the researchers know that they will be evaluated in terms of their success in achieving it, the motivation to adhere to relevant work is strengthened. Coordination of the work is easier than when parts of the work are being done in a number of separate and separated units. Moreover, the interaction of several disciplines and the periodic shifting of personnel helps to promote productivity.[52]

14. RESEARCH MANAGEMENT

The administration and control of research and development tends to be looser and more informal than in most other areas of industry. Although there may exist a rather formidable formal control structure, many of the decisions tend in fact to be made quite informally. In research, but not development, it is generally believed that administrators should resist the temptation to manage projects in much detail. Usually, management's job is limited to providing general guidelines and goals, selecting capable persons, and providing a climate conducive to good work. "When, like a band of explorers, researchers penetrate into the unknown, they are on their own, and decisions for action must be taken in the light of the new and strange situations that arise. As the size of the band increases, the need

[52] See A. Stanley and K. White, *Organizing the R and D Function*, American Management Association, 1965; and R. Anthony, *Management Controls in Industrial Research Organization*, Cambridge, Mass.: Harvard University Press, 1952.

for management goes up, but it is emphasized that the important decisions must be made by those closest to the front line." [53]

This does not mean that management does not—and should not—guide research. Whereas overmanagement of research is likely to lead to technical hack work, totally unguided research is likely to lead to waste and frustration. Management must learn to guide research in the directions most likely to contribute to company goals, yet not constrain it so that it produces excessively narrow and short-range work. Moreover each company must decide, in the light of expected scientific and commercial developments, the scientific areas where it will concentrate its efforts, those where it will merely keep in touch with the scientific community, and those where it will virtually ignore developing knowledge. Top management's ultimate control over the scope, emphasis, and efficiency of research lies largely in the selection of key personnel. Research and general managers decide in what broad fields to do research, and staff the program accordingly. Within these fields, they tend to rely heavily on the judgment of researchers to select specific inquiries and particular approaches to the problem.

In development, management plays a more dominant role. In part, this is because there is less uncertainty. Management can define the problems and goals more closely, and it can be more confident of a correlation between resources utilized and achievement. Another important reason for the greater role of management is the high cost of development. If a project proceeds beyond the exploratory stages, its costs begin to increase considerably. Moving from a design study to the later stages of the development work typically involves greater labor requirements for working out and testing the details of the design. Testing the full system involves considerable expense, particularly when the production of test items requires many special tools and buildings. From a sample of large projects in widely different product fields, it appears that the cumulative number of man-years devoted to a project can be approximated reasonably well by a logistic function of time.[54] Due to their more expensive nature, development projects are scrutinized carefully, and major commitments are not made until the design concept seems both technically feasible and economically attractive.

[53] R. Gibson, "A Systems Approach to Research Management," *Research Management*, 1962. For a similar view, consider the following comment by C. Mees, Vice President in Charge of Research at Eastman Kodak: "The best person to decide what research shall be done is the man who is doing the research. The next best is the head of the department. After that you leave the field of best persons and meet increasingly worse groups. The first of these is the research director, who is probably wrong more than half the time. Then comes a committee, which is wrong most of the time. Finally there is a committee of company vice-presidents which is wrong all the time." Quoted in J. Jewkes, D. Sawers, and R. Stillerman, *op. cit.*

[54] P. Norden, "Curve Fitting for a Model of Applied Research and Development Scheduling," *IBM Journal of Research and Development*, July 1958. See R. Gibson, *op. cit.* and M. O'Brien, *op. cit.*

The management of research and development is presently far from a science. Numerous propositions are put forth, but few are testable and practically none are tested in any formal way. Nonetheless, it is worthwhile noting some of the observations that appear in the literature. First, it is frequently pointed out that a company's research aims should be clearly spelled out and communicated to the scientists, and that its research should be undertaken in broad areas relevant to its economic goals. If one simply hires teams of scientists and allows them to do research in their favorite fields, the results may be novel and interesting, but they are unlikely to have much commercial value to the company. There is a much greater chance of obtaining commercially useful results if the firm's research aims are specified and researchers are hired who offer a good match, as to both qualifications and interests, with these aims. It is surprising how frequently firms seem to have lost sight of this seemingly obvious point.

Second, top management's responsibilities do not end with the definition of the objectives of research and development. Management must also make sure that its organization performs certain critical planning functions. Research and development should be responsive to technological flows from three sources: the company's competitors, the company's present and prospective customers, and the scientific community in general. Despite the difficulties in technological forecasting described in Chapter II, the firm must attempt to forecast, as best it can, the new developments that will come from these sources. Although many firms make rather informal forecasts, others have developed quite formal procedures to forecast technological threats and opportunities.

Third, management must pay proper attention to the transfer of new technology into operations. This is sometimes an extremely difficult task. On the one hand, this transfer may be restricted because the researcher does not recognize the commercial implications of his work or will not release his findings until he has covered all of its scientific ramifications. On the other hand, operating groups sometimes resist new technology on the ground that it is "impractical" or because, although it is desirable in the long run, it will add to their short-run marketing or engineering costs. Various devices, cited in section 18, have been used to help reduce the resistance to the transfer of new technology.

Fourth, particularly in the case of large military and space projects, it is often claimed that managers tend to underestimate the uncertainties involved, that they do not maintain enough flexibility, and that they settle too quickly on a particular design. When there is considerable uncertainty, it often pays to proceed sequentially, maintaining flexibility and using the experience that is gained to reduce uncertainty. This is illustrated by the use of parallel R and D efforts, discussed in section 11. Fifth, it is important to prevent the isolation of research from development. In a company where this is the case, the research people may be divorced from practical applications and their work may have little practical value. On the other hand, according to many observers, there are dangers if no line is drawn between research and development. The program may become dominated by short-term, product-oriented projects, and the exploration of fundamentally new areas may be neglected.

Sixth, it is frequently pointed out that a reasonable limit should be placed on the amount of "firefighting" activities to be done by researchers. In most companies, management tends to value technical service to customers and to the company's manufacturing divisions as one of the most important products of its technical groups. Sometimes management feels that whenever an emergency service call comes in, longer range R and D projects can be dropped temporarily. Too much work of this sort produces resentment among scientists and engineers, and detracts considerably from a laboratory's power to produce important new ideas in the long run. Seventh, it is also important to recognize that the firm's R and D department is only one of many sources of new ideas. There is sometimes a tendency for R and D managers to focus too much attention on new developments arising from their laboratories, and to neglect developments in other firms and industries. If something is "not invented here," it may be neglected or resisted.[55]

15. MANAGEMENT CONCEPTS AND PROBLEMS

We have seen that American industry, stimulated by the wartime accomplishments of science and technology, devoted increased attention and resources to research and development after World War II. In the fifties, Sputnik further increased industry's acceptance of the idea that scientific activity undertaken on a large scale would yield commercially important results. With the attendant growth in research and development came new and difficult management problems—and a variety of answers. According to one view, which was very popular during the fifties, the best way to manage research is simply to hire a good man and leave him

[55] See Stanley and White, op. cit.; S. Kingsburg, L. Bass, and W. Lothrop, "Organizing for Research," Handbook of Industrial Research Management, ed. by C. Heyel, New York: Reinhold Publishing Corporation, 1959; S. Marcson, The Scientist in American Industry, New York: Harper & Row, Publishers, 1960; J. Quinn, "Long-Range Planning of Industrial Research," Harvard Business Review, July 1961; J. Quinn and R. Cavanaugh, "Fundamental Research Can be Planned," Harvard Business Review, January 1964; H. Shepard, "Patterns of Organization for Applied Research and Development," Journal of Business, January 1956; N. Kaplan, "Some Organizational Factors Affecting Creativity," IRE Transactions on Engineering Management, 1960; and D. Marquis, "Organization and Management of R and D," Proceedings of the 17th Conference on Administration of Research, Denver: University of Denver, 1964.

alone. He will produce new knowledge which eventually will be profitable to the firm without the corporation's peering over his shoulder. This theory led to the establishment at that time of some central research laboratories led by distinguished scientists who were left essentially to their own devices.

According to another view, the processes of research, development, and innovation are essentially similar to the other major functions of the firm and, like them, are subject to rational management, at least within limits. These two views competed for popularity and influence. In recent years, there seems to have been some disillusionment with the first view. Firms seem to have recognized that it is not enough simply to hire good men and leave them alone. This is apt to result primarily in scientific papers and little else. Moreover, it is becoming more widely recognized that, unless one recognizes the uncertainties that mark research and development, the second view has very important shortcomings too. Firms sometimes underestimate the true uncertainties and attempt to manage projects in too much detail and with too little flexibility. The job of putting research and new technology to work for corporate goals is a difficult one, which may require modifying both the goals and the style of the firm.[56]

A related problem that has received considerable attention is the tension that may arise between the traditions and values of management on the one hand, and science on the other. The scientist comes from a tradition where he is privileged to choose his own topics of work, the objective is new knowledge, and his performance is evaluated by his peers and colleagues in science. On the other hand, management operates in a tradition of passing on, specifying, and executing decisions made by others, the objective is to make money, and evaluation is done by hierarchical superiors. Given these differences, it is not difficult to see why scientists and managers sometimes find it difficult to deal effectively with one another.[57]

Existing knowledge regarding the effects of various organizational and other factors on the productivity of an industrial research laboratory is very limited. Based on their experience, research directors and other qualified observers often stress the importance of the following factors. First, scientists should be permitted to choose and change problems. The overall program and research goals of the organization should be kept in mind, but within reasonable limits, the scientist should be allowed to plan his own work. Second, management should recognize the professional status of the scientist. For example, research personnel should be consulted about plans or proposals which will affect their work. Third, a positive and enthusiastic reception should be given to new ideas, even when they do not appear

---

[56] See D. Schon, *op. cit.*, Chapter III.
[57] See Kaplan, *ibid.*; C. Orth, J. Bailey, and F. Wolek, *Administering Research and Development*, Homewood, Ill.: Richard D. Irwin, Inc., 1964; and W. Kornhauser, *Scientists in Industry*, Berkeley and Los Angeles: University of California Press, 1962.

to be relevant to the immediate problems at hand. Fourth, scientists who are nonconformists—people who like to work at night instead of during the day, for example—should be tolerated, so long as the resulting disruptions remain within reasonable bounds.

The hierarchy within the laboratory may be quite different from that in other parts of the firm. In some laboratories there is both a "technical ladder" and a "managerial ladder." For example, the rungs of the managerial ladder may be Group Head, Section Head, and Department Head; those of the technical ladder may be Research Associate, Senior Research Associate, and Scientific Adviser. Since no managerial responsibilities are placed on the scientists on the technical ladder, this system allows the firm to give recognition and reward to scientists who do an excellent job without removing them from scientific work. Thus, the scientist has two ways up in the organization.[58]

There are two sides to the role played by the firm's highest research administrators. They must guide research in directions that are useful to the organization and at the same time represent the scientists' interests to top management. Research executives vary in their ability and will to protect the interests of researchers, as well as to establish the lines research is to follow in the interests of the firm. At lower levels in the organization a central problem of supervisors is to decide how tight their supervision should be. A study of twenty laboratories of the National Institutes of Health identified three kinds of supervision: "participatory" (high rate of interaction and joint decision making between supervisor and researcher), "directive" (low rate of interaction and unilateral decision making by supervisor), and "laissez-faire" (low rate of interaction and little decision making by supervisor). According to the study, research performance was highest for "participatory" supervision, intermediate for "laissez-faire" supervision, and lowest for "directive" supervision.[59]

16. SCIENTISTS, TECHNOLOGISTS, AND INDUSTRY

It is worthwhile to note some of the characteristics of eminent scientists. Most of them have the following factors in common: a childhood environment where knowledge and intellectual effort were highly valued, an unusual degree of independence and an early dependence on personal resources, an intense drive that generated hard work, a secondary school

---

[58] See H. Shepard, "Nine Dilemmas in Industrial Research," *Administrative Science Quarterly*, December 1956; "The Dual Hierarchy in Research," *Research Management*, Autumn 1958; and Kornhauser, *op. cit.*

[59] See H. Baumgartel, "Leadership Style as a Variable in Research Administration," *Administrative Science Quarterly*, 1957; and S. Marcson, *op. cit.*

training that emphasized science rather than the humanities, and high, though not necessarily remarkably high, intelligence. The creative scientist tends to be distinguished from his less creative colleagues by his rejection of the frame of reference in which questions are posed at him. He is likely to redefine the problem and think about it in rather unusual ways. Moreover, there seems to be a fertile fund of metaphors in his flow of fantasy, resulting in a large number of rather absurd ideas which he is more willing than the less creative scientist to express. Eventually, he is willing to reject many of these ideas as bad ones, but premature censorship may tend to stifle imagination.

Sociologists have distinguished between the professional and organizational orientation of people engaged in industrial research and development. Some people—the "cosmopolitans"—are low on loyalty to the employing organization, high on commitment to specialized role skills, and likely to use a professional reference group orientation. Other people— the "locals"—are high on loyalty to the employing organization, low on commitment to specialized role skills, and likely to use an organizational reference group orientation. Cosmopolitans tend to be strong producers of technical results; locals tend to assume administrative duties; and people who combine these orientations are especially capable of facilitating the use of technical results. Of course, many engineers and scientists who are originally recruited into research come to aspire to management positions, and many firms use the research and engineering departments as sources of recruitment for other parts of the company.[60]

Pelz and Andrews have carried out a study of 1,300 scientists and engineers, the purpose being to determine the factors associated with the quality of a scientist's performance. According to their results, effective scientists, although directed by their own ideas and valuing freedom, allow other people a voice in shaping their directions and tend to interact vigorously with colleagues. Rather than limiting their activities to the world of application or the world of pure science, they tend to maintain an interest in both. They tend to be motivated by the same kinds of things as their colleagues (although they are not fully in agreement with their organization in terms of their interests), but they differ from their colleagues in the styles and strategies with which they approach their work. Pelz and Andrews also present results concerning the geriatrics of technical groups. When a new group is formed, its scientific contribution is likely to be highest during its first two years and its overall usefulness is likely to peak in its fourth and fifth years, after which there is a steady decline.[61]

---

[60] See W. Kornhauser, *ibid.*; and Alvin Gouldner, "Cosmopolitans and Locals," *Administrative Science Quarterly*, 1957–1958.

[61] D. Pelz and F. Andrews, *Scientists in Organizations*, New York: John Wiley & Sons, Inc., 1966. These are only a small sample of the findings of this very interesting book. Also see A. Roe, *The Making of a Scientist*, New York: Apollo Editions, William Morrow and Company, Inc., 1961; J. Bruner, *On Knowing: Essays for the*

Another important, if sometimes overdrawn, distinction is between the scientist and the technologist. For example, according to Schon, the scientist "identifies himself with the pursuit of knowledge, the development of true theory." [62] He has little concern for what the theory can be used for, its applications being important only insofar as they lead to further theory. The technologist, on the other hand, is "the practical man who does things, makes things work. He uses skills and knowledge of the mechanisms of things in order to build, to put together, to solve problems." [63] Although the distinction is exaggerated by these descriptions, it is true that members of the technical community do tend to fall in a very rough way into these types, that each type has its own social system, and that each type has a hierarchy of status which, by and large, excludes the other.

When a scientist, and to a lesser extent an engineer, leaves school and enters industry, he is entering a quite different culture. His experience in graduate school is largely with professors who are members of the scientific culture and with students who, temporarily at least, share this culture. He has learned to value what he does by its contribution to science. Now he must get used to the idea that it must contribute, sooner or later, somehow or other, to profit. He has learned to value negative as well as positive results, but must now face business management's attitude toward project failures. Moreover, in graduate school, the young scientist has learned that real scientific achievement is the work of a small elite, concentrated heavily in universities and research institutes, and that industry attracts the lesser talents. (Whether or not this is true is beside the point.) Faced with the problems of making this transition, he may respond in a number of ways. He may attempt to maintain the attitudes and values of science, he may become as much as possible like the businessmen with whom he works, or he may find some middle ground.[64]

17. INFORMATION FLOWS AND COMMUNICATION PATTERNS

How do industrial scientists and engineers acquire the information required for the performance of research and development tasks? How do they keep abreast of the state of the art? A number of studies indicate that most information is acquired primarily from sources within the firm in an

Left Hand, Cambridge, Mass.: Harvard University Press, 1962; J. Weisner, *Where Science and Politics Meet,* New York: McGraw-Hill, Inc., 1965; and I. Pool, "The Social Environment for Sustained Technological Growth," *Patents and Progress,* Homewood, Ill.: Richard D. Irwin Inc., 1965.

[62] D. Schon, *op. cit.,* p. 98.

[63] *Ibid.*

[64] See D. Allison, "The Industrial Scientist," *International Science and Technology,* February 1967; and D. Schon, *op. cit.,* Chapter IV.

informal way, commonly through oral communication. Information useful for a particular need is often obtained through a specific search, but just as often it is pointed out by others or encountered when the individual is seeking to expand his general competence. Sources external to the firm play a more important role when the information is acquired to develop general competence than when information for a specific need is being sought. According to Rosenbloom and Wolek, a minority of engineers and scientists with a broader orientation, particularly toward their professional disciplines, are the principal linkage to information outside the organization.[65]

Regardless of where they stand along the spectrum from extremely basic to applied work, engineers and scientists must keep abreast of the state of the art. However, there are important differences in the way in which "basic scientists" and "applied technologists" accomplish this goal. The technologist publishes less and devotes less time to reading than does the basic scientist. In technological activity, the primary mode of information transfer is oral. Moreover, even in oral communication, the technologist differs from the basic scientist. The basic scientist, often associated with a university, keeps track of the work of others through visits, conferences, informal exchange of preliminary written materials, and association in what Derek Price calls "invisible colleges." The technologist, on the other hand, keeps abreast of his field primarily through close association with other technologists in his own organization. He is limited in forming and utilizing informal channels outside his organization by the requirement that he refrain from disclosing information of value to his company.[66]

It is sometimes said that new results of basic science are transmitted to applied technologists only after having been put in textbook form, the result being that there are two long delays between a discovery and its utilization—the period of several years between the publication of the original research and its appearance in textbooks and the period of variable length between the education of the technologist and his utilization of the knowledge. This hypothesis may be true in many fields. However, it is important to recognize that some technologies are much more closely connected with science than others. Moreover, it sometimes happens that technology encounters a problem, the solution of which requires an under-

[65] See Bureau of Applied Social Research, *The Flow of Information Among Scientists,* New York: Columbia University Press, 1958, and *Review of Studies in The Flow of Information Among Scientists,* New York: Columbia University Press, 1960; C. McLaughlin, R. Rosenbloom, and F. Wolek, "Technology Transfer and the Flow of Information in a Large Industrial Corporation," unpublished; and R. Rosenbloom and F. Wolek, "The Flow of Technical Information in Industrial R and D Organizations," unpublished.

[66] See D. Marquis and T. Allen, "Communication Patterns in Applied Technology," and D. Price and D. Beaver, "Collaboration in an Invisible College," both in *The American Psychologist,* November 1966.

standing of the scientific basis of the phenomena involved. For example, progress in electron tube technology appeared at one time to have reached an upper limit of a few megacycles in frequency response; this forced a return to basic physics and a more detailed study of the interactions of free electrons and electromagnetic waves. When the connection between science and technology is of this sort, little delay occurs in the transfer of new results of basic science to technologists.[67]

In recent years, there has been an enormous increase in the printed record of science and technology, the result being that the storage, organization, and retrieval of information are becoming the objects of widespread concern. Besides the old array of published abstracts and indexes and the traditional library services, new systems have been and are being added— published lists of titles, citation indexes, clearing-houses, information evaluation centers, referral services, automated searching services, selective dissemination services, and so forth. The professional societies have been very active in this field. For example, the American Psychological Association has conducted studies of the process of scientific communication, and the American Institute of Physics has analyzed the needs of physicists and planned an array of services to meet them. In addition, the Federal government is engaged in a major effort to improve the use and availability of scientific and technical information; this effort involves the national libraries, the National Referral Services for Science and Technology, the Science Information Exchange, the Clearinghouse for Federal Scientific and Technical Information, the National Standard Reference Data Center, and other agencies.[68]

18. Interaction with Other Parts of the Firm

The effectiveness of an R and D department depends heavily on its relations with other parts of the firm. To illustrate how the efforts of the research, marketing, production, and legal staffs interact, let us consider the development of a hypothetical metal-to-metal adhesive. It begins in the laboratory when a chemist notices an unanticipated adhesive effect and reproduces it. He shows the effect to the research director who authorizes

---

[67] See Marquis and Allen, *ibid.;* D. Price, "Is Technology Historically Independent of Science?," *Technology and Culture,* 1965; and J. Morton, "From Physics to Function," *IEEE Spectrum,* 1965.

[68] See W. Knox, *Recommendations for National Document Handling Systems in Science and Technology,* Federal Council for Science and Technology, 1965; W. Garvey and B. Griffith, "Scientific Information Exchange in Psychology," *Science,* 1964; and J. Licklider, "A Crux in Scientific and Technical Communication," *The American Psychologist,* November 1966.

a search of the report and patent literature and a first examination of the potential market. After a few months of additional experimentation, the research director presents the idea to management, which approves a full-scale development project. The development team attempts to improve the adhesive and explores variations of the chemistry involved. A detailed analysis of the market is carried out by the marketing department, and a thorough patent search is undertaken by the legal staff. The marketing analysis suggests the desirability of modifications in the product, and the patent search points to areas where work should be done to reduce the chance of later competition from an equally effective product. The firm files its patent application and establishes a pilot production line. The line has a number of bugs in it; quality control is a problem; shelf life must be examined. About six months after the pilot line is set up, a full production line is established, the marketing strategy is settled, the sales force is educated to the product, the use tests are done, and quality-control techniques are established. Finally, the company markets the product—although bugs in production, quality, and reliability still occur.[69]

What part do the marketing people play in a project of this sort? They estimate the performance characteristics that consumers think a new product should have, as well as the nature and extent of the demand. They also play an important role in determining what the new product looks like, since compromises generally have to be made between what the engineers would like and what the market desires. If the firm considers the profit potential for the product satisfactory and product development continues, the marketing people go on to design advertising and distribution programs and carry out test marketing. Whether the output of the R and D department is used is often dependent on the marketing people. It is easy to cite cases where good ideas emerging from the R and D department were blocked by marketing people who failed to grasp their significance. It is also easy to cite cases where scientists had little or no appreciation of the styling, pricing, and distribution problems faced by a marketing manager.

Relations with the production department are also very important. The production people must produce the new item emerging from the R and D department. Often there are considerable problems in translating jobs to be done from the language and methods appropriate to R and D engineers into terms that are useful to draftsmen, production engineers, production supervisors, and ultimately, operatives. Moreover, the linguistic and communication difficulties are often compounded by problems of status and power. For example, the development engineers may tend to look down on the production people. Whether the results of the R and D department come to fruition may be dependent on the production staff as well as the marketing staff. It is not uncommon for good ideas stemming

[69] See D. Schon, "The Fear of Innovation," *International Science and Technology*, November 1966.

from the R and D department to be blocked by production managers who feel threatened by the problems involved in the change.[70]

Research departments have a vested interest in change, but to other departments, it may represent a threat that disrupts the established way of doing things, and that is resisted. Top management can help reduce such resistance by locating and examining the critical technological transfer points, by providing the information to target research toward company goals, by fostering the proper motivational environment, and, if necessary, by creating specific organizations to ride a new technology through to commercialization. A major strategy that research groups use to overcome such resistance is to report directly to top management, which generally is more receptive to research utilization. Nonetheless, a research director often has a difficult time in selling certain research results to top management, as well as to the constituent departments of a firm. Various devices are used to break down resistance to the effective use of research. For example, scientists and engineers are moved back and forth from research to other parts of the firm to provide management and operating units with people whose views and experience bridge the gap between research and the rest of the organization. Also, the research department can hold lectures and seminars, and perform other informational and liaison services. Despite these devices, research departments often complain that their results are not utilized as extensively and as quickly as they consider optimal.

19. ANALYTICAL TECHNIQUES

During the past few years, firms have become more inclined to question and analyze the productivity of their expenditures on research and development. The optimism, permissiveness, and faith of the post-World War II era have given way to a greater emphasis on measurement and control in the management of R and D resources. Paralleling the search for better ways to choose, implement, and apply the results of R and D is the steady growth in the number and variety of analytical techniques proposed to aid decision making in this area. In this section, we note a few of the techniques used to promote better planning and scheduling of R and D projects, as well as better project selection.

A variety of network techniques—like the Program Evaluation and Review Technique (PERT)—have been used in planning and scheduling

[70] See T. Burns, "Research, Development, and Production," *IRE Transactions on Engineering Management*, March 1961; and J. Quinn, "Transferring Research Results to Operations," *Harvard Business Review*, January 1963. Schon points out that marketing and technology sometimes "attempt to create a work situation in which each group makes true, safe statements within its professional territory. But since uncertainty is inherent in technological innovation, the result is that marketing and technology attempt to put themselves in the role of providing "givens" for the other, judging the output of the other by their own professional criteria, and leaving the other with the major burden of uncertainty." D. Schon, *op. cit.*, p. 109.

development projects. In employing these methods, the first step is to analyze the work that must be done, break it down into individual activities, and estimate how long each will probably take and how much it will cost. The results are diagramed as a network showing which activities cannot be begun before the completion of other jobs and which work can be carried out in parallel with other activities. Then, using these techniques, it is possible to estimate how long the entire project will take and how much it will cost. In addition, one can calculate the "critical path"— the sequence of jobs in which any slowdown will delay the completion of the entire project. A knowledge of this path is important in deciding which jobs to rush in order to keep the entire project on schedule.[71]

Under certain circumstances, these techniques can be useful in determining the allocation of expenditures among jobs. For example, suppose that the sequence of events and activities in the development project is known with certainty and that the time needed to complete each activity can vary over a known range. If the cost of performing an activity is a decreasing function of the length of time needed to perform the activity, these techniques can be used to find that set of activities that minimizes the total cost of completing the project in a given length of time. Moreover, if there is a delay cost which is directly related to the length of time needed to complete the project, it is possible to find the completion time that minimizes the total cost of completion and delay, as well as the schedule of activities which gives this optimal completion time.

Network techniques have proved useful in large development projects. For example, PERT, which was invented in the course of the Polaris program, has been given considerable credit for the fact that the development of this missile took two years less time than originally estimated. In the case of research projects, these techniques are much less useful, since they make the unrealistic assumption that the sequence of events and activities to be carried out is known with certainty. In research (and sometimes in development too), this sequence is extremely unpredictable. Attempts have been made to extend these techniques to take account of these uncertainties, but this work is only beginning.[72]

Turning to project selection, mathematical programming techniques— linear, integer, and dynamic programming—have been formulated to assign resources among alternative projects so as to maximize an overall profit-

---

[71] For descriptions of PERT and the Critical Path Method, see D. Malcolm, S. Rosenbloom, C. Clark, and W. Fazar, "Application of a Technique for Research and Development Program Evaluation," *Operations Research*, 1959; R. Rosenbloom, "Notes on the Development of Network Models for Resource Allocation in R and D Projects," *IEEE Transactions on Engineering Management*, June, 1964; and the articles by Malcolm, Ashley and Austin in B. Dean (ed.), *Operations Research in Research and Development*, New York: John Wiley & Sons, Inc., 1963.

[72] For example, see M. Yovits, D. Gilford, R. Wilcox, E. Staveley, and H. Lerner, *Research Program Effectiveness*, New York: Gordon and Breach Science Publishers, 1966.

ability measure subject to budget constraints. Decision-theoretic concepts have also been proposed to help take account of the fact that the choice is ordinarily made under conditions of risk and uncertainty. For example, according to the simple scheme proposed by Freeman, the analyst is advised to estimate for each project the discounted net profits if it is successful, as well as the probability of success. On the basis of such estimates, he obtains the expected discounted profits for each project; and using programming techniques, he chooses the set of projects that maximizes the sum of the expected discounted profits subject to resource constraints.[73]

The available evidence suggests that these selection techniques are not being used very extensively. In part, this is because they often are based on highly simplified views of the research and development process. In most cases, they fail to recognize that R and D project selection is a sequential decision process, they take only limited account of the uncertainties involved, and they ignore possible interdependence among projects. Another important reason why these techniques seem to have found only limited use is that managers and scientists, particularly those involved in more basic work, often find it difficult to provide the estimates of project profitability and probability of success that these techniques require. Although these selection techniques are useful in focusing attention on many of the relevant factors, they have had much less practical impact than the network techniques.[74]

20. THE IMPORTANCE OF THE INDEPENDENT INVENTOR

In the last three sections of this chapter, we consider the role of the independent inventor in promoting technological change, as well as certain aspects of the role of the large firm. Although the growth of organized research and development has led to many attempts to administer the last rites to the independent inventor, he is by no means dead. Over the last sixty years, he has contributed a great deal to the stream of important inventions. For example, in their study of sixty-one significant twentieth-century inventions, Jewkes, Sawers, and Stillerman [75] estimated that over half were produced by individuals not doing company-directed research. Nonetheless, this century has seen a notable shift in the source of inven-

[73] R. Freeman, "A Stochastic Model for Determining the Size and Allocation of the Research Budget," *IEEE Transactions on Engineering Management*, March 1960. The brief description in the text only covers part of Freeman's proposal. For a survey of such techniques, see N. Baker and W. Pound, *op. cit.*; and Yovits *et al.*, *op. cit.*

[74] See Baker and Pound, *op. cit.*; Yovits *et al.*, *op. cit.*; Dean, *op. cit.*; and E. Mansfield, "Decision Making with Respect to Industrial Research and Development," paper presented at United Aircraft Research Laboratories, January 12, 1967.

[75] Jewkes, Sawers, and Stillerman, *op. cit.*

tions away from the independent inventor and toward the corporation. In 1900, about 80 percent of all patents (issued to individuals and United States firms) were issued to individuals; in 1957, about 40 percent were issued to individuals. The reasons for this shift are not difficult to find. Technology in most industries has become more complex, a division of labor among specialists in various scientific fields has become more necessary, and the instruments required to research and develop new processes and products have become more expensive.

Despite these factors, the independent inventor, the inventor who works outside industrial R and D organizations, continues to be an important source of new technology. The independent inventor tends to move into areas where the costs of inventing are low, and where time and ingenuity can be substituted for expensive equipment. For example, Jacob Rabinow invested only about $20,000 in his invention of the clock regulator.[76] The independent inventor sometimes is willing to undertake projects that company R and D is not imaginative enough to pursue. For example, it was an independent inventor, Frank Whittle, who, without the support of the British Air Ministry or aircraft industry contributed so much to the development of the early jet engine.[77] Incidentally, it is by no means true that all independent inventors are uneducated tinkerers. On the contrary, some are highly trained scientists and engineers, sometimes university faculty members. Examples are Leo Baekeland, who invented Bakelite, Eugene Houdry, who invented catalytic cracking, Edwin Armstrong, who invented FM radio broadcasting, and Edwin Land, who invented the Polaroid camera.

Independent inventors often turn their inventions over to larger companies for development, because they lack the financial resources and necessary facilities. This was true in the case of Jacques Brandenberger, a French chemist, who is generally credited with the invention of cellophane. The Comptoir de Textiles Artificiels, the biggest French rayon producer, became interested in his results and agreed to finance the development work. A new company, La Cellophane, was formed, Brandenberger's patents were transferred to it, and Brandenberger was employed to direct the development. La Cellophane was the first commercial manufacturer of plain cellophane.[78] Turning to personal characteristics, independent inventors have the reputation of being a stubborn and nonconforming breed. Many observers claim that the successful independent inventor often is marked by a persistence bordering on obsession and that he tends to be more of a maverick than his corporate counterpart.

[76] See the testimony of D. DeSimone before the Senate Subcommittee on Antitrust and Monopoly, May 18, 1965.
[77] See the testimony of R. Schlaifer before the Senate Subcommittee on Antitrust and Monopoly, May 25, 1965.
[78] Jewkes, Sawers, and Stillerman, *op. cit.*

Xerography provides a further illustration of the work of an independent inventor. After graduating from Caltech in 1930, Chester Carlson worked at the Bell Telephone Laboratories, where he transferred to the patent department and studied patent law. In 1934, he took a job as patent attorney at Mallory and Company. Noticing how difficult and costly it was to copy documents, he set out to examine the problem. By 1937, he had developed the basic concept of xerography and filed a patent application although he had yet to verify his ideas experimentally. After several years of improving his process, he went to the Battelle Memorial Institute, the world's largest nonprofit research organization, and made an agreement whereby Battelle acquired the patent rights and Carlson acquired a substantial share in the proceeds of any future development. Battelle improved the process to the point where industry became interested. In 1946, the Haloid Corporation (later renamed the Xerox Corporation) accepted an exclusive sublicense, developed the process further, and in 1950 announced its first commercial application.[79]

21. THE SOURCES OF RADICAL INVENTIONS

Some observers claim that the bulk of the commercial R and D carried out by large corporations is aimed at fairly modest advances in the state of the art.[80] They say that the really major inventions seldom stem from the laboratories of the large firms, which are primarily contributors of minor "improvement" inventions. If true, these hypotheses have important implications regarding the role of the large firm in promoting technological change.

The evidence cited in support of these hypotheses are of two types. First, the McGraw-Hill surveys indicate that about 90 percent of the firms expected their R and D outlays to pay off in five years or less (Table 3.7). Since it usually takes considerably longer than this before a radically new process or product even hits the market, the emphasis on short pay-off periods is taken to indicate that most R and D in these firms is geared toward improvements or minor changes in existing products. Moreover, the stated objectives of the research programs of various firms indicate

---

[79] See the testimony of D. DeSimone before the Senate Subcommittee on Antitrust and Monopoly, May 18, 1965.

[80] Of course, no one denies that the risks are greater than in most other aspects of business. Thus, there is no disagreement with section 10. The comparison is with very far-reaching R and D projects. See D. Hamberg, "Invention in the Industrial Laboratory," *Journal of Political Economy*, April 1963, J. Jewkes, D. Sawers, and R. Stillerman, *op. cit.*, and R. Nelson M. Peck, and E. Kalachek, *Technology, Economic Growth and Public Policy*, Washington, D.C.: The Brookings Institution, 1967; and E. Mansfield, *op. cit.*, Chapter IV.

an emphasis on immediate and short-term benefits. Second, studies of the origins of various major twentieth-century inventions seem to indicate that only a fairly small proportion originated in the laboratories of large corporations. Jewkes, Sawers, and Stillerman [81] found that such laboratories accounted for only twelve of the sixty-one major inventions they studied. Thirty-three of the inventions—including air conditioning, automatic transmission, Bakelite, cellophane, and the jet engine—were the product of independent inventors. Hamberg [82] found that the laboratories of large firms accounted for only seven of the twenty-seven major post-World War II inventions he studied. The rest—including the ENIAC computer, the oxygen converter, stereophonic sound, and neomycin—came from independent inventors, small firms, universities, and an agricultural experiment station.

There is probably a good deal of truth in these hypotheses, although they certainly do not hold for all firms. From the point of view of the individual large firm, it is often wise to leave the pioneering to others and to stick to less far-reaching research and development. Whether this is wise from the point of view of society is a different and more difficult question. Some economists assert that, from the point of view of society, large firms tend to spend too little on more fundamental, risky, and radical types of R and D. Even if this is the case (and it may well be), it does not deny the importance of the laboratories of large corporations. On the contrary, as we pointed out in Chapter II, technological change in many industries may be due in considerable measure to the cumulative effect of many "improvement" inventions. Although they may be a less important source of really major inventions than is socially desirable, their contribution is nonetheless of great significance. Whether or not very large firms are required to make this contribution is another question, and one which will be discussed below and in subsequent chapters.

22. Size of Firm, Market Structure, and Research and Development

In Chapter I, we pointed out that some economists believe that very large firms are needed to produce the technical achievements on which economic progress depends. For example, J. K. Galbraith has asserted that only such firms can carry out the activities required in the modern world to develop new products and processes; and on this basis, he has argued that an industry composed of a few large oligopolists will be technically more progressive than an industry composed of a larger number of smaller firms. Various reasons have been given for the alleged importance of great size: a large firm can finance R and D more easily, it can afford bigger

[81] J. Jewkes, D. Sawers, and R. Stillerman, *op. cit.*
[82] D. Hamberg, *op. cit.*

projects, the results of R and D are more likely to be useful because of its greater diversity, it can wait longer for the pay-off, and it can capture a larger portion of the social gains from its research because it has a larger share of the market.[83] Not all economists agree with Galbraith; many do not believe that very large firms are required to produce rapid technological change.[84]

In studying this issue, a relevant question is: do large firms spend more, relative to their size, than small firms on R and D? Although the National Science Foundation's data cast only a limited amount of light on this issue, it is worthwhile to see what they suggest. Table 3.8 shows the relationship in various industries between the amount spent on R and D as a percent of sales and a firm's size, for those firms that engaged in R and D. Looking at R and D performance, there seems to be a tendency in most industries for the largest firms to carry out relatively more R and D than the other firms. Only in lumber, drugs, and nonferrous metals is this not the case. Looking at company-financed R and D, there is a somewhat weaker tendency for the largest firms to support a larger amount of R and D (as a percent of sales) than smaller firms, but in most industries such a tendency exists. If data were available for all firms (not just those that perform R and D), this tendency would be strengthened, because a larger proportion of large firms than small ones perform R and D.

Thus, the results seem to favor the hypothesis that large firms support more R and D than do small ones. However, from the point of view of antitrust policy, the more relevant question is: Do the largest few firms in an industry spend more on R and D (as a percent of sales) than firms which are relatively large but still only a fraction of the size of the leaders? Table 3.8 cannot answer this question because, in most industries, the "smaller" firms as well as the giants have more than 5,000 employees, and, consequently, they are lumped together. Some light is thrown on this question by a study [85] that investigates the relationship between size of firm and the level of R and D expenditures among the major firms in the chemical, petroleum, drug, steel, and glass industries. Except for the chemical industry, the results provide no evidence that the largest firms in these industries spent more on R and D, relative to sales, than did somewhat smaller firms. In the petroleum, drug, and glass industries, the largest firms spent significantly less; in the steel industry, they spent less but the difference

[83] See J. K. Galbraith, *American Capitalism*, Boston: Houghton Mifflin Company, 1952; J. Schumpeter, *Capitalism, Socialism, and Democracy*, New York: Harper & Row, Publishers, 1947; and H. Villard, "Competition, Oligopoly, and Research," *Journal of Political Economy*, December 1958.

[84] See J. Jewkes, D. Sawers, and R. Stillerman, *op. cit.*; G. Nutter, "Monopoly, Bigness, and Progress," *Journal of Political Economy*, June 1956; and E. Mansfield, *Monopoly Power and Economic Performance*, New York: W. W. Norton & Company, Inc., 1964.

[85] E. Mansfield, *op. cit.*, Chapter II.

TABLE 3.8

Research and Development Performance and Company-Financed
R and D Costs of Firms Performing R and D, by Industry and Size
of Firm's Work Force, 1961

	R AND D PERFORMANCE EMPLOYMENT			COMPANY-FINANCED R AND D EMPLOYMENT		
INDUSTRY	UNDER 1,000	1,000–4,999	5,000 OR MORE	UNDER 1,000	1,000–4,999	5,000 OR MORE
	(PERCENT OF SALES)					
Food	n.a.	0.3	0.4	n.a.	0.3	0.4
Textiles	n.a.	0.5	0.5	n.a.	n.a.	0.4
Lumber	1.8	0.6	0.3	n.a.	n.a.	0.3
Paper	n.a.	0.7	0.7	n.a.	0.8	0.7
Chemicals	2.2	3.7	5.2	n.a.	3.4	3.9
Industrial	3.1	4.4	5.8	n.a.	3.2	4.7
Drugs	3.8	5.8	4.4	n.a.	6.4	4.6
Others	1.5	2.1	3.8	n.a.	2.1	1.6
Petroleum	n.a.	0.6	1.0	n.a.	0.6	1.0
Rubber	0.8	0.9	2.6	n.a.	0.9	1.7
Stone, clay, and glass	n.a.	1.1	2.1	n.a.	1.1	2.1
Primary metals	n.a.	0.9	0.8	n.a.	0.8	0.8
Ferrous	n.a.	0.4	0.7	n.a.	0.4	0.8
Nonferrous	n.a.	1.3	1.0	n.a.	1.1	0.8
Fabricated metal products	1.0	1.0	1.7	n.a.	1.0	1.2
Machinery	3.0	2.0	6.2	n.a.	1.9	4.1
Electrical equipment	5.6	5.9	12.1	n.a.	2.8	4.2
Motor vehicles	n.a.	1.3	3.5	n.a.	0.9	2.7
Aircraft	6.9	12.6	25.7	n.a.	1.7	2.5
Instruments	4.8	4.3	9.6	1.7	3.3	5.3

Source: Research and Development in Industry, 1961, National Science Foundation, 1964.
n.a. Not available.

was not statistically significant. A study by Scherer provides similar results for a wider range of industries, the ratio of R and D expenditures to sales usually being no higher among the largest firms than among their somewhat smaller competitors.[86]

Needless to say, these findings pertain to only one of many questions relating to the effects of firm size and market structure on the rate of tech-

---

[86] See F. Scherer, Testimony before the Senate Subcommittee on Antitrust and Monopoly, May 25, 1965, and "Size of Firm, Oligopoly, and Research: A Comment," *Canadian Journal of Economics and Political Science,* May 1965.
A difference is not statistically significant if the chances are better than one in twenty that it could be due to chance.

nological change. Little can be concluded from these results alone. In Chapter VII, we bring together a variety of findings that bear on this subject.

23. SUMMARY

The organized application of science to advance technology is a relatively new thing. At the turn of the twentieth century, as science and technology gradually moved closer together, industry began to support organized research and development. The distinction between research and development is based largely on the orientation of the work, the degree of uncertainty inherent in the problem, and the length of time work can be expected to proceed without demonstrable payoff. Total R and D expenditures in the United States have increased spectacularly during the last several decades, much of the R and D performed by industry being financed by the Federal government. The performance of R and D is spread very unevenly among industries, R and D as a percent of sales being highest in the aircraft, electrical equipment, instruments, and chemical industries. When company-financed R and D rather than R and D performance is considered, the differences among industries are reduced, but the industries remain in much the same rank order. These inter-industry differences may reflect differences among industries in the profitability of research and development; obviously, however, this hypothesis is difficult to test.

Ideas and proposals for R and D projects arise from customers and from the marketing and production departments of a firm, as well as from its R and D department. To evaluate these proposals, most large firms use relatively simple extensions of the criteria—like the pay-out period and the rate of return—used in capital budgeting. When projects are first proposed, the screening is often cursory and informal, since there is considerable uncertainty regarding the results and the costs are small. However, as projects go into development, costs increase and uncertainties decrease, the consequence being that detailed economic evaluation of the project becomes both more necessary and more feasible. Most of the projects that are accepted initially are scrapped before the development stage. In the short run, there often is a tendency for firms to maintain a fairly constant ratio between R and D expenditures and sales, but in the longer run, this ratio changes in response to changes in the prospective profitability of research, bandwagon effects, and other factors.

One of the most difficult problems in this area is the measurement of the returns from research and development. There is some evidence that the number of significant inventions carried out by a firm is highly correlated with the level of its R and D expenditures. Beyond this very little is known, although a limited amount of experimental work has been carried out. Chance plays a crucial role in research and development, and a long string of failures often occurs before any sort of success is achieved. R and D can be regarded as a process of uncertainty reduction or learning. Viewed in this way, it obviously is desirable under certain circumstances to run in parallel several approaches to the same problem, the optimal number of approaches being inversely related to the cost of each approach and directly related to the prospective amount of learning. This result is important because it puts in proper perspective some of the criticisms of "duplication" and "waste" in research and development.

In large decentralized firms, there is frequently a central research laboratory, which emphasizes research and is organized by academic subject, and separate R and D departments in each of the operating divisions, these departments doing product and process development of a more immediate nature. The administration and control of research and development tends to be looser and more informal than in most other areas of business. To obtain maximum results, it is often stated that a firm's research aims should be clearly spelled out, that proper account should be taken of the uncertainties involved, that a reasonable limit should be placed on the amount of "firefighting" activities to be done by researchers, and that the potential importance of ideas originating outside the R and D department should be recognized. Also, top management must insure that its organization performs certain critical planning functions and that various devices are used to reduce the resistance to the transfer of new technology into operations. The effectiveness of an R and D department depends heavily on its relations with other parts of the firm. There sometimes are important communications difficulties, as well as problems of status and power, that separate the production and marketing people from the R and D staff.

There are many differences between the ideal working atmosphere of an industrial research laboratory and that of other parts of the firm. In part, these differences stem from the conflicts that may arise between the traditions and values of management, on the one hand, and of science, on the other. Many studies have been carried out to determine the characteristics of eminent scientists and the factors that apparently are associated with the quality of a scientist's performance. Also, investigations have been made of the ways in which industrial scientists and engineers acquire the information required for the performance of their research and development tasks. In recent years, there has been an enormous increase in the printed record of science and technology, the result being that the storage, organization, and retrieval of information has become the object of widespread concern. There are important differences in the methods used by basic scientists and applied technologists to keep abreast of the state of the art.

In development, management generally plays a more dominant role than in research. The cost of a particular development project depends on the size and complexity of the product being developed, as well as on the extent of the advance in performance that is sought. More resources are required to redesign a product with a large number of interdependent components than a product with few, relatively independent components. In addition, some economists postulate that the expected total quantity of resources used in a development effort is related to the expected development time. They argue that over a considerable range, time can be decreased only by increasing total cost. Finally, development cost is also related to the stock of basic knowledge and of components and materials and to the development strategy that is used. A great deal of attention has been devoted to development strategy, particularly with regard to the development of military aircraft. It is often argued that the proper strategy when trying to carry out a considerable advance in the state of the art is to stay flexible and search for significant new knowledge, rather than to try to force the development along a predetermined route. In recent years, there has been a steady growth in the number of analytical techniques—like PERT—that have been proposed to aid the planning and scheduling of R and D projects.

Despite the growth of industrial laboratories, the independent inventor continues to contribute a great deal to technology, particularly in areas where the costs of inventing are low, and time and ingenuity can be substituted for expensive equipment. The independent inventor, who sometimes is a highly trained scientist or engineer, frequently turns over his invention to a large company for development, because he lacks the financial resources and necessary facilities. It is often claimed that the bulk of the commercial R and D carried out by large corporations is aimed at fairly modest advances in the state of the art. There is some evidence that the really major inventions often arise outside the laboratories of the large firms, which are primarily contributors of more minor "improvement" inventions. The evidence also indicates that, although large firms tend to carry out more R and D (as a percent of sales) than small firms, the largest firms generally do no more R and D (as a percent of sales) than the merely big firms.

CHAPTER IV

INNOVATION AND THE DIFFUSION OF NEW TECHNIQUES

<><><><><><><><><><><><><><><><><>

1. INNOVATION: DEFINITION AND IMPORTANCE

An invention, when applied for the first time, is called an innovation. Traditionally economists have stressed the distinction between an invention and an innovation on the ground that an invention has little or no economic significance until it is applied. This distinction becomes somewhat blurred in cases like DuPont's nylon, where the inventor and the innovator are the same firm. Under these circumstances, the final stages of development may entail at least a partial commitment to a market test. However, in many cases the inventor is not in a position to—and does not want to—apply his invention, because his business is invention, not production, or because he is a supplier, not a user, of the equipment embodying the invention, or for some other reason. In these cases, the distinction remains relatively clear-cut.

Regardless of whether the break between invention and innovation is clean, innovation is a key stage in the process leading to the full evaluation and utilization of an invention. The innovator—the firm that is first to apply the invention—must be willing to take the risks involved in introducing a new and untried process, good, or service. In many cases, these risks are high. Although R and D can provide a great deal of information regarding the technical characteristics and cost of production of the invention—and market research can provide considerable information regarding the demand for it—there are many areas of uncertainty which can be resolved only by actual production and marketing of the invention. By obtaining needed information regarding the actual performance of the invention, the innovator plays a vital social role. In this chapter, we take up the nature of the innovative process and the characteristics of innovators, as well as the factors determining how rapidly, once an innovation occurs, its use spreads.

2. THE LAG FROM INVENTION TO INNOVATION

How long is the lag between invention and innovation? This lag must vary substantially, since some inventions require changes in tastes, technology, and factor prices before they can profitably be utilized, whereas others do not. Moreover, some inventions constitute major departures from existing practice, whereas others are more routine "improvement" inventions.[1] Restricting our attention to relatively important inventions, the only data are extremely rough,[2] since concepts such as "invention" and "innovation" are not easy to pinpoint and date, and the available samples are not random. Nonetheless, these data provide some feel for the distribution of the lag. John Enos estimated the time interval between invention and innovation for eleven important petroleum refining processes and thirty-five important products and processes in a variety of other industries. Table 4.1 shows that the lag averaged eleven years in the petroleum industry and about fourteen years in the others. Its standard deviation is about five years in the petroleum industry and sixteen years in the others. He concludes that: "Mechanical innovations appear to require the shortest time interval, with chemical and pharmaceutical innovations next. Electronic innovations took the most time. The interval appears shorter when the inventor himself attempts to innovate than when he is content merely to reveal the general concept." [3]

---

[1] The distinction between "major" and "improvement" inventions is made by many writers. Tables 4.1 and 4.2 pertain to "major" inventions. The results regarding patent utilization (cited in Chapter VII) may be of use in describing the lag for "improvement" inventions.

[2] J. Enos, "Invention and Innovation in the Petroleum Refining Industry," *The Rate and Direction of Inventive Activity*, Princeton, N.J.: Princeton University Press, 1962; F. Lynn, "An Investigation of the Rate of Development and Diffusion of Technology in Our Modern Industrial Society," *Report of the National Commission on Technology, Automation, and Economic Progress*, Washington, D.C.: 1966.

[3] J. Enos, *op. cit.*, p. 309.

TABLE 4.1

Estimated Time Interval between Invention and Innovation, Forty-Six Inventions, Selected Industries [a]

INVENTION	INTERVAL (YEARS)	INVENTION	INTERVAL (YEARS)
Distillation of hydrocarbons with heat and pressure (Burton)	24	DDT	3
		Electric precipitation	25
Distillation of gas oil with heat and pressure (Burton)	3	Freon refrigerants	1
		Gyrocompass	56
Continuous cracking (Holmes-Manley)	11		
Continuous cracking (Dubbs)	13	Hardening of fats	8
"Clean circulation" (Dubbs)	3	Jet engine	14
Tube and tank process	13	Turbojet engine	10
Cross process	5	Long-playing record	3
Houdry catalytic cracking	9	Magnetic recording	5
Fluid catalytic cracking	13	Plexiglass, lucite	3
Gas lift for catalyst pellets	13	Cotton picker	53
Catalytic cracking (moving bed)	8	Nylon [b]	11
Safety razor	9	Crease-resistant fabrics	14
Fluorescent lamp	79	Power steering [c]	6
Television	22	Radar	13
Wireless telegraph	8	Self-winding watch	6
Wireless telephone	8	Shell molding	3
Triode vacuum tube	7	Streptomycin	5
Radio (oscillator)	8	Terylene, dacron	12
Spinning jenny	5	Titanium reduction	7
Spinning machine (water frame)	6	Xerography	13
Spinning mule	4	Zipper	27
Steam engine (Watt)	11	Steam engine (Newcomen)	6
Ball point pen	6		

Source: J. Enos, *op. cit.*, p. 307–308.

[a] The first eleven inventions in the left-hand column were those that occurred in petroleum refining.

[b] Actually, this is the length of time between the beginning of fundamental research by DuPont on superpolymers and the production of nylon on the first commercial unit.

[c] This figure pertains to Vickers' booster units, not Davis's system. See section 3.

In a more recent study, Frank Lynn estimated the average number of years elapsing from the basic discovery and establishment of an invention's technical feasibility to the beginning of its commercial development, as well as the average number of years elapsing from the beginning of its commercial development to its introduction as a commercial product or process.

The results, based on brief histories of twenty major innovations during 1885–1950, seem to indicate that the lag has been decreasing over time, that it is much shorter for consumer products than industrial products, and that it is much shorter for innovations developed with government funds than for those developed with private funds (Table 4.2).[4] Finally, there have

TABLE 4.2

Average Rate of Development of Selected Technological Innovations [a]

Factors Influencing the Rate of Technological Development	Average Time Interval (years)		
	Incubation Period[b]	Commercial Development[c]	Total
Time Period			
Early twentieth century (1885–1919)	30	7	37
Post-World War I (1920–1944)	16	8	24
Post-World War II (1945–1964)	9	5	14
Type of Market Application			
Consumer	13	7	20
Industrial	28	6	34
Source of Development			
Private industry	24	7	31
Federal government	12	7	19

Source: Frank Lynn, "An Investigation of the Rate of Development and Diffusion of Technology in Our Modern Industrial Society," *Report of the National Commission on Technology, Automation, and Economic Progress,* Washington, D.C., 1966.

[a] Based on study of twenty major innovations whose commercial development started in the period 1885–1950.

[b] Incubation Period—begins with basic discovery and establishment of technological feasibility, and ends when commercial development begins.

[c] Commercial Development—begins with recognition of commercial potential and the commitment of development funds to reach a reasonably well-defined commercial objective, and ends when the innovation is introduced as a commercial product or process.

been studies in the defense, electronics, and mining machinery industries of the lead time required to go from the first idea for a new product to the first commercial deliveries. This lead time seems closer conceptually to Lynn's "commercial development period" than to the entire lag between invention and innovation. The results are shown in Table 4.3.

[4] There are many pitfalls in this area. For example, even if there is no tendency for the lag to decrease over time, there can appear to be such a tendency because many recent inventions that have not yet been applied—and which experience long lags between invention and innovation—are necessarily omitted.

TABLE 4.3

Estimated Lead Times, Selected Products

PRODUCT	PREPARA- TION OF PROJECT REQUIRE- MENT AND BASIC SPECIFI- CATION	DESIGN PRODUC- TION OF PROTO- TYPE AND TESTING	PRODUC- TION DRAWINGS AND QUANTITY PRODUC- TION AND TOOLING	MANU- FACTURING TIME BEFORE FIRST PRODUC- TION MODELS FLOW OFF LINE	TOTAL
			(YEARS)		
Landing ship, tank	0.5	0.7	0.9	0.8	2.9
Minesweeper	0.7	0.8	0.8	0.8	3.2
Recoilless rifle	0.3	1.7	1.0	1.3	4.3
Medium tank	0.3	2.3	0.5	1.1	4.3
Destroyer	0.8	2.1	1.3	1.0	5.1
Transport plane	0.5	2.4	0.5	1.8	5.3
Bomber	0.5	3.0	0.8	1.8	6.0
Jet fighter plane	0.8	3.3	0.7	2.4	7.3
New mining machine (new principle)	0.3	2.5	1.0	1.0	3.3
New cutting and loading machine	2.0	2.5	1.5	1.0	4.8
Electronic computer	—	—	—	—	5.0
Telephone exchange	—	—	—	—	6.0
Machine tool control equipment	—	—	—	—	3.0
Communication satellite	—	—	—	—	5.0

Source: C. Freeman, "Research and Development in Electronic Capital Goods," *National Institute Research Review,* November 1965; and A. Saville, "Mining Machine Industry," *Iron and Coal Trades Review,* September 19, 1958. Note that the figures regarding mining machinery and electronic equipment (other than computers) pertain to Western Europe.

3. POWER STEERING:
AN ILLUSTRATIVE CASE

Some of the factors that can delay the occurrence of an innovation are illustrated by the history of power steering, an important product improvement in the automobile industry. Francis Davis, a Harvard-trained consulting engineer who formerly had worked for Pierce Arrow, invented power steering in the mid-twenties. Taking a car whose steering system had been modified to incorporate his invention, Davis went to Detroit in 1926, confident that the automobile industry would quickly adopt his idea. In ten days, he called on ten different individuals and the car was driven by twenty-six persons. General Motors, after many negotiations and tests, signed an option agreement for one year which gave it first shot at a license.

In 1928, Davis signed a license agreement with General Motors. During the next few years, General Motors built several power-steering gears, and in 1932 the Cadillac division had a car equipped with power steering and ready for manufacture. However, worried about public acceptance of the innovation, the company finally decided that the tooling costs could not be justified and they did not introduce it. In 1941, two experimental vehicles equipped with power steering were built by Buick, and plans were made for the introduction of a power-steered Buick to the public. But World War II began and there were no new Buicks, power-steered or otherwise. Nonetheless, power steering was used in a great many British and American armored cars and trucks, and Davis expected that when the war ended, his invention would quickly be introduced commercially.

Again, however, his confidence proved ill-founded. When the war ended, the automobile manufacturers refused to install power steering. They had a seller's market and there was no pressure to install it. Also, what worked in wartime, they believed, might not work so well in the family sedan; and there might be serious maintenance problems. It was not until 1951, when Chrysler made power steering available for its vehicles, that the innovation finally occurred. Then the other automobile manufacturers quickly followed suit, in the face of widespread public acceptance of the innovation. Twenty-five years after Davis's trip to Detroit, power steering was on its way.[5]

4. THE DECISION TO INNOVATE

What factors should a firm consider in deciding whether or not to innovate? For present purposes, it is sufficient to provide a broad and highly simplified sketch, a detailed analysis being available elsewhere.[6] To begin with, the firm should estimate, of course, the expected rate of return from introducing the new product or process. In the case of a new product, the result obviously will depend on the capital investment that is required to introduce the innovation, the forecasted sales, the estimated costs of production, and the effects of the innovation on the costs and sales of the firm's existing product line. These factors depend in part on a firm's pricing policy, as well as on the characteristics of the new product. In addition, the firm should estimate, as best it can, the risks involved in innovating. These

[5] See the testimony of D. DeSimone before the Senate Subcommittee on Antitrust and Monopoly, May 18, 1965.

[6] For example, in E. Pessemier, *New-Product Decisions*, New York: McGraw-Hill, Inc., 1966.

risks tend to be substantial, as witnessed by Booz, Allen, and Hamilton's estimate that, out of every ten products which emerge from research and development, five fail in product and market tests, and of the five that pass these tests, only two become commercial successes.[7]

If the expected returns from the introduction of the innovation do not exceed those obtainable from other investments by an amount that is large enough to justify the extra risks, the innovation should be rejected. If they do exceed those obtainable elsewhere by this amount, the profitability and risks involved in introducing the innovation at present must be compared with the profitability and risks involved in introducing it at various future dates. There are often considerable advantages in waiting, since improvements occur in the new product or process and more information becomes available regarding its performance and market. For example, in the case of new products, firms often employ test marketing to obtain additional information before making a full-scale commitment. (In test marketing, a sample of potential buyers is exposed to the product under more or less normal market conditions; from the results, the firm attempts to infer how some larger population of potential buyers will behave.)

There are disadvantages, as well as advantages, in waiting, perhaps the most important being that a competitior may beat the firm to the punch or that the conditions favoring the innovation may become less benign. In the case of new products, there is often a considerable disadvantage in not being first; sales opportunities will be lost in the interval that competitors are in the market ahead of this firm, and part of the market may be preempted. If the expected returns exceed those obtainable from other investments by an amount that is large enough to justify the risks and if the disadvantages of waiting outweigh the advantages, the firm should introduce the innovation. Otherwise it should wait. Pioneering is a risky business; whether it pays off is often a matter of timing.[8]

In recent years, a number of analytical devices have been developed to aid management in making decisions of this sort. Bayesian statistical techniques can be used to help decide whether or not to collect additional information before acting and if so, how much the additional information is worth. Such techniques can be useful in various ways. For example, they can help prevent market research from being carried out under circumstances where, regardless of the outcome of the research project, the optimal choice is unaffected or unclear; according to some marketing experts, such mistakes are common. Also, the network techniques described in Chapter III can sometimes help management to plan and schedule the activities leading up to the introduction of the new product or process. For

[7] Booz, Allen and Hamilton, Inc., *Management of New Products*, New York, 1960.
[8] See C. Carter and B. Williams, *Investment in Innovation*, New York: Oxford University Press, 1958; E. Pessemier, *ibid.*; and S. Marglin, *Approaches to Dynamic Investment Planning*, Amsterdam: North-Holland Publishing Company, 1963.

example, PERT can be used to identify critical schedule slippages and cost overruns in time for corrective action.

Assuming that the innovation is a new product and that it is successful, the innovator will have invested many times the original research costs leading to the basic invention by the time the new product is brought to market. According to the Department of Commerce's Panel on Invention and Innovation, the research and advanced development leading to the basic invention typically constitutes only about 5 to 10 percent of the total costs. The subsequent engineering and design of the product typically represent about 10 to 20 percent, while tooling and manufacturing engineering represent about 40 to 60 percent of the total costs. Finally, the manufacturing start-up expenses typically constitute about 5 to 15 percent and the marketing start-up expenses constitute about 10 to 25 percent of the total costs.[9]

5. THE GROWTH OF INNOVATORS AND TIMING OF INNOVATION

How large is the payoff for a successful innovation? The best single measure of a firm's reward is the rate of return on its investment; but because of data limitations, we are forced to study the effect of a successful innovation on a firm's growth rate, another interesting, if incomplete, measure of its success. A comparison of the rates of growth of the innovating firms with those of other firms of comparable initial size and with their own pre-innovation growth rates helps to indicate how great the payoff was, in terms of growth, for a successful innovation. Results for the steel and petroleum industries show that, in every time interval and in both industries, the successful innovators grew much more rapidly (during a five- to ten-year period after the innovation occurred) than the other firms, their average growth rate often being more than twice that of the others. However, in the period immediately before they introduced the innovations, there was no persistent tendency for the successful innovators to grow more rapidly than other comparable firms. According to the best available estimates, the average effect of a successful innovation was to raise a firm's annual growth rate by 4 to 13 percentage points, depending on the time interval and the industry.[10] As one would expect, a successful innovation

---

[9] See U.S. Department of Commerce, *Technological Innovation*, Washington, January 1967. For a discussion of various analytical techniques, see E. Pessemier, *op. cit.* and the literature cited there.

[10] Of course, the observed differences in growth rate may be due in part to other factors that are associated both with a firm's willingness to innovate and the timing of the innovation. Although the methods used go part way toward eliminating the problem, there is no way to be sure of its total elimination. See E. Mansfield, *Industrial Research and Technological Innovation*, New York: W. W. Norton & Company, Inc., 1968, Chapter VI.

had a much greater impact on the growth rate of a small firm than a large one.

There are many theories regarding the way in which innovations are distributed over the business cycle. One "commonly accepted view is that inventions are introduced when industry is operating at low levels and when the pressure of competition is most unrelenting . . ." [11] New designs tend to be postponed during good times, and ideas that accumulate are tried out, and new ones explored, during recessions.[12] Another commonly accepted view is that a strong seller's market is most favorable to the introduction of new processes and products.[13] When the economy is approaching the top of the cycle, entrepreneurs "will welcome cost-reducing or output-expanding inventions. [But when the economy turns downward,] . . . entrepreneurs will be chary of taking up inventions, except such as offer great cost reductions at a small increase in fixed costs." [14]

An econometric study of the steel, petroleum refining, and bituminous coal industries attempts to throw new light on the timing of innovation.[15] The principal conclusions of this study are as follows: First, it appears that new processes were most likely to be introduced during periods when these industries were operating at about 75 percent of capacity.[16] Contrary to the opinion of many economists, there was no tendency for innovations to cluster during periods when operating rates were extremely high or extremely low. Apparently, innovation was discouraged by the meagerness of profits and the bleakness of future prospects at a trough and by the lack of unutilized capacity, where changes could be made cheaply and without interfering with production schedules, at a peak. Second, the timing of innovation had a statistically and quantitatively significant effect on the level and timing of expenditures on plant and equipment.

6. INNOVATION AND SIZE OF FIRM

In the previous chapter, we described the debate within the economics profession over the effects of firm size and market structure on the amount spent on research and development. There has been a similar debate over

[11] E. Graue, "Inventions and Production," *Review of Economics and Statistics,* November 1953, p. 222.

[12] W. Brown, "Innovation in the Machine Tool Industry," *Quarterly Journal of Economics,* August 1957; and R. Mack, *The Flow of Business Funds and Consumer Purchasing Power,* New York: Columbia University Press, 1941.

[13] B. Keirstead, *The Theory of Economic Change,* New York: The Macmillan Company, 1948; and C. Carter and B. Williams, *Industry and Technical Progress,* New York: Oxford University Press, 1957.

[14] Keirstead, *op. cit.,* p. 145.

[15] E. Mansfield, *Industrial Research and Technological Innovation, op. cit.,* Chapter VI.

[16] The rate of innovation means, in this context, the rate at which major innovations occur.

the extent to which very large firms are required to do the innovating. Several decades ago, Schumpeter [17] challenged the then prevailing view and asserted that in recent times innovations have been carried out primarily by very large firms. More recently, Galbraith [18] and others have taken much the same position, resting their case in considerable part on the following three arguments: First, the costs of innovating are so great that only large firms can now become involved; second, projects must be carried out on a large enough scale so that successes and failures can in some sense balance out; third, for innovation to be worthwhile, a firm must have sufficient control over the market to reap the rewards.

This position has been questioned by Mason [19] and others. According to this group, no conclusive evidence supports the view that a disproportionately large share of the significant innovations has been carried out by very large firms. However, neither Mason and his followers nor Schumpeter and Galbraith have carried out the empirical studies to settle the question. A study of three basic industries—iron and steel, petroleum refining, and bituminous coal—provides some of the data that are needed. The findings are very rough, both because these industries may not be entirely representative and because of the obvious difficulties in defining a particular innovation, in singling out the innovators, and in gauging the relative importance of various innovations.

To obtain the data, trade associations and trade journals in each of the three industries were asked to list the important processes and products first introduced in the industry since 1918. They were also asked to rank them by importance. Then through research in technical journals and correspondence with various firms within and outside the industry, it was determined which firm first introduced each innovation commercially and when this took place. This information was obtained for about 80 percent of the innovations, about 150 innovations in all. Finally, after obtaining data regarding the size of each firm in each industry, it was possible to determine how many of these innovations were first introduced by the largest four firms in each industry. Since the recent situation probably differed from that prevailing prior to World War II, innovations that occurred during 1939–1958 were separated from those that occurred during 1919–1938.

Do the results indicate that the largest firms introduced a disproportionately large share of the innovations? Of course, the answer depends on what one means by a disproportionately large share. But if the largest firms devoted the same proportion of their resources as did smaller firms both to

[17] J. Schumpeter, *Capitalism, Socialism, and Democracy*, New York: Harper & Row, Publishers, 1942.

[18] J. Galbraith, *American Capitalism*, Boston: Houghton Mifflin Company, 1952.

[19] E. Mason, "Schumpeter on Monopoly and the Large Firm," *Review of Economics and Statistics*, May 1951.

inventive activity and to the testing and development of other persons' ideas, if they obtained applicable results as easily as the smaller firms, and if they were as efficient and as quick to apply the results, one would expect their share of the innovations to equal their share of the market. Did the relative number of innovations carried out by the largest firms exceed their relative share of the market? According to the rather crude measurements in Table 4.4, the largest four coal and petroleum firms carried out a larger number of innovations than their share, but the largest four steel producers

TABLE 4.4

Innovations and Capacity (or Output) Accounted for by Largest Four Firms, Steel, Petroleum Refining, and Bituminous Coal Industries, 1919–1938 and 1939–1958 (Percent of Industry Total)[a]

	STEEL[b]		PETROLEUM[c]		COAL[d]	
ITEM	WEIGHTED	UN-WEIGHTED	WEIGHTED	UN-WEIGHTED	WEIGHTED	UN-WEIGHTED
			PERIOD: 1919–1938			
Process innovations	39	41	34	36	27	18
Product innovations	20	20	60	71	—	—
All innovations [e]	30	32	47	54	27	18
Capacity (or output)	62	62	33	33	11	11
			PERIOD: 1939–1958			
Process innovations	58	64	58	57	30	27
Product innovations	27	27	40	34	—	—
All innovations [e]	43	51	49	43	30	27
Capacity (or output)	63	63	39	39	13	13

Source: E. Mansfield, *Industrial Research and Technological Innovation, op. cit.,* Chapter VI.

[a] In the columns headed "weighted," each innovation is weighted roughly according to the respondents' views of its importance. More precisely, each is weighted in proportion to its average rank in the lists obtained. For processes, we suggested that total savings be used to judge relative importance; for new products, we suggested that sales volume be used. Obviously, this is very rough.

[b] Ingot capacity is used to measure each firm's size. The industry is defined to be those firms with ingot capacity, but firms engaged primarily in some other business were excluded. For the earlier period, a firm's size refers to 1926; for the later period it refers to 1945.

[c] Crude capacity is used to measure each firm's size. The industry is defined to be those firms with crude capacity. For 1919–1938, a firm's size refers to 1927; for 1939–1958, the figures refer to 1947. The product innovations included here are petrochemicals. In each case, the innovator is the first petroleum company that produced it.

[d] Annual production is used to measure each firm's size. The industry is defined to include all who produced bituminous coal. For 1919–1938, a firm's size refers to 1933; for 1939–1958, these figures refer to 1953. The innovations included here are all new devices for preparing coal. This was the only kind of data we could obtain.

[e] For the weighted data, this is just the unweighted average of the figures for process and product innovations.

carried out fewer. Thus, if the Schumpeterean hypothesis is taken to mean that the largest firms accounted for a larger share of the innovations than of the market, it seems generally to hold in petroleum and coal but not in steel.

Why did the largest firms account for a disproportionately large share of the innovations in some cases but not in others? According to one theory, they would account for a disproportionately large share of the innovations in cases where: (1) the innovation requires a large investment relative to the size of the potential users of the innovation, (2) the minimum size of firm to which the innovation would apply is large relative to the average size of firm in the industry, and (3) the average size of the largest four firms in the relevant industry is much greater than the average size of all firms which are potential users of the innovation. This theory can account for a large proportion of the differences observed in Table 4.4.

Finally, three additional points should be noted. First, these results are based entirely on a comparison of the largest four firms with the rest of the industry. If we compare firms of various sizes, there is some evidence that, in all of these industries, the top few firms carried out no more innovations, relative to their size, than did somewhat smaller firms (considerably smaller ones in steel). Second, there is evidence that the smallest steel, petroleum refining, and bituminous coal firms did less innovating recently—relative to large and medium-sized firms—than in the period before World War II. The rising costs of development and the greater complexity of technology may have been responsible in part for this change. Third, there is also a limited amount of data pertaining to the railroad industry. On the basis of a small sample of the most important innovations occurring in the twentieth century, the largest four railroads seemed to do a disproportionately large share of the innovating, relative to the rest of the industry. Their share seemed to be in accord with the theory set forth in the preceding paragraph.[20]

7. IMPORTANCE OF EXTERNAL SOURCES

To what extent do new firms, firms in other industries, independent inventors, and universities play a leading role as innovators or as sources of the ideas underlying major innovations? Many economists[21] emphasize the

[20] The results in this section are based on E. Mansfield, *Industrial Research and Technological Innovation, op. cit.*, Chapter V; and "Innovation and Technical Change in the Railroad Industry," *Transportation Economics*, National Bureau of Economic Research, 1965.

[21] For example, see J. Schumpeter, *Business Cycles*, New York: McGraw-Hill Inc., 1939; E. Domar, "Investment, Losses, and Monopoly," *Income, Employment, and Public Policy*, New York: W. W. Norton & Company, Inc., 1948; and W. Mac-Laurin, "The Sequence from Invention to Innovation and Its Relation to Economic Growth," *Quarterly Journal of Economics*, Vol. 67, February 1953. For related dis-

importance of these external sources of ideas and innovation, particularly in the less science-based industries. Recently, Arthur D. Little carried out an empirical study that sheds new light on the validity of this hypothesis.[22] The Little study is concerned with the origins of the recent major innovations occurring in three mature industries—textiles, machine tools, and construction. The results indicate that there have been relatively few innovations with major economic impact in these industries over the last twenty or thirty years. Those that have occurred have come primarily from outside the industry. To some extent, the ideas underlying them have come from independent inventors, from foreign technology, and from the formation of small new firms. But the most important source has been through the flow of technology from one industry to another. In some cases, these industries have borrowed technology from other industries; in other cases, another industry has entered their business, supplying new components, materials, or equipment; in still other cases, another industry has manufactured a new version of their product.

To illustrate the importance of external sources, let us take the case of numerically controlled machine tools, a very significant new development in metal-working technology. Numerical control provides instructions to machine tools in the form of coded instructions punched on paper tape and enables the machine tool itself to perform most of the functions done by the operator on conventional tools. Numerical control was not developed by the machine tool industry but by Massachusetts Institute of Technology which carried out the work for the U.S. Air Force. The first successful demonstration of a numerically controlled machine tool was held in 1951 at M.I.T., and the first commercial version appeared at the Machine Show of 1955. It was used at first primarily by the aircraft industry on government projects. Although machine tool manufacturers like Giddings and Lewis played a significant role in its commercialization, the concept was developed outside the industry and much of the impetus behind the innovation came from the U.S. Air Force.[23]

The proportion of really major innovations developed and introduced by established firms is lower in these older industries than in technically sophisticated industries like chemicals, electronics, and aerospace. According to Donald Schon, the director of the Little study, the basic innovations

cussion of the flow of technology from one industry to another, the importance of independent inventors, and the tendency for radical inventions to arise outside the large, established firms, see Chapters II and III.

[22] Arthur D. Little, "Patterns and Problems of Technical Innovation in American Industry," *The Role and Effect of Technology in the Nation's Economy*, Hearings before a Subcommittee of the Select Committee on Small Business, United States Senate, 88th Congress, First Session.

[23] See E. Schwartz and T. Prenting, "Automation in the Fabricating Industries," *Report to the President by the National Commission on Technology, Automation, and Economic Progress*, February 1966; and E. Mansfield, *Numerical Control: Diffusion and Impact in the Tool and Die Industry*, forthcoming.

in textiles over the past twenty years have come from the chemical industry, and the principal wave of technological change in the building industry has been a wholesale borrowing of methods from industrial manufacturing. In machine tools, we have seen that the concept leading to one of the most important innovations stemmed largely from external sources. In Schon's opinion, the older industries have difficulty in developing and introducing major innovations because they are fragmented into many small firms, the work of the industry is divided into many small, separately-controlled steps, they are committed to present methods and machines, and they spend little on research and development.[24] Finally, to put all of this in perspective, it should be noted that the many minor innovations, as well as the few major ones, play a very important role in determining the state and evolution of an industry. This point has, of course, been stressed before.

8. THE DIFFUSION OF NEW TECHNIQUES

As pointed out in Chapter II, technological change results in a change in the production function of an existing product or in an addition to the list of technically feasible products. In the American economy, firms and consumers are free to use new technology as slowly or as rapidly as they please, subject, of course, to the constraints imposed by the marketplace. How rapidly an innovation spreads is obviously of great importance; for example, in the case of a process innovation, it determines how rapidly productivity increases in response to the new process. In the remainder of this chapter, we discuss the nature of the diffusion process, the determinants of the rate of diffusion, and the characteristics of technological leaders and followers.

The diffusion process, like the earlier stages of the process of creating and assimilating new processes and products, is essentially a learning process. However, rather than being confined to a research laboratory or to a few firms, the learning takes place among a considerable number of users and producers. When the innovation first appears, potential users are uncertain of its nature and effectiveness, and they tend to view its purchase as an experiment. Sometimes considerable additional R and D is required before the innovation is successful; sometimes, despite attempts at redesign and improvement, the innovation never is a success. Information regarding the existence, characteristics, and availability of the innovation is disseminated by the producers through advertisements and salesmen; information regarding the reaction of users to the innovation tends to be disseminated informally and through the trade press.

Learning takes place among the producers of the innovation, as well as

[24] D. Schon, "Innovation by Invasion," *International Science and Technology*, March 1964. For further discussion and evaluation of these opinions, see Chapters II, III, and VII.

the users. Early versions of an innovation often have serious technological problems, and it takes time to work out these bugs. During the early stages of the diffusion process, the improvements in the new process or product may be almost as important as the new idea itself. For example, there were very important improvements in the catalytic cracking of petroleum in the period following the Sun Oil Company's first introduction of the process, the original Houdry fixed-bed process being outmoded in less than a decade. Moreover, when a new product's design is stabilized, costs of production generally fall in accord with the "learning curve." Thus, in the case of new machine tools, unit costs tend to be reduced by 20 percent for each doubling of cumulated output.[25]

Finally, the diffusion process involves the reallocation of resources. For example, if a new type of equipment is to replace an old type, labor, capital, and materials must be available to produce the new equipment, as well as the fuel and material it uses. The resources used to make the old equipment, and the fuel and material it uses, must be transferred to other employment. Some workers may be thrown out of work, at least temporarily; others must be retrained to operate the new equipment. Since physical capital, once constructed, tends to be relatively inflexible, changes in its allocation must occur largely through the building of new plant and equipment and the scrapping of old. The process of adjustment is often intricate and far-reaching, and the full exploitation of the social benefits from technological change requires that the process be as smooth as possible. Some of the problems of adjustment are discussed in detail in Chapter V.

9. The Diesel Locomotive: A Case Study

The nature of the diffusion process can be illustrated by the case of the diesel locomotive, which was first used in this country in 1924, eleven years after the diesel-electric system was introduced in Europe. The early diesel locomotives were heavy, slow, and without much power. By 1930, eleven American railroads used them at some point on their properties, but they were usually installed where there was a smoke nuisance or a fire hazard. During the thirties, diesel locomotives became more important in the United States. In 1933, General Motors came out with an improved locomotive that was smaller, faster, and more powerful than previous types; and in 1934 began the era of the diesel "streamliners." By 1935, 50 percent of the major American railroads had begun to use diesel locomotives, these leaders generally being large firms and firms where the investment in such locomotives was particularly profitable. In particular, they tended to haul

[25] See J. Enos, *op. cit.*, and W. Hirsch, "Manufacturing Progress Functions," *Review of Economics and Statistics*, May 1956.

little coal. The "coal roads" were reluctant to install diesel locomotives because this might alienate their important customers and because coal was relatively cheap for them.

By 1940, most major American railroads seemed to regard the diesel switcher as being completely out of the experimental stages, although there was still considerable uncertainty regarding its maintenance costs and other factors governing its profitability. When we entered World War II, the diesel locomotive had gained considerable acceptance for switching and limited acceptance for other purposes. By that time it accounted for about three fourths of new orders. Defense needs and priorities governed the production and allocation of diesel locomotives during the war. The allocation of diesel power among the nation's railroads was controlled by the Office of Defense Transportation, and the locomotive builders were allocated material by the War Production Board. Because of the wartime increases in traffic and the change in traffic flows, there was a considerable need for new motive power to replace many of the old steam locomotives. At first, materials (particularly for the diesel power plant) were very tight; but as time went on and the need became more pressing, controls were relaxed and the production of diesel locomotives was stepped up considerably. During the war, about 2,800 diesel locomotives were acquired by American railroads, and by the end of 1945, they constituted almost 10 percent of the total locomotive stock.

When the war ended, the acceptance of the diesel locomotive was widespread, but few firms expected it to displace the steam locomotives for all types of work. However, as time went on, several developments helped to make the advantages of complete dieselization more obvious. First, further refinements were made in diesel design, and the price per horsepower of the diesel locomotive continued to decline relative to steam. Second, it became obvious that large savings could be effected by completely eliminating the facilities needed to service and repair steam locomotives. Third, the remaining uncertainties regarding the diesel locomotive's performance and maintenance were largely dispelled, and the problems in training crews and ancillary personnel were met—with the assistance of the locomotive manufacturers. Between 1946 and 1955, most firms decided to dieselize completely, and by 1959, the diesel locomotive had almost completely displaced the steam locomotive.[26]

10. Rates of Diffusion

Once an innovation has been introduced by one firm, how rapidly does its use spread? Perhaps the earliest noteworthy study of this question was made

[26] This section is based on E. Mansfield, *Industrial Research and Technological Innovation, op. cit.,* Chapter IX.

in 1934.[27] The findings, based on data for twenty-three machines for periods ranging from eleven to thirty-nine years, indicate

. . . the following estimates of the typical duration of periods in their life histories: commercial trial, three to eleven years; rapid increase in use, four to eleven years; slackened increase (with a customary annual gain of less than 10 percent), three to six years; decline, of undefined length. Processes and types of equipment suffer declines for long periods before they pass completely out of use. They linger on in small plants and for special uses long after they have been replaced by new processes or equipment in the major part of the industry.[28]

A more recent study [29] shows how rapidly the use of twelve innovations spread from enterprise to enterprise in four industries—bituminous coal, iron and steel, brewing, and railroads. The innovations are the shuttle car, trackless mobile loader, and continuous-mining machine (in bituminous coal); the by-product coke oven, continuous wide strip mill, and continuous annealing line for tin plate (in iron and steel); the pallet-loading machine, tin container, and high-speed bottle filler (in brewing); and the diesel locomotive, centralized traffic control, and car retarders (in railroads). Figure 4.1 shows the percentage of major firms that had introduced each of these innovations at various points in time. To avoid misunderstanding, three points should be noted in regard to these data. First, because of difficulties in obtaining information concerning smaller firms (and because the smaller firms often were unable to use the innovation in any event), only firms exceeding a certain size are included. Second, the percentage of firms having introduced an innovation, regardless of the scale on which they did so, is given. Third, in a given industry, most of the firms included in the case of one innovation are also included for the others. Thus the data for each of the innovations are quite comparable in this regard.

Two conclusions emerge from Figure 4.1. First, the diffusion of a new technique is generally a slow process. Measuring from the date of the first successful commercial application, it took twenty years or more for all the major firms to install centralized traffic control, car retarders, by-product coke ovens, and continuous annealing. Only in the case of the pallet-loading machine, tin container, and continuous-mining machine did it take ten years or less for all the major firms to install them. Second, the rate of imitation varies widely. Sometimes it took decades for firms to install a new technique, but in other cases they imitated the innovator very quickly. For example, fifteen years elapsed before half of the major pig-iron producers had used the by-product coke oven, but only three years elapsed before half of the major coal producers had used the continuous-mining machine.

[27] H. Jerome, *Mechanization in Industry*, National Bureau of Economic Research, 1934.
[28] *Ibid*, pp. 20–21.
[29] E. Mansfield, *Industrial Research and Technological Innovation, op. cit.*, Chapter VII.

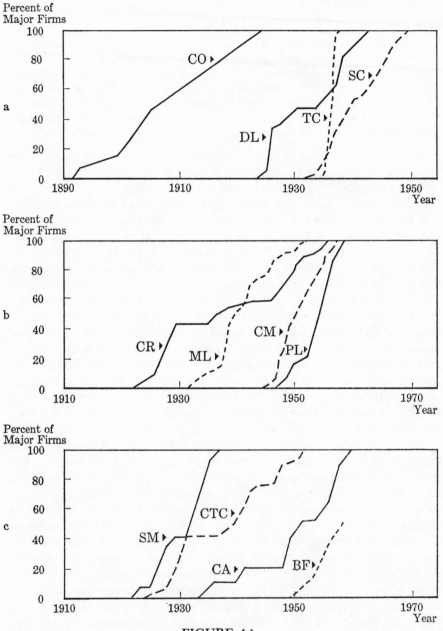

FIGURE 4.1

Growth in the Percentage of Major Firms that Introduced Twelve
Innovations, Bituminous Coal, Iron and Steel, Brewing, and Railroad
Industries, 1890–1958

"Footnotes to Figure 4.1 are at the bottom of the next page."

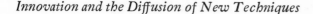

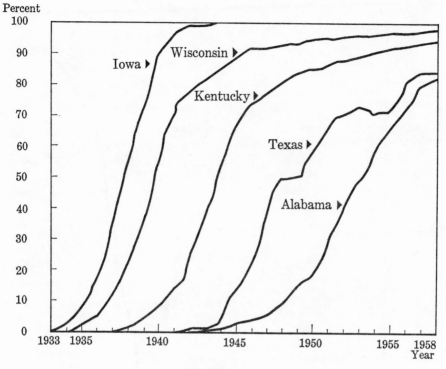

FIGURE 4.2

Percentage of All Corn Acreage Planted to Hybrid Seed

Source: Z. Griliches, *op. cit.*

The number of years elapsing before half the firms had introduced an innovation varied from 0.9 to 15.

In addition, studies have been made of the diffusion of hybrid corn, an important agricultural innovation. Griliches [30] made a valuable study of the differences among regions in the rate of diffusion of hybrid corn. Although serious research on hybrid corn was begun early in the century, the first

[30] Z. Griliches, "Hybrid Corn: An Exploration in the Economics of Technological Change," *Econometrica*, October 1957. For a review of other studies of the diffusion process, see E. Rogers, *Diffusion of Innovation*, New York: The Free Press of Glencoe, 1962.

a. By-product coke oven (CO), diesel locomotive (DL), tin container (TC), and shuttle car (SC).

b. Car retarder (CR), trackless mobile loader (ML), continuous-mining machine (CM), and pallet-loading machine (PL).

c. Continuous wide strip mill (SM), centralized traffic control (CTC), continuous annealing (CA), and high-speed bottle filler (BF).

Source: E. Mansfield, *Industrial Research and Technological Innovation, op. cit.*, Chapter VII.

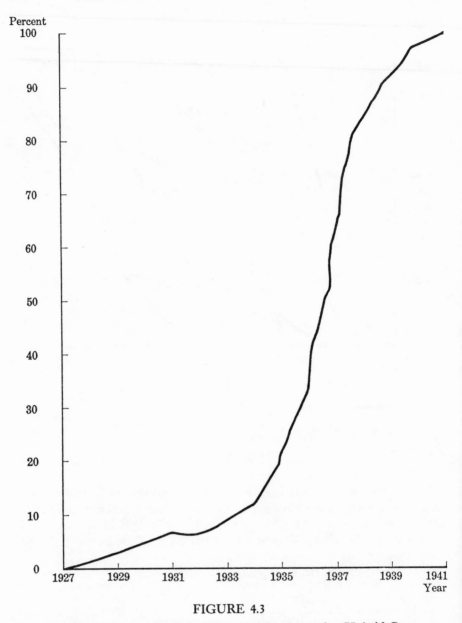

FIGURE 4.3

Percentage of Farmers in Iowa Community Accepting Hybrid Corn

Source: B. Ryan and N. Gross, *op. cit.*

application of the research results on a substantial commercial scale did not occur until the thirties. As shown in Figure 4.2, some regions began to use hybrid corn earlier than others; and once they had begun, some regions made the transition to full (or almost full) adoption more rapidly than others. For example, the time interval from 20 to 80 percent of full adoption required eight years in Alabama but only three years in Iowa. Ryan and Gross[31] confined their attention to about 250 farms in two small Iowa communities, some of their findings being as follows: First, the growth in the percentage of users followed an S-shaped curve, as shown in Figure 4.3. Second, the late adopters were not late because of lack of information concerning the existence of the innovation. By 1934, more than 90 percent of the farmers had heard of the new seed, but fewer than 20 percent had tried it. Third, the earliest adopters were very conservative in the percent of their acreage planted to hybrid corn during the year of their initial adoption.

11. DETERMINANTS OF THE RATE OF DIFFUSION

What determines an innovation's rate of diffusion? Before taking up this question, we should say a few words about the determinants of the ultimate, or equilibrium, level of use of the innovation. For a new process used to make an existing good or service, the equilibrium level of use depends upon the extent of its economic advantages over the other inputs it replaces, and on the sensitivity of the demand of the product it produces to any decline in price or increase in quality induced by the innovation. For a new final good, the equilibrium level of use depends on how much of this product consumers are willing to purchase at the price at which it can be produced and marketed profitably.

Four principal factors seem to govern how rapidly the innovation's level of utilization approaches this ultimate, or equilibrium, level: (1) the extent of the economic advantage of the innovation over older methods or products, (2) the extent of the uncertainty associated with using the innovation when it first appears, (3) the extent of the commitment required to try out the innovation, and (4) the rate of reduction of the initial uncertainty regarding the innovation's performance. Based on these factors, a simple mathematical model[32] has been constructed to explain the differences in the rate of diffusion shown in Figure 4.1. This model is based on the following four hypotheses:

First, as the number of firms in an industry adopting an innovation in-

[31] B. Ryan and N. Gross, "The Diffusion of Hybrid Seed Corn in Two Iowa Communities," *Rural Sociology*, March 1943.

[32] E. Mansfield, *op. cit.*, Chapter VII. Also see E. Mansfield, "Technological Change: Measurement, Determinants, and Diffusion," *Report to the President by the National Commission on Technology, Automation, and Economic Progress*, February 1966. Note that this model pertains to the rate at which firms begin using the innovation. For the discussion to be complete, the intrafirm rate of diffusion must be considered too—and we shall do so in section 13.

creases, it is assumed that the probability of its adoption by a nonuser increases. This assumption seems reasonable because, as experience and information regarding an innovation accumulate, the risks associated with its introduction grow less, competitive pressures mount, and bandwagon effects increase.

Second, the expected profitability of an innovation is assumed to be directly related to the probability of its adoption. This seems reasonable because the more profitable the investment in an innovation promises to be, the greater will be the probability that a firm's estimate of its potential profitability will compensate for the risks involved in its installation.

Third, for equally profitable innovations, the probability of adoption is assumed to be smaller for innovations requiring relatively large investments. This is because firms will be more cautious before committing themselves to large, expensive projects, and they will have more difficulty in financing them.

Fourth, the probability of adoption of an innovation is assumed to be dependent on the industry in which the innovation is introduced. For equally profitable innovations requiring the same investment, the rate of adoption in one industry might be higher than in another because firms in that industry are more inclined to experiment and take risks, the industry's markets are more keenly competitive, or the industry is healthier financially.

If these hypotheses are correct, and if some subsidiary assumptions hold, it can be shown [33] that β, a particular measure of the rate of diffusion, will be linearly related to the profitability of the innovation and the size of the investment required (the intercept of the linear equation differing among industries). Rather than define β explicitly, we provide in Figure 4.4 the values of β corresponding to various intervals between the time when a few firms (20 percent of those considered) had introduced the innovation and the time when most firms (80 percent) had done so. This chart indicates the rate of diffusion implied by any particular value of β.

To test the theory and to see how it can be used in explaining the observed differences among the rates of diffusion, the values of β were computed for the twelve innovations in Figure 4.1 and tests were made to determine if they are in fact linearly related to the variables discussed above. The results seem to indicate that they are. Figure 4.5 compares the actual values of β for the twelve innovations with those computed from the formula

$$\beta = \begin{Bmatrix} -0.57 \\ -0.52 \\ -0.29 \\ -0.59 \end{Bmatrix} + 0.53P - 0.027S,$$

[33] *Ibid.*

Elapsed Time
(in years)

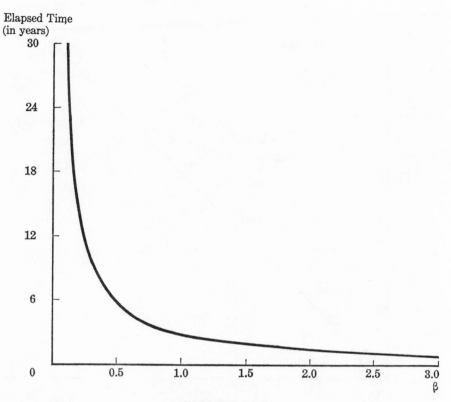

FIGURE 4.4

Relationship between β [a] and the Number of Years Elapsed from the
Time 20 Percent of Major Firms Had Introduced the Innovation to
the Time when 80 Percent Had Done So

[a] A particular measure of the rates of diffusion (see text).

in which the figures in the brackets pertain to the bituminous coal industry, the iron and steel industry, the brewing industry, and the railroad
industry, respectively. P is a measure of the relative profitability of an
innovation, and S is a measure of the size of the investment.[34]

It appears that this theory explains almost all the observed variation in
the rates of diffusion. As shown in Figure 4.5, the theoretical relationship
between β, on the one hand, and P and S, on the other, seems to hold very
well. Although the model is still in the experimental stages, it seems to be a
promising forecasting device. In addition, two other points should be noted:

[34] P = average pay-out period to justify investments (during the relevant period)
divided by average pay-out period for investment in the innovation. S = average
initial investment in the innovation divided by average total assets (from *Moody's*)
for the relevant period. For a more detailed description of P and S, *ibid*. The figures
in the formula are least-square estimates.

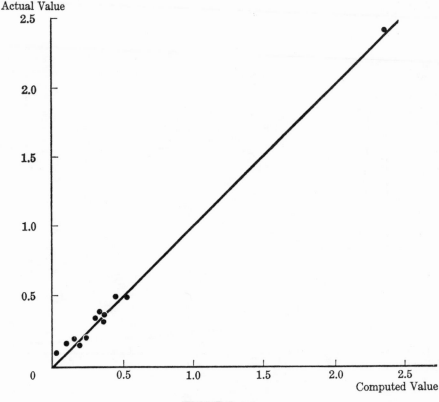

Actual Value

Computed Value

FIGURE 4.5

Comparison of Actual and Computed [a] Values of β for Twelve
Innovations

Source: E. Mansfield, *Industrial Research and Technological Innovation, op. cit.,*
Chapter VII.
  [a] Computed from the equation given in the text. Difference in values is measured
by the vertical distance from the circle to the line; the line represents perfect correspondence.

First, there is an apparent tendency for the rate of diffusion to be higher
when the innovation does not replace very durable equipment and when
an industry's output is growing rapidly. However, neither of these apparent
tendencies is statistically significant. Second, although there is too little
data to warrant a conclusive statement, the interindustry differences seem
roughly consistent with the hypothesis that rates of diffusion are higher in
less concentrated industries.

Of course, this simple theory cannot include all of the important factors
influencing the rate of diffusion. The frequency and extent of advertising
and other promotional devices used by producers will also have an influence. So will the innovation's requirements with regard to knowledge and

coordination, the diffusion process being delayed if the innovation requires new kinds of knowledge on the part of the user, new types of behavior, and the coordinated efforts of a number of organizations. In addition, the diffusion process may be impeded by bottlenecks in the production of the innovation; for example, it took years before all the early orders for the Boeing 707 could be filled. Also, if an innovation requires few changes in socio-cultural values and behavior patterns, it is more likely to spread rapidly. And the more apparent the profitability of an innovation and the easier it is to explain and demonstrate the advantages of the innovation, the more quickly it is likely to spread. In addition, the policies adopted by relevant labor unions can have an important influence on the rate of diffusion, as we shall see in Chapter V.

12. TECHNICAL LEADERS AND FOLLOWERS

What are the characteristics of firms that are relatively quick—or relatively slow—to begin using new techniques?[35] Seven characteristics of a firm and its operations might be expected to affect a firm's speed of response to a new technique: (1) size of firm, (2) expectation of profit from the new technique, (3) rate of growth of the firm, (4) the firm's profit level, (5) the age of the firm's management personnel, (6) liquidity of the firm, and (7) the firm's profit trend. Let us consider these characteristics in order.

Size of Firm. One would expect larger firms to introduce a new technique quicker than small ones. In industries where the larger firms are most progressive, this would certainly be expected.[36] But even if the larger firms are not relatively progressive and do not introduce more than their share of the innovations, one would expect them to be quicker, on the average, to begin using new techniques than smaller firms. To illustrate this, we assume an industry with two firms, one large (80 percent of the market), one small (20 percent of the market). If the large firm does its share of the innovating, it will be first in 80 percent of the cases—and it will be quicker on the average than the small firm.[37] Empirical studies substantiate the

[35] The results in this section are based on E. Mansfield, *op. cit.*, Chapter VII. They are based on data pertaining to the steel, coal, railroad, and brewing industries.

[36] The advantages of the large firm are fairly obvious—greater financial resources, bigger engineering departments, better experimental facilities, closer ties with equipment manufacturers, and so forth.

[37] We have shown elsewhere that if firms differ only in the number of machines, the probability distribution of the lag before adoption of a new technique being the same for each machine, the larger firms will be quicker, on the average, than the smaller firms to begin using the new technique. See E. Mansfield, *op. cit.*, Chapter VIII.

A very important thing to note in this connection is that the results of this section are quite compatible with those in section 6. Even if the largest firms in some industries do less than their share of the innovating, there is likely to be an inverse relationship, on the average, between size of firm and how long a firm waits before it begins to use a new technique.

hypothesis that large firms are quicker, on the average, than small ones to begin using new techniques. Moreover, they provide estimates of the extent of this effect; in the coal, steel, railroad, and brewing industries, the elasticity of delay with respect to firm size is about —0.4.[38]

Expected Profit from The New Technique. The higher the expected return from the new technique, the quicker it would be expected to be adopted. Introduction of a new technique would be delayed if the return was not deemed adequate to offset the risk involved. Unfortunately, only partial data can be obtained regarding firms' profit expectations with respect to various new techniques. However, on the basis of available data, there are strong indications that the profitability of the investment is important in determining how rapidly a firm adopts a new technique.

Growth Rate of the Firm. The more rapidly a firm is growing, the more responsive it could be expected to be in adopting a new technique. An expanding firm can introduce a new technique into its new plants, whereas a firm that is not growing has to wait until it can profitably replace existing equipment. Several studies suggest that this factor may often be important; but our own results revealed no close relationship between a firm's rate of growth and the rate at which it adopts a new technique. The effect of the factor was not statistically significant.

The Firm's Profit Level. More prosperous firms might be expected to adopt a new technique more quickly than firms with low levels of profit. Since less prosperous firms have smaller cash inflows and poorer credit ratings, they experience greater difficulty in financing the investment. They are, therefore, in a less favorable position to take the risk involved in being one of the first to adopt a new technique. Despite these factors, however, the available data show no close relationship between a firm's profit rate and the rate at which it adopts a new technique. The effect of this factor was not statistically significant.

The Age of Management Personnel. Firms with younger top management personnel might be expected to adopt a new technique more quickly than those with older top managements. It is often asserted that younger managements are less bound by traditional ways, and some evidence does indicate that this is true in agricultural enterprises. However, for industrial firms there is no evidence that this is the case, the effect of the factor being statistically nonsignificant.

Liquidity of the Firm. The more liquid firms might be expected to begin using a new technique more quickly than the less liquid firms, because the former are better able to finance the investment. The testing of this hypothesis was limited to only a few cases because of the lack of sufficient data. In these cases, the effect of liquidity on a firm's speed of response was not statistically significant.

The Firm's Profit Trend. Firms with decreasing profits might be ex-

[38] *Ibid.*

pected to be more responsive to a new technique, because they might be expected to search more diligently for new alternatives. This hypothesis could be tested for only a few cases because of insufficient data, and in these cases the effects of a firm's profit trend were not statistically significant.

13. INTRAFIRM RATES OF DIFFUSION OF A NEW TECHNIQUE

Sections 11 and 12 were concerned with the rate at which firms begin to use new techniques. This section examines the influence of various factors on the intrafirm rate of diffusion, that is, the rate at which a firm, once it has begun to use a new technique, continues to substitute it for older methods. We report the findings of a study of the diffusion of the diesel locomotive. Table 4.5 shows, for thirty randomly chosen railroads, the

TABLE 4.5

Time Interval between Date When Diesel Locomotives Were 10 Percent of All Locomotives and Date When They Were 90 Percent of All Locomotives in Thirty Randomly Chosen Class I Railroads

TIME INTERVAL	NUMBER OF FIRMS
14 or more years	3
11–13 years	7
8–10 years	11
5–7 years	3
3–4 years	6
	—
Total	30

Source: E. Mansfield, *Industrial Research and Technological Innovation, op. cit.,* Chapter IX.

number of years that elapsed between the time when diesel locomotives were 10 percent of the total locomotive stock and the time when they were 90 percent.[39] There is wide variation among firms in the intrafirm rate of diffusion. Although an average of nine years was required for the thirty firms to increase dieselization from 10 to 90 percent of complete conversion, six firms took only three or four years to convert and three took fourteen years or more.

The results of an econometric study show that about two thirds of the variation in the rate of intrafirm dieselization among the railroads can be

[39] We present results based on utilization data, as well as these ownership data, in *ibid*, Chapter IX.

explained by the following factors: profit expectation of the investment in diesel locomotives, the date when a firm began to dieselize, size of the firm, the age distribution of its steam locomotives, and a firm's initial liquidity. Several points should be noted regarding these findings. First, together with previous results, the findings suggest that there exists an important economic analogue to the classic psychological laws relating reaction time to the intensity of the stimulus. The profitability of an investment opportunity acts as a stimulus, the intensity of which seems to govern quite closely a firm's speed of response. Second, small firms, once they began, were quicker than their larger rivals to substitute the new technique for the old. Third, the results point up the importance of when a firm begins to use the new technique, the age of its equipment at that time, and its liquidity. All of these factors have a statistically significant effect on the intrafirm rate of diffusion, (measured in terms of either ownership or utilization data or both).[40] However, as so often has been the case in studies of investment behavior, the effect of the profitability of the firm is not statistically significant.

14. SOURCES OF INFORMATION

When a firm introduces a technique it has not used before, where does it obtain the technical information leading to and entering into this decision, and what role is played by this information? To throw new light on these questions, the National Planning Association has studied 560 such decisions in three industries: railroads, housing, and computers. Although the data are not intended to represent a random sample, Sumner Myers, the author of the study, believes that they are free from any important bias and that the results are highly suggestive. According to the findings, about half of the decisions were based largely on technical information transferred horizontally to the firm, that is, on information generated by one organization and used by another. About half were based on knowledge generated within the using firm. The single most important source of information transferred horizontally was the vendor or potential supplier, which received credit for supplying the information in 15 percent of all cases. The government, which received credit in 10 percent of all cases, was also an important source of information transferred horizontally. Apparently, there are important differences in the way in which government and vendor information is used. Government information often requires further development, whereas vendor information tends to be used "as is." Government information tends to be acquired through conversations with an employee's fellow workers and by reading publications. Vendor informa-

---

[40] As one would expect, the intrafirm rate of diffusion was faster for firms that were later to begin using the innovation, that had older equipment, and that were more liquid. The age of a firm's old equipment and size of firm have a statistically significant effect only when the utilization, rather than the ownership, data are used.

tion tends to be sold to the using firm and is acquired through personal contacts with sales engineers and other vendor representatives.

Regardless of its source, what role did the information play? On the one hand, it could have been used to solve a problem that was defined, however roughly, and being worked on; in this case, it plays a passive role. On the other hand, it could have stimulated the relevant decision by defining hitherto undefined needs and problems; in this case, it plays an active role. The distinction is not as clear as it may seem at first sight, but it nonetheless is useful. In the sample studied by the National Planning Association, Myers concluded that the information played a passive role in three quarters of the cases and an active role in one quarter. It is interesting to note that government-supplied information played an active role much more often than information from other sources. Finally, in about two thirds of the cases, it was a simple matter for the firm to recognize the applicability of the information. For example, the railroads can hardly have had much trouble in recognizing the applicability of the diesel locomotive to their business. But in one third of the cases, a creative act was required to utilize the seemingly irrelevant research results or technical information that entered into the decision. In the cases where information played a passive role, the technical information was generally well diffused in the relevant field of expertise; however, the information often was not immediately at hand and required substantial effort to get.[41]

15. TECHNICAL LEADERSHIP
IN AGRICULTURE

Rural sociologists and economists have made a number of interesting studies of the characteristics of technical leaders and followers in agriculture. They often categorize farmers as innovators (the first 2.5 percent to adopt a new process), early adopters (the next 13.5 percent to adopt it), early majority (the next 34 percent), late majority (34 percent), and late adopters (final 16 percent). The studies indicate important differences among these five categories with regard to attitudes, values, social status, abilities, group memberships, and farm business characteristics.

Attitudes and Values. Innovators have more favorable attitudes toward science and are more likely than others to have direct contact with scientists. Laggards place more faith in agricultural "magic" and traditional

---

[41] See S. Myers, "Industrial Innovations and the Utilization of Research Output," paper presented at the National Conference on the Administration of Research, University of Florida, October 28, 1966, and "The Role and Impact of Government R and D Information," paper presented before the National Association of Business Economists, Southern Methodist University, December 2, 1966. These results are part of a larger study of technological transfer carried out by the National Planning Association.

beliefs than do innovators and early adopters. Innovators tend to place less value on being debt free and are more willing to borrow money. They have more venturesome attitudes and reach decisions more quickly than do the others. Although the findings have not been entirely consistent, most studies have found laggards to be older than innovators.

Abilities and Social Status.   Research generally indicates that farmers who are quickest to adopt new techniques have the most formal education, have special mental abilities, and read more farm magazines and extension bulletins than do laggards. Innovators have a higher social status than do laggards. They generally have greater community prestige, larger farms, higher incomes, and more wealth than the others. However, their farming methods may not be respected by other farmers in the community.

Group Memberships.   Farmers who are early in using new techniques are more active in farm organizations, cooperatives, PTA's, and churches. Innovators are more active in state-wide and county-wide organizations; to the extent that laggards are in any groups at all, they are in neighborhood and community groups. Family ties are stronger for the late majority and late adopters than for innovators and early adopters. The friendship patterns of the laggard tend to be restricted to his community, while the innovator's tend to be more cosmopolitan. Innovators travel more widely than other farmers. "Community norms on adoption affect the respect that innovators receive. In 'progressive' communities, innovators may be looked to by their neighbors for information and advice. In 'backward' communities, their farming methods are viewed with suspicion by their neighbors who are less prone to change." [42]

The Economic Characteristics of the Farmers and their Farms.   Innovators tend to have larger farms, higher gross farm incomes, greater farm efficiency, more specialized enterprises, and greater farm ownership. Of course, many of these economic characteristics are by no means surprising.

Finally, some data are available regarding the sources of information obtained by farmers regarding new techniques. The results indicate that the sources vary depending on the stage of the process through which an individual passes from first hearing about a new idea to its final adoption. Table 4.6 shows that mass media sources are most important at the awareness and interest stages; neighbors and friends are most important at the evaluation and trial stages. Also, there is evidence of a "two-step flow of communication," as Katz [43] calls it. The early users of a new technique tend to rely on sources of information beyond their peer group's experience; after they have begun using the new technique, they become a model for their less expert peers, who can imitate their performance.

---

[42] J. Bohlen *et al.*, *Adopters of New Farm Ideas*, North Central Regional Extension Publication No. 13, October 1961, p. 4.

[43] E. Katz, "The Social Itinerary of Technical Change," *Human Organization*, Summer 1961.

TABLE 4.6

Rank Order of Information Sources by Stage in the
Adoption Process

	STAGE				
RANK	AWARENESS (LEARNS ABOUT A NEW IDEA OR PRACTICE)	INTEREST (GETS MORE INFORMATION ABOUT IT)	EVALUATION (TRIES IT OUT MENTALLY)	TRIAL (TRIES A LITTLE)	ADOPTION (ACCEPTS IT FOR FULL-SCALE USE)
	(SOURCES OF INFORMATION)				
1	Mass media—radio, TV, newspapers, magazines	Mass media	Friends and neighbors	Friends and neighbors	Friends and neighbors
2	Friends and neighbors —mostly other farmers	Friends and neighbors	Agricultural agencies	Agricultural agencies	Agricultural agencies
3	Agricultural agencies— Extension, Vo Ag, and the like	Agricultural agencies	Dealers and salesmen	Dealers and salesmen	Mass media
4	Dealers and salesmen	Dealers and salesmen	Mass media	Mass media	Dealers and salesmen

Source: J. Bohlen *et al., op. cit.,* Table 1.

16. THE DIFFUSION OF NEW CONSUMER GOODS

Sections 10 to 15 focused attention primarily on the diffusion of new producer goods. What determines the rate of diffusion of a new consumer good? Whereas the profitability of a new producer good plays a key role in its diffusion, the tastes and preferences of consumers play the analogous role in the case of a new consumer good. If the public likes a new product much better than existing substitutes, its use will spread quickly; if it is only marginally superior, the diffusion process will go on more slowly. In addition, as in the case of producer goods, a new consumer good will spread more rapidly if only a small financial commitment is required to try it, if there is relatively little uncertainty regarding its performance, and if the initial uncertainty decreases at a rapid rate.

To illustrate some of the factors at work, consider the case of television. Although the Federal Communication Commission authorized the start of commercial television broadcasting in 1941, the diffusion process did not really begin until after World War II. The rate of diffusion was very rapid, the combined revenues from the sales of television sets and television broadcasting exceeding $1.5 billion during 1950. According to Dernburg, the percentage ownership of television sets in a particular area in 1950 was directly related to the length of time television was available and the extent of television coverage. It was directly related to average income up to about $7000 and inversely related to it thereafter; holding average income constant, it was inversely related to the dispersion of income except in very low income areas. It was highest where the average educational level was ten to twelve years; for higher and lower levels of education, it was lower.[44]

There has been considerable interest among sociologists and anthropologists in the relationship between social class and the propensity to accept change, many observers claiming that the upper socioeconomic classes tend to be conservative and the lower socioeconomic classes tend to be the innovators. However, empirical studies seem to suggest that whether this is so depends on the extent to which the innovation is compatible with the cultural characteristics of a particular class. For example, the consumers who are quickest to introduce new consumer durables tend to be young, highly educated, prosperous, and concentrated in the professional and managerial groups. Moreover, fashions in consumer goods sometimes are introduced via the socioeconomic elite and pass down through the status hierarchy, sometimes in the form of inexpensive copies.[45]

17. HAS THERE BEEN AN INCREASE IN THE RATE OF DIFFUSION?

A number of economists, led by Charles Killingsworth,[46] have claimed that innovations spread much more rapidly now than in the past. Presumably the reasons for such a difference are the development of improved communication channels, more sophisticated methods for determining the time at which equipment should be replaced, and greater receptivity to new ideas and new ways of doing things. Since the question of whether or not the rate of diffusion has been increasing is of considerable importance, it is unfortunate that the available evidence is so limited. Killingsworth admits that he has little or no quantitative evidence to support his proposition. The only attempts to provide such evidence are contained in my study of twelve major innovations and in a more recent study of twenty

[44] T. Dernburg, R. Rosett, and H. Watts, *Studies in Household Economic Behavior*, New Haven, Conn.: Yale University Press, 1958.

[45] S. Graham, "Class and Conservatism in the Adoption of Innovation," *Human Relations*, 1956; H. Barnett, *Innovation*, New York: McGraw-Hill, Inc., 1953; L. Fallers, "A Note on the 'Trickle Effect'," *Public Opinion Quarterly*, Fall 1954; W. Bell, "Consumer Innovators"; R. Frank and W. Massy, "Innovation and Brand Choice"; and C. King, "Fashion Adoption: A Rebuttal to the Trickle-Down Theory"; all in *Toward Scientific Marketing*, American Marketing Association, 1964. The latter paper challenges the "trickle-down" theory. Also, see T. Berg and A. Shuchman, *Product Strategy and Management*, New York: Holt, Rinehart, and Winston, Inc., 1963.

[46] C. Killingsworth, Testimony before Senate Subcommittee on Employment and Manpower, 1963.

major innovations by Lynn.[47] The findings must be viewed with considerable caution.

To see whether the rate of diffusion has tended to increase over time, "time," as well as the profitability of the innovation and the size of the investment required to introduce the innovation, was included as an explanatory variable in the analysis of rates of diffusion in section 11. In this way, we attempted to hold constant the effects of profitability and size of investment. The results indicated some apparent tendency for the rate of diffusion to increase over time. However, this tendency was very weak —the time interval between 20 percent adoption and 80 percent adoption declining on the average by only about 4/10th of 1 percent per year— and this could easily have been due to chance.[48] Lynn's results indicate a more definite acceleration of the rate of diffusion. Between the early part of the century and the interwar period, he found a considerable speed-up, with only slight further acceleration after 1945.

Of course, a higher rate of diffusion is not always desirable. It would obviously be unwise, both privately and socially, to introduce a new technique quickly and find out subsequently that it was uneconomic. Given that there is considerable uncertainty regarding an innovation's performance, it makes good sense to adopt it gradually. Moreover, the existence of old equipment frequently makes it wasteful to introduce an innovation very quickly. In many cases, it does not pay to replace the old equipment until it has deteriorated and become more costly to operate. In addition, if one expects important improvements in the innovation, it is often rational to wait before adopting it.[49] Although many observers suspect that the diffusion process often goes on more slowly than it should, this does not imply that increases in the rate of diffusion are always a good thing.

18. SUMMARY

An invention, when applied for the first time, is an innovation. Regardless of whether the break between invention and innovation is blurred or clearcut, innovation is a key stage in the process leading to the full evaluation and utilization of an invention. The innovator must be willing to take the risks involved in introducing a new and untried process, good, or service. The lag between invention and innovation varies substantially, the average lag being between ten and twenty years for the innovations for which data are presented. In deciding whether or not to innovate, a firm

[47] E. Mansfield, *op. cit.*, Chapter VII; and F. Lynn, *op. cit.*

[48] However, in the stochastic version of the model, the effect of "time" was statistically significant. See E. Mansfield, *ibid.*

[49] There is an extensive literature on the economics of machine replacement. For example, see E. Grant and W. Ireson, *Principles of Engineering Economics*, New York: The Ronald Press Company, 1964; and G. Terborgh, *Dynamic Equipment Policy*, New York: McGraw-Hill, Inc., 1949.

must weigh the advantages of waiting to obtain additional information against the chance that a competitor will beat the firm to the punch or that the conditions favoring the innovation may become less benign. According to the best available estimates, a successful innovation has a significant impact on the innovator's growth rate, the effect being greater for a small firm than for a large one.

There is considerable interest in the characteristics of innovators and in the timing of innovation. Although it is often alleged that the largest firms do more than their share of the innovating, this is not always the case, the steel industry being a notable exception. However, it seems to be true in most of the industries for which we have data—petroleum refining, bituminous coal, railroads.[50] Whether or not it is true in a particular industry seems to depend on the average size of the investment required to innovate, the minimum size of firm required to use the innovations, and the size distribution of firms in the industry. Many economists emphasize the importance of innovation by invasion, and studies of mature industries seem to confirm the significance of external sources of innovations. Turning to the timing of innovation, there is no evidence that innovations tend to cluster during periods when operating rates were extremely high or extremely low. On the contrary, at the trough of the business cycle, innovation seems to be discouraged by the meagerness of profits and the bleakness of future prospects; at the peak, it seems to be discouraged by the lack of unutilized capacity.

In the American economy, firms and consumers are free to adopt innovations as slowly or as rapidly as they please; subject, of course, to the constraints imposed by the marketplace. The diffusion process, like the earlier stages of the process of creating and assimilating new processes and products, is essentially a learning process. Potential consumers learn of the innovation and are persuaded to try it; the producers of the innovation work out the bugs and learn how to reduce costs. The diffusion process generally entails the reallocation of resources. Some workers may be thrown out of work, at least temporarily; others must be retrained to operate the new equipment. Since capital, once constructed, tends to be relatively inflexible, changes in its allocation must occur largely through the building of new plants and equipment and the scrapping of old. The process of adjustment is often intricate and far-reaching, and the full exploitation of the social benefits from technological change requires that the process be as smooth as possible.

How rapidly an innovation spreads is obviously of great importance; for example, in the case of a process innovation, it determines how rapidly productivity increases in response to the new process. The available evidence indicates that the diffusion of a new technique has generally been a

---

[50] This statement is based on a comparison of the largest four firms with the rest of the industry. See the last paragraph of section 6 for the results of other comparisons.

slow process, twenty years or more being required in many cases before all the major firms in an industry have begun using an innovation. The evidence also indicates that the rate of imitation varies widely; sometimes it took decades for an innovation to be widely adopted, but in other cases, firms imitated the innovator very quickly. In the twelve cases shown in Figure 4.1, the number of years elapsing before half the firms had introduced an innovation varied from 0.9 to 15. Although it is frequently claimed that innovations spread more rapidly now than in the past, there is very little evidence on this score. The available data suggest some tendency of this sort, but the findings must be viewed with considerable caution.

An innovation's rate of diffusion is determined in large part by four factors: the extent of the economic advantage of the innovation over older methods or products, the extent of the uncertainty associated with using the innovation when it first appears, the extent of the commitment required to try out the innovation, and the rate at which the initial uncertainty regarding the innovation's performance can be reduced. A simple mathematical model has been constructed to help explain differences among process innovations in the rate of imitation. This model is built largely around one hypothesis—the probability that a firm will introduce a new technique is an increasing function of the proportion of firms already using it and the profitability of doing so, but a decreasing function of the size of the investment required. When confronted with data for twelve innovations, this model seems to stand up surprisingly well. Although the model is still in the experimental stages, it seems to be a promising forecasting device.

Studies have also been made of the factors associated with a firm's speed of response to a new technique. Among industrial firms, the size of a firm and the profitability of its investment in the technique seem to be directly related to the speed with which it begins using it. However, there is no evidence that a firm's speed of response is related to the firm's rate of growth, profit level, liquidity, profit trend, or age of a firm's management. Among farmers, the technical leaders seem to have relatively advanced formal education, higher social status, more cosmopolitan interests and social contacts, larger farms, higher gross farm incomes, greater farm efficiency, more specialized enterprises, and greater farm ownership than their slower competitors. Both for industry and agriculture, studies have been made of the sources of technical information entering into the decision to adopt a new technique. Turning to consumers, some observers claim that the upper socioeconomic groups tend to be conservative and the lower socioeconomic groups tend to be the innovators. However, with regard to many types of goods, the opposite is true; for example, the consumers that are quickest to introduce new consumer durables tend to be young, highly educated, prosperous, and concentrated in the professional and managerial groups.

CHAPTER V

AUTOMATION, LABOR DISPLACEMENT, AND ADJUSTMENT PROBLEMS

◆◇◆◇◆◇◆◇◆◇◆◇◆◇◆◇◆◇◆◇◆◇◆

1. TECHNOLOGICAL UNEMPLOYMENT

When technological change is mentioned, the first thing many people think of is unemployment. The fear of technological unemployment is by no means new. During the mid-1700's, a mob of worried English spinners smashed into James Hargreave's mill, and destroyed the first workable multi-spindle frames. Similar forms of labor resistance to the adoption of new techniques are chronicled in the histories of most major nations. Moreover, resistance of this kind is not confined to unskilled workers. Although new techniques often result in the displacement of unskilled workers, there have been many cases where skilled journeymen were as much affected as unskilled. For example, the Owens automatic glass-blowing machines largely destroyed the bottle glassblowers craft.[1]

[1] See K. Van Auken, "Personnel Adjustment to Technological Change," in H. Jacobsen and J. Roucek, *Automation and Society*, New York: Philosophical Library, Inc., 1959; and P. Taft, "Organized Labor and Technical Change: A Backward Look," in G. Somers, E. Cushman, and N. Weinberg, *Adjusting to Technological Change*, New York: Harper & Row, Publishers, 1963.

Early social attitudes contributed to the fear of and resistance to new techniques by many worker groups. In the late 1800's and the early part of this century, the prevailing attitude was "sink or swim." Little or no help was available to displaced workers. If a worker's skills were outmoded, he was often forced into jobs (when they were available) which were far below his previous status. In accord with the mores of the times, it was felt that any efforts to help would be quite wrong; each man should stand on his own two feet. In recent years, attitudes have changed. There is a growing feeling that society, which is, by and large, a beneficiary of technological change, has an obligation to minimize the losses and assist the readjustment of those who are hurt. In this chapter, we discuss the relationship between technological change and aggregate unemployment, the ways in which private and public policies can ease the problems involved in the displacement of labor, and the attitudes of unions toward management's adoption of new techniques.

2. AUTOMATION

Although the dread of technologically induced mass unemployment is not new, it was revived with great effect in the late fifties and early sixties, the new scare word being "automation." For example, Professor Crossman of Oxford University, addressing an international conference in 1964, said that "unemployment due to automation will grow steadily over the next few decades, perhaps centuries, and in the end it is likely to reach a very high figure, say 90 percent of the labor force, unless radical changes are made in the present pattern of working."[2] Although "automation" means different things to different people, it generally refers to processes designed to mechanize the human cognitive, conceptual, and informational processes. First, there are automatic control mechanisms, which introduce the closed-loop feedback principle and make possible the creation of an automatic remote-controlled, self-contained production system. "Feedback" is a concept of control by which the input of a machine is regulated by the machine's own output, the consequence being that the output meets the conditions of a predetermined objective—as in a thermostatically controlled heating system. Process control machines have found use in oil refineries and chemical plants, as well as many other industries. Second, there are transfer machines, commonly called "Detroit automation," which have been employed in the automobile industry. Such equipment has been used to machine cylinder blocks.[3] Third, there are a variety

[2] Organization for Economic Cooperation and Development, *The Requirements of Automated Jobs*, Paris, 1965, p. 21.
[3] See C. Killingsworth, "The Automation Story: Machines, Manpower and Jobs," in C. Markham, *Jobs, Men, and Machines*, New York: Frederick A. Praeger, Inc., 1964; Organization for Economic Cooperation and Development, *ibid;* and C. Silberman, "The Real News About Automation," *Fortune*, January 1965.

of uses of computer technology. Although we have described some of these uses in Chapter II, it may be worthwhile citing others. For example, consider American Airlines' reservation system. A central computer is connected to small desk machines displaying flight information. By pushing various buttons, a ticket agent can report a sale (or cancellation) or request information. The central computer flashes back replies to inquiries on space availability. When a sale or cancellation is made, the correct number of seats is added to, or deducted from, the inventory of seats in the computer's memory. Thus, sales are not approved if space is not available, and expensive time lags are eliminated. It requires only a tenth of a second to tell if a seat is available on any flight leaving New York.[4]

Another example is furnished by Westinghouse Electric Corporation's Tele-Computer Center. Westinghouse, which probably uses computers as widely as any American firm, uses this center to provide up-to-date information regarding costs, sales, and other critical variables and to simulate various aspects of its business. In addition, the center handles about 2,000 orders a day for various products, prepares invoices, and does the bookkeeping; sends incoming orders to the nearest warehouse with the product in stock; and automatically adjusts warehouse stocks to optimum level by sending a reorder to the factory. It has enabled the firm to close six of its twenty-six warehouses, to cut inventories by 35 percent, and to provide better service.[5]

3. TECHNOLOGICAL CHANGE, AGGREGATE DEMAND, AND STRUCTURAL UNEMPLOYMENT

Is it true that increases in the rate of technological change necessarily result in increases in aggregate unemployment? Contrary to much popular opinion, the answer is no. Changes in aggregate unemployment are governed by the growth in the aggregate demand for goods and services and the growth in the labor force, as well as the growth in output per man-hour.[6] If the rate of increase of aggregate demand equals the rate of increase of productivity plus the rate of increase of the labor force, there will be no increase in aggregate unemployment, regardless of how high the rate of increase of productivity may be. Although there will be increases in some types of jobs and decreases in others, the total number of unemployed will not be affected.

Thus, rapid technological change need not result in increased aggregate

[4] See W. Buckingham, "Gains and Costs of Technological Change," in G. Somers, E. Cushman, and N. Weinberg, *op. cit.*

[5] See *Business Week*, June 25, 1966; and E. Mansfield, *Managerial Economics and Operations Research*, New York: W. W. Norton & Company, Inc., 1966, Part IV.

[6] Changes in the average hours of work also influence aggregate unemployment, but their effect has been quantitatively less important in recent years.

unemployment. The important thing is that the government increase aggregate demand at the proper rate. If aggregate demand increases too slowly, increases in aggregate unemployment will take place. If aggregate demand increases too rapidly and resources are already fully employed, inflation will result. Unfortunately, there is nothing that insures that aggregate demand will grow at the right pace—as witnessed by the fact that it grew too slowly in the thirties and too rapidly immediately after World War II. However, through appropriate fiscal and monetary policies, the Federal government can compensate for inadequate or too rapid rates of growth of aggregate demand. The job of choosing and carrying out appropriate fiscal and monetary policies is not always easy, but the problems are by no means insoluble.[7]

During the fifties and early sixties, there was considerable concern that workers and jobs were becoming more and more mismatched. According to the "structuralists," new methods and equipment were increasing the skill and educational requirements of available jobs, and making it more likely that shortages of highly educated workers would coexist with unemployed pools of unskilled workers. Other economists denied that there was a substantial increase in the amount of structural unemployment, that is, unemployment that exists because the workers available for employment do not possess the qualities that employers with unfilled vacancies require. An important and lively debate took place, both inside and outside the government.

The important question was how unemployment would respond to an increase in the general level of demand. If an increase in demand would result in a reduction of unemployment, then evidently at least that much unemployment was not structural; if it would fail to reduce unemployment, then the unemployment that remained could be called structural. To put the structuralist hypothesis to a test, attempts were made to compare various periods when the general pressure of demand was about the same, the purpose being to see whether the level of unemployment was higher or more strongly concentrated in certain skill categories, industries, or regions in more recent periods than in the past.

The results, as well as the course of events since the 1964 tax cut, provided little support for the structuralist view. There was no evidence that unemployment was becoming more concentrated in particular geographical regions. Moreover, after adjusting for the effect of the over-all unemployment rate on the unemployment rate in particular occupations and industries, there were very few occupations or industries showing a statistically significant tendency for unemployment to increase with time. Also, after adjusting for the effect of the over-all unemployment rate, there was

[7] For an elaboration of this point, see the National Commission on Technology, Automation and Economic Progress, *Technology and the American Economy*, Washington, D.C., 1966.

no significant tendency for unemployment rates among Negroes to rise during the late fifties and early sixties. Although a substantial portion of all unemployment may have been structural, there has been no evidence that unemployment of this type increased greatly in recent years.[8]

4. CHANGES IN SKILL REQUIREMENTS

The debate over structural unemployment prompted a number of studies of the effects on skill requirements of the new methods and equipment adopted in recent years. Was it true that automatic machinery required extensive training of large segments of the work force or replacement of these workers with people of higher skills? Case studies were carried out to determine the effects of new methods and equipment on job content and occupational structure in industries like oil refining, electronic equipment, pulp and paper, slaughtering and meat packing, rubber tires and tubes, machine-shop trades, and medical services. The results did not indicate any sharp or consistent increase in skill requirements as a consequence of switching to newer techniques. The extent of the increase, if it existed at all, varied enormously among innovations, and seemed quite modest on the average.

For example, consider the effects of automation in the office. Case studies indicated that, after a changeover to an electronic computer system, few employees where the machine was placed were doing exactly the same jobs. Moreover, the more rationalized work process resulted in employees working under tighter time schedules and being monitored by an integrated system that checked and rechecked. Nonetheless, although new jobs such as programmers, operators, and managers of electronic data-processing machines were created, skill requirements seemed to remain relatively stable for such routine jobs as posting, filing, tabulating, and key punching. Despite extensive changes in job content, the introduction of electronic data processing seemed to raise the average grade of office occupations only slightly.[9]

[8] For example, see R. Solow, *The Nature and Sources of Unemployment in the United States*, Stockholm: Almqvist and Wiksell, 1964; J. Knowles and E. Kalachek, *Higher Unemployment Rates, 1957–60*, Washington, D.C.: U.S. Government Printing Office, 1961; L. Gallaway, "Labor Mobility, Resource Allocation, and Structural Unemployment," *American Economic Review*, September 1963; N. Simler, "The Structural Hypothesis and Public Policy," *American Economic Review*, December 1964; R. Gordon and M. Gordon, *Prosperity and Unemployment*, John Wiley & Sons, Inc., 1966; B. Berman and D. Kaun, "Characteristics of Cyclical Recovery and the Measurement of Structural Unemployment"; and A. Gantt, "Requirements for Structural Adjustment by the Labor Force, 1952–63"; both presented at the December 1964 meetings of the American Statistical Association; and E. Mansfield, "Comment," *Proceedings of the Business and Economics Section, American Statistical Association*, 1965.
[9] For example, see F. Mann, "Psychological and Organizational Aspects," in J. Dunlop, *Automation and Technological Change*, Englewood, N.J.: The American Assem-

Within factory occupations, the results seemed much the same. In some occupations, skill requirements increased. For example, more complicated metalworking equipment increased the technical skills required of tool and die makers, as a knowledge of mathematics and the basic sciences became more and more necessary to perform this work. However, in other occupations, skill requirements decreased. For example, the use of numerically controlled machine tools sometimes reduced the skills of machine-tool operators, the duties of the operator being limited generally to loading and unloading the machine and monitoring the machine during operation. On balance, there was no indication that new techniques required a much higher order of skill in most occupations.[10]

The reasons why automatic machinery had a relatively modest impact on skill requirements were given by Bright and others. As new processes become routinized, it becomes possible to use less skilled labor. For example, during the early days in the manufacture of transistors, chemical engineers had to supervise the vats where crystals were grown; however, as processes were perfected, these engineers were replaced with less skilled labor. Another important factor is technological change itself. Whereas new techniques often require highly skilled labor at first, they generally become adapted to use less skilled—and less expensive—labor. As Bright put it, "the machine designer ceases his efforts to simplify operation and maintenance only when the machine manning needs have been reduced to a standard that is normally available in the local labor force." [11]

The fact that the educational attainment of the work force has increased does not contradict these findings. In large part, jobs have been filled with better educated people because the educational level of the population has increased and such people have become available. If the available human resources are of high quality, a market economy will adjust to the use of such resources, one consequence being that unskilled,

---

bly, 1962; E. Hardin, "Computer Automation, Work Environment and Employee Satisfaction: A Case Study," *Industrial and Labor Relations Review*, 1960; E. Hardin, "The Reactions of Employees to Office Automation," *Monthly Labor Review*, 1960; and I. Hoos, "Impact of Automation on Office Workers," *International Labor Review*, 1960.

[10] For example, see C. Walker, *Toward the Automatic Factory*, New Haven, Conn.: Yale University Press, 1957; C. Walker, "Changing Character of Human Work Under the Impact of Technological Change," *Report of the National Commission on Technology, Automation, and Economic Progress*, Washington, D.C., 1966; W. Faunce, "The Automobile Industry: A Case Study in Automation," in H. Jacobson and J. Roucek, *op. cit.*; and F. Mann and L. Hoffman, *Automation and the Worker*, New York: Holt, Rinehart, and Winston, Inc., 1960.

[11] J. Bright, "The Relationship of Increasing Automation and Skill Requirements," *Report of the National Commission on Technology, Automation, and Economic Progress*, Washington, D.C., 1966, p. 221. Also, see M. Horowitz and I. Herrnstadt, "Changes in Skill Requirements of Occupations in Selected Industries," *ibid*; and E. Clague, "Effects of Technological Change on Occupational Employment Patterns in the United States," in *The Requirements of Automated Jobs, op. cit.*

untrained labor will earn less than average income and will experience above-average unemployment when aggregate demand is too low. This has always been the case and is not due to technological change. If the relative position of the unskilled has deteriorated, it is probably due more to the growing abundance of highly educated people than to the newer techniques that have come into being.[12]

Needless to say, the issue here is not whether the adoption of new techniques alters occupational and skill requirements. Clearly it does, although other factors are probably at least as important. Instead the important issue is whether the changes are so great that unskilled labor will be unable to find work in the future. According to the Bureau of Labor Statistics' projections (Tables 5.1 and 5.2), the number of white-collar

[12] Report of the National Commission on Technology, Automation, and Economic Progress, op. cit.

TABLE 5.1

Employment, by Major Occupation Group, 1964, and Projected Requirements, 1975 [a]

MAJOR OCCUPATION GROUP	1964		1975		PERCENT CHANGE 1964–1975
	NUMBER (IN MILLIONS)	PERCENT	NUMBER (IN MILLIONS)	PERCENT	
Total employment	70.4	100.0	88.7	100.0	26
White-collar workers	31.1	44.2	42.8	48.3	38
Professional, technical, and kindred workers	8.6	12.2	13.2	14.9	54
Managers, officials, and proprietors, except farm	7.5	10.6	9.2	10.4	23
Clerical and kindred workers	10.7	15.2	14.6	16.5	37
Sales workers	4.5	6.3	5.8	6.5	30
Blue-collar workers	25.5	36.3	29.9	33.7	17
Craftsmen, foremen, and kindred workers	9.0	12.8	11.4	12.8	27
Operatives and kindred workers	12.9	18.4	14.8	16.7	15
Laborers, except farm and mine	3.6	5.2	3.7	4.2	—[b]
Service workers	9.3	13.2	12.5	14.1	35
Farmers and farm managers, laborers, and foremen	4.4	6.3	3.5	3.9	−21

Source: Report of the National Commission on Technology, Automation, and Economic Progress, op. cit.
Note: Because of rounding, sums of individual items may not equal totals.
[a] Projections assume a national unemployment rate of 3 percent in 1975.
[b] Less than 3 percent.

TABLE 5.2

Employment of Nonagricultural Wage and Salary Workers, by
Industry, 1964, and Projected Requirements, 1975 [a]

Industry	1964 (in thousands)	1975 (in thousands)	Percent Change 1964–1975
Total	58,156	75,875	30
Mining	633	620	— [b]
Contract construction	3,056	4,190	37
Manufacturing	17,259	19,740	14
Durable goods	9,813	11,500	17
Ordnance and accessories	247	250	— [b]
Lumber and wood products except furniture	603	550	−9
Furniture and fixtures	406	510	26
Stone, clay, and glass products	612	675	10
Primary metal industries	1,231	1,290	5
Fabricated metal products	1,187	1,460	23
Machinery	1,606	2,050	28
Electrical equipment and supplies	1,548	2,000	29
Transportation equipment	1,605	1,730	8
Motor vehicles and equipment	755	800	6
Aircraft and parts	604	575	−5
Instruments and related products	369	510	38
Miscellaneous manufacturing industries	399	475	19
Nondurable goods	7,446	8,240	11
Food and kindred products	1,746	1,665	−5
Tobacco manufactures	89	80	−10
Textile mill products	891	880	— [b]
Apparel and related products	1,302	1,525	17
Paper and allied products	625	775	24
Printing, publishing, and allied products	951	1,100	16
Chemicals and allied products	877	1,125	28
Petroleum refining and related industries	183	160	−13
Rubber and miscellaneous plastics products	434	580	34
Leather and leather products	348	350	— [b]
Transportation and public utilities	3,947	4,425	12
Trade, wholesale and retail	12,132	16,150	33
Finance, insurance and real estate	2,964	3,725	26
Services and miscellaneous	8,569	12,275	43
Government	9,595	14,750	54
Federal government	2,348	2,525	8
State and local government	7,248	12,225	69

For source and footnotes, see Table 5.1.

and service workers will increase much more rapidly than the number of blue collar workers during 1964–1975, and the prospects for farm employment will continue to be bleak, a 21 percent decrease in requirements being forecasted by the Bureau. However, despite the widespread concern that new techniques will drastically reduce requirements for laborers, the Bureau forecasts no decline in these requirements, although they will decline as a percent of the total. Whereas these results suggest that commentators like W. Ferry and E. Crossman [13] have exaggerated the magnitude of the problem, they do not deny the need for retraining programs and increased educational efforts of various sorts. On the contrary, with such manpower policies full employment targets can be raised. But without such policies, it appears that, when unemployment rates are pushed much below 4 percent, an expansion in aggregate demand will only reduce unemployment at a politically unacceptable cost in terms of inflationary pressure.[14]

5. LABOR DISPLACEMENT

Although an adequate level of aggregate demand can go a long way toward assuring that aggregate unemployment will not exceed a socially acceptable minimum, it cannot prevent labor from being displaced from particular occupations, industries, and regions, and being drawn to others. Nor would we want to eliminate such movements of labor, without which it would be impossible to adjust to changes in technology, population, and consumer tastes. However, regardless of the long-run benefits of this adjustment process, important problems may arise in the short run, great distress being imposed on the workers who are displaced. It is important that these movements of labor be carried out as efficiently and painlessly as possible.

The most serious adjustment problems have occurred when massive displacement has occurred in isolated areas among workers with specialized skills and without alternative sources of employment. Coal miners are a good example. About two-thirds of the nation's bituminous coal miners in 1960 were located in West Virginia, Pennsylvania, and Kentucky, and most of the coal mining was concentrated in isolated towns. Employment in bituminous coal started to decline after World War II, due partly to shifting demand and to the adoption of new techniques. Between 1947

[13] For Ferry's position, see the *Bulletin* of the Center for the Study of Democratic Institutions, Santa Barbara, Calif., January 1962. For Crossman's position, see section 2.
[14] This appears to be the present view of the Council of Economic Advisers. See Gardner Ackley's statement, quoted in *Business Week*, November 5, 1966.

and 1959, total employment in the industry declined by more than 60 percent, the consequence being that about 10 percent of the labor force in five major bituminous coal areas were unemployed during most of the fifties. In twenty-five smaller areas where coal mining was of more importance, the unemployment rate was even higher.[15]

The biggest of all displacements has been in agriculture, where the number of farm owners and farm workers declined by over 40 percent during the postwar period. Modern farm techniques—ranging from chemical fertilizers and insecticides to the cotton picker and huge harvesting combines—have contributed to this exodus, although they are by no means the only reason. Of those who left agriculture, many "suffering from deficient rural educations, lacking skills in demand in urban areas, unaccustomed to urban ways, and often burdened by racial discrimination, exchanged rural poverty for an urban ghetto." [16]

Displaced older workers have encountered particularly serious problems. Seniority rights have functioned to hold down the displacement of older workers; but once unemployed, they are less likely than younger workers to be re-employed. For example, one year after the shutdown of the Packard plant in Detroit, 77 percent of the under-forty-five-year-old workers were working at another job, whereas the percentages were 67 for the forty-five to fifty-four age group and 62 for the fifty-five to sixty-four age group. Even if skill is held constant, the older workers had more serious unemployment problems that the younger workers, at least as measured by length of unemployment. Another study obtained similar results for a period when the general level of employment was higher than in the Packard case.[17]

It is easy to understand why older workers have more difficulties in finding another job. Many of their skills are specific to a particular job, and much of their income and status may be due to seniority, the consequence being that they cannot command as high a wage on the open market as they previously earned. Moreover, employers naturally are reluctant to invest in hiring and training a worker who will only be available for a relatively few years and who often has relatively limited education. Finally, because of their roots in the community, older workers are less likely to move to other areas where jobs are more plentiful.[18]

[15] S. Levitan and H. Sheppard, "Technological Change and the Community," in G. Somers, E. Cushman, and N. Weinberg, *op. cit.*

[16] *Report of the National Commission on Technology, Automation, and Economic Progress, op. cit.*, p. 20.

[17] See H. Sheppard, L. Ferman, and S. Taber, *Too Old to Work—Too Young to Retire: A Case Study of Permanent Plant Shutdown*, Senate Special Committee on Unemployment Problems, 1959.

[18] See A. Ross and J. Ross, "Employment Problems of Older Workers," *Studies in Unemployment*, Senate Special Committee on Unemployment Problems, 1959.

Displaced Negroes seem to find it even more difficult than older workers to obtain suitable re-employment at their previous status and earnings. For example, among workers who had been earning the same wage at Packard, Negroes experienced a higher average length of unemployment than whites. Moreover, the prestige and economic level of the new job were more likely to be lower for Negroes than whites.[19] Needless to say, prejudice often plays an important role in preventing displaced Negroes from obtaining new jobs.

6. Private Adjustment Policies

Although private policies alone cannot solve all of the problems associated with labor displacement, they can do a great deal. First, there is general agreement that, if possible, reductions in employment due to the adoption of new techniques (and other forms of change) should be carried out by attrition—retirements and voluntary quits. The use of attrition is widely accepted, but a firm's ability to use it depends on its turnover experience, the age and sex of its labor force, and the skill mix necessary to maintain its operations.[20] If there were better manpower planning, attrition could be used more widely. By analyzing attrition rates and the age structure of the labor force and by trying to forecast manpower requirements, companies could improve the integration of hiring and lay-off policies with the introduction of new techniques.[21]

Second, it is generally agreed that advance notice should be given by employers of the possibility or inevitability of major layoffs or plant shut-downs. Firms have hesitated to enter into formal agreements stipulating such advance notice because they fear that their employees will leave before the change is effected, that worker productivity will decline, and that the firm's competitive position will be endangered. Recent research seems to indicate that these fears are exaggerated.[22] The benefits to workers of advanced notice are obvious, but it is not a cure-all. For example, even when a close down is announced, some workers refuse to believe that the plant will not reopen.

Third, another line of attack has been to combine job protection for more senior people with various types of limited income protection for less senior ones. Some firms and unions have attempted to broaden senior-

---

[19] See J. Hope, "The Problem of Unemployment as it Relates to Negroes," *Studies in Unemployment, ibid.*

[20] President's Advisory Committee on Labor-Management Policy, *Seminars on Private Adjustments to Automation and Technological Change,* May–June 1964, Washington, D.C., U.S. Government Printing Office, 1965.

[21] The National Commission on Technology, Automation, and Economic Progress, *op. cit.*

[22] G. Schultz and A. Weber, *Strategies for the Displaced Worker,* New York: Harper & Row, Publishers, 1966.

ity jurisdictions to give longer tenure workers more effective protection against displacement. Interplant transfer systems have been established, whereby workers who are displaced from one plant are given priority when applying for jobs at other plants of the same company. Severance pay is widely used to give some help to workers that are displaced, about 40 percent of the workers covered by major collective bargaining agreements being eligible for benefits.[23]

Fourth, it is often suggested that employers should help displaced workers to find alternative jobs or to obtain additional training or education. This assistance can take the form of counseling, job-referral service, or on-the-job training. According to the National Commission on Automation, on-the-job training, in particular, offers "great potential benefit to employers, employees and the community at large. It is now generally conceded that the most efficient method of training workers for existing job vacancies is by instruction on the job. However, sufficient knowledge about the potential capability of employees is lacking; consequently, many are not given jobs at the highest levels of their capabilities."[24] Whether or not on-the-job training is more efficient than other types, it seems clear that additional training is often called for.

7. TWO EXPERIMENTS: ARMOUR AND KAISER

Armour and Company and the Kaiser Steel Corporation have experimented with pioneering plans to ease the problems of adjusting to the adoption of new techniques and other forms of change. Armour, after closing six of its plants involving 5,000 production workers in 1959, agreed to set up a tripartite committee, composed of union, company, and public members, to study the problems of adjustment, including the training of employees for new jobs. To finance the activities of this committee, the company agreed to contribute 1 cent per hundredweight of tonnage shipped from its plants (up to $500,000). In the period since 1959, the committee has reassigned displaced workers within the company, facilitated the search for new employment in the labor market at large, and developed a pattern of private-public cooperation in the administration of programs for handling labor displacement.

The committee began by undertaking comprehensive studies to assess

[23] See Organization for Economic Cooperation and Development, *op. cit.*; and A. Weber, "The Interplant Transfer of Displaced Employees," in G. Somers, E. Cushman, and N. Weinberg, *op. cit.* For an important early protective arrangement, see the famous Washington agreement between railroad carriers and several unions, including IAM, May 1936.

[24] The National Commission on Technology, Automation, and Economic Progress, *op. cit.*, p. 103.

the dimensions of the problem. While this fact-finding stage was going on, the Oklahoma City plant was closed, prompting the committee to launch an experimental effort to aid in the placement and retraining of the displaced workers. The resulting research findings and experiences were considered in the labor negotiations in 1961, and several changes were made in the contract. Severance payments were increased, the retirement plan was changed, the company agreed to give 90 days' notice of plant shutdowns, and an interplant transfer program was established. Since 1961, the committee has continued its work. Although not all of its efforts have been successful, the parties seem to regard the experiment as useful and worthwhile.

According to members of the committee, some of the lessons learned from this experience are as follows: First, the success of any program for the transfer, training, and placement of workers is closely dependent on the extent of over-all unemployment in the labor market. Second, advance notice is a procedural prerequisite for constructive action. Third, when a fall in employment is foreseen for a particular establishment, preventive measures can be taken even if the precise magnitude and incidence of the displacement cannot be predicted. Fourth, the possibility of interplant transfer does not mean that workers will exercise this option. However, under propitious circumstances, transfer plans can be moderately successful. Fifth, severance pay appears to play a very constructive role in the adjustment process. Sixth, the "cumulative experience of the committee with various placement efforts suggests that the most useful role a private group can play in facilitating the re-employment of displaced workers is to supplement the activities of public agencies and to concentrate on cases that involve unique problems of individual adjustment."[25]

In 1959, the Kaiser Steel Corporation entered into a labor agreement establishing a tripartite committee to develop a formula for sharing the fruits of growing productivity and to bring under continual study the problems of labor-management relations. The committee established a scheme whereby savings in costs are shared with the workers; using 1961 as a base, reductions in cost (after making proper allowance for the cost of capital improvements) are split—32.5 percent going to the employees, 67.5 percent going to the corporation. Moreover, it was decided that no worker would lose his job because of displacement by improved equipment or methods; instead, he would be put into a reserve labor pool and paid his average hourly earnings for a period of one year or more.[26]

[25] G. Schultz and A. Weber, op. cit., p. 195. Also see E. Young, "The Armour Experience: A Case Study in Plant Shutdown," in G. Somers, E. Cushman, and N. Weinberg, op. cit.; and Armour Automation Committee, Progress Report, Chicago, June 19, 1961.

[26] See D. Cole, "The Kaiser-Steelworkers Long Range Sharing Plan," in C. Markham, op. cit.

Members of the committee are quick to point out that Kaiser is in many respects a unique operation and that some features of the plan may not work elsewhere. For example, since the rate of attrition over the years at Kaiser has been about equal to the rate at which workers have been displaced, the reserve labor pool is likely to be small. Nonetheless, it is an interesting and promising experiment which has attracted considerable attention. Recently the plan has run into difficulties because workers have been distressed by reduced bonuses. In early 1968, the workers approved the extension of the plan, but with modifications that increased bonuses.[27]

8. Public Manpower and Training Policies

Beyond insuring an adequate level of aggregate demand, perhaps the most important way that the government can facilitate adjustment to the adoption of new techniques is by promoting the necessary adaptability of the labor force through education and training. Education can increase the versatility and flexibility of the work force and increase its ability to adjust to change. It can open up greater opportunities and increase the productivity of workers at any level of skill or ability. The available evidence indicates the importance of a broad-based secondary education, rather than a narrow vocational education. The training for many—perhaps most—specific jobs can and should be done on the job.

Turning from the education of tomorrow's work force to the retraining of today's, it is generally agreed that the government should help workers who are casualties of technological (and other) change to obtain the skills required to return to productive employment. A coordinated, integrated system of adult retraining, which takes proper account of nationwide needs and supplies and which reaches the underprivileged and the hard-core unemployed, is useful and important. However, it should be recognized that industry quite properly plays the predominant role in the vocational training and retraining of the work force, and that the government plays only a residual role. The difficulties faced by government-sponsored training programs are considerable, given the limitations of capacity of the vocational education system and the lack of basic education among the trainees.[28]

[27] See A. Weber, "Variety in Adaptation to Technological Change," in Organization for Economic Cooperation and Development, *op. cit.;* and "Labor Test Near for Kaiser Steel," *The New York Times,* October 1, 1967.
[28] For example, see J. Walsh, "Implications of Government-Sponsored Training Programs," in Organization for Economic Cooperation and Development, *op. cit.,* pp. 345–355.

In recent years, a number of Federal training programs have been started. The Manpower Development and Training Act established programs in 1962 to offer occupational retraining for unemployed and underemployed workers who lack the personal resources to adjust to changing labor market conditions. The Vocational Education Act of 1964 makes a major commitment to the expansion and improvement of the nation's public vocational education facilities. The Job Corps and the Neighborhood Youth Corps are aimed wholly at the disadvantaged.[29] In addition, there has been some re-orientation of the U.S. Employment Service and related state agencies, new emphasis being placed on the counseling of unemployed workers to expand their occupational horizons and to assess manpower trends.

The early experience with the Manpower Development and Training Act was disappointing. Selection procedures restricted training opportunities generally to those workers with the most marketable characteristics in terms of age, race, and education. Fortunately, the reluctance to deal with the more difficult cases was overcome to a great extent by the 1963 amendments to the Manpower Act and by experience gained in administering the statute. Significant steps have been taken toward directing government resources to the unskilled and unschooled. In addition, some endorsement has been given to the principle of government encouragement of geographical mobility.

The government can also promote greater efficiency of labor markets and better adjustment to change by providing better labor market information and by experimenting, in its role as employer, with new adjustment techniques. Job seekers typically have relatively little information available to them regarding alternative job openings. To expand the amount and quality of available information, it has been suggested that the government establish a computerized nation-wide service providing detailed information regarding the requirements of job vacancies and the personal characteristics of job seekers.[30] With regard to Federal experimentation with new adjustment techniques, it has been suggested that the government explore new ways of disseminating information to those who need and want work, and that it investigate new educational technologies to recognize individual potential and to promote faster and better learning.[31]

[29] For a discussion of these programs, see the 1967 Annual Report of the Council of Economic Advisers.

[30] For some dissenting remarks, see A. Rees, "Information Networks in Labor Markets," *American Economic Review*, May 1966.

[31] See the National Commission on Technology, Automation, and Economic Progress, *op. cit.*, pp. 49–53 and 70–72. For a discussion of manpower policies in Western Europe, see J. Stieber, "Manpower Adjustments to Automation and Technological Change in Western Europe," *Report of the National Commission on Technology, Automation, and Economic Progress*, Washington, D.C., 1966.

9. PROPOSALS OF THE NATIONAL AUTOMATION COMMISSION

In late 1964, President Johnson appointed a National Commission on Technology, Automation, and Economic Progress to study the role of technological change in the American economy and to recommend relevant administrative and legislative steps that should be taken to cushion the adverse effect on workers of the adoption of new techniques. Three of the commission's proposals, submitted in 1966, have received considerable publicity. First, it recommended that serious study be given to a "negative income tax" program, which would approach by stages the goal of establishing a minimum income level for all families. According to such a program, persons with incomes below an acceptable minimum would receive a tax rebate, just as persons above certain levels now pay taxes.

Second, it recommended "a program of public service employment, providing, in effect, that the government be an employer of last resort, providing work for the 'hard-core unemployed' in useful community enterprises."[32] Aimed at those left behind in an otherwise prosperous society, this program called for the Federal government to underwrite the employment of otherwise unemployed workers in hospitals, schools, parks, libraries, and other parts of the nonprofit and public sectors of the economy. Third, it recommended

compensatory education for those from disadvantaged environments, improvements in the general quality of education, universal high school education and opportunity for 14 years of free public education, elimination of financial obstacles to higher education, lifetime opportunities for education, training and retraining, and special attention to the handicaps of adults with deficient basic education.[33]

Thus, the commission proposed a triple-barreled approach to the alleviation of the adverse impact on workers of the adoption of new techniques. For those with reasonable abilities and no basic handicaps, an adequate level of aggregate demand, plus a strong dose of education, if needed, should assure ample job opportunities. For those less able to compete in the labor market, the government is an employer of last resort.

---

[32] *Ibid*, p. 110.
[33] *Ibid.*, pp. 110–111. For further discussion of proposals dealing with the poverty problem, see R. Lampman, "Approaches to the Reduction of Poverty," *American Economic Review*, May 1965; M. Friedman, *Capitalism and Freedom*, Chicago: Chicago University Press, 1962; and S. Levitan, "Programs in Aid of the Poor," *Report of the National Commission on Technology, Automation, and Economic Progress*, Washington, D.C., 1966.

For those who cannot or should not work, the negative income tax guarantees an acceptable income. This is a bold program, which thus far has received no strong or widespread support. Whether it will be accepted, wholly or in part, in the next twenty years is difficult to say.

10. Union Policies Toward New Techniques

Union policies toward management's adoption of new methods and equipment can be classified into five types. First, there is willing acceptance, which is the most frequent policy. This policy is adopted in the numerous cases where the new technique makes little difference with respect to skill requirements and number of jobs, but where the productivity gains make it attractive to labor by providing greater opportunity to bargain for wage increases. Moreover, unions may be led by the bargaining process or by the nature of the economic situation to accept willingly new techniques that involve a mixture of advantages and disadvantages. For example, the United Mine Workers gave the employers a free hand in making such changes, despite the fact that the industry had not been an expanding one. John L. Lewis, the head of the union until 1960, preferred to allow the employers to raise productivity and then compel them to pass on much of the gains to the workers in the form of higher wages.

Second, there is outright opposition to change. Although this policy is not rare, it is adopted in only a small proportion of cases, because unions know that it is unlikely to succeed for more than a short period and because bargaining is likely to be more advantageous than uncompromising opposition. When it occurs, opposition takes various forms. In some cases, the union has refused to use the new technique; for example, some locals of the painters' union have refused to use the spray gun. In other cases, the union has refused to use the new equipment efficiently; for example, the compositors' union has restricted the use of the teletypesetter by requiring that the machine be operated by a journeyman printer or apprentice. In still other cases, where the use of the new technique requires new rates or changes in seniority rules, the union may block the change by refusing to negotiate on them.

Third, there is competition with the new technique. According to this policy, which is a form of opposition, the union tries to compete with the innovation either by encouraging the more efficient use of an old method or the use of an alternative one. This policy is adopted when there are some types of work for which the new technique has little advantage or when the new technique is less costly but the old process produces better quality. For example, the lathers' and plasterers' unions, in cooperation with their contractors, have advertised the alleged deficiencies of dry wall.

Fourth, there is encouragement of technological change and the adoption of new techniques. The difference between this policy and a policy of acceptance is that in this case the union plays an active role in promoting change. This policy is usually pursued when the union is worried about the competitive position of an industry or a plant. For example, in the needle trades, profit margins tend to be small and mortality rates of firms tend to be high. The International Ladies' Garment Workers Union and the Amalgamated Clothing Workers have engineering departments; and although it is not their principal purpose to help employers adopt better techniques, they do provide such help in cases where the union has special reason to assist an employer.

Fifth, there is adjustment to change. The essence of this policy is an effort by the union to control the use of the new technique and to deal with the opportunities and problems it presents. Since no two innovations are alike, carrying out a policy of adjustment means negotiating tailor-made agreements on a wide assortment of issues. For example, who will do the work on the new equipment? A new technique may alter the kind of skill needed, it may transfer work from one seniority district to another, or it may greatly reduce the degree of skill required. Such changes often pose extremely difficult problems for the union. Jurisdictional disputes may occur with other unions, and internal conflicts may occur within a particular union.

What will be the rate of pay? If the new method increases or maintains the degree of skill required, the union may attempt to negotiate a wage increase. For example, the pulp and sulphite workers found that new methods usually did not reduce the number of workers but often increased skill requirements. Thus the union concentrated on trying to make these changes yield wage increases. If the new method reduces the skill requirements, the union may try hard to get an agreement that men operating the new equipment will receive the same rates as workers on old processes. When a new method is introduced that obviously means large savings to the company, it is difficult, and often foolish, for management to refuse to share the gains.

If workers are displaced, what is to be done for them? The union may want to increase the number of jobs on the new process, thus making work for some or all of these workers. (Make-work policies of this sort are discussed more fully below.) If the amount of displacement is small, the major concern of the union may be to find them other jobs and to obtain severance pay for them. For example, there was a strike in 1958 against Columbia Broadcasting System over job security for the men expected to be displaced by the introduction of video tape. The strike was settled when provision was made for severance pay of up to thirteen weeks' wages for layoff or dismissal due to automated processes.[34]

11. DETERMINANTS OF UNION POLICY

The policy adopted by a union depends primarily on three factors. First, it depends on the nature of the union. A policy of opposition, when it occurs, is usually adopted by craft unions. Industrial unions usually find that the adverse effect of a new technique is limited to a small portion of their membership and that, whereas some members are hurt, others are better off. Consequently, they are likely to pursue a policy of adjustment. Moreover, industrial unions are usually less interested than craft unions in who will hold the jobs on the new process. Since the industrial union covers all workers in the plant, the workers on the new process remain within the bargaining unit; but a craft union faces the possibility that the work on the new process will be outside of its jurisdiction.

Second, the union's policy depends on the nature of the industry, firm, or occupation. If the employers face serious competition and if employment would be increased if better methods were used, the union may encourage the adoption of new techniques. If the industry or firm is experiencing rapid growth, the union may try to negotiate the best possible rates on the new jobs, whereas the union's policy is less predictable if the industry or firm is contracting. If the union believes that new techniques will have no effect on the rate of contraction, it may try to limit displacements through make-work rules. This, for example, has been the reaction of some of the railroad unions.

Third, the union's policy depends on the nature of the new technique. If the change results in a large and immediate reduction in the number of jobs, the union may elect to oppose it. However, the effect on the number of jobs in the bargaining unit tends to be more important than the effect on the number of jobs in the particular department affected by the change. Thus, although a particular change may reduce the number of jobs in one department, a local union covering the entire plant may not make an important issue of it. Also, the change in the degree and kind of skills required by the new process is of great importance, since it may transfer the work to a new craft or result in a conflict between two crafts over which one will do the work.[35]

If it becomes clear that some workers must be displaced, the union's reaction tends to occur in three stages. First, an attempt is made to maintain the employment and earnings of existing job holders. Second, once

---

[34] See S. Slichter, J. Healy, and R. Livernash, *The Impact of Collective Bargaining on Management*, Washington, D.C.: The Brookings Institution, 1960.
[35] *Ibid.*

the union recognizes that a decrease in jobs and earnings cannot be prevented, it advocates transitional measures to reduce the shock of displacement. For example, attempts are made to widen the seniority unit to include interplant, interfirm, and interarea transfers as a matter of right for displaced employees; also, requests are made for advance notice of shutdowns. Third, the union claims that the job losses should be compensated for by a financial settlement in exchange for which management obtains greater freedom in deploying manpower. The West Coast longshoreman agreement—which essentially bought out union restrictions—is a notable example that is discussed below.[36]

12. MAKE-WORK RULES AND FEATHERBEDDING

We have noted that, when the adoption of a new technique reduces the number of workers that are needed, unions sometimes resist the employer's efforts to dispense with the unneeded employees. The resulting make-work rules take various forms. Limits may be placed on the load that a worker may handle, and restrictions may be placed on the duties of workers. Some work may have to be done twice, the best-known example of this being the "bogus" rule of the International Typographical Union.[37] Modern equipment may be prohibited, and excessive crews may be required. For example, the railroad running crafts have sought—and in many states, obtained—full crew laws that regulate the size and composition of crews. The loss of output attributable to deliberately restrictive practices cannot be estimated with any accuracy. In some industries, like entertainment and railroad operation, there is a considerable amount of useless labor; in other industries, it is a minor problem. The reason why only a minority of unions pursue make-work policies to any considerable extent is that only a minority of their membership would benefit even temporarily from such policies.

The ability of unions to impose make-work rules depends primarily on two things—the extent of the union's control of the market and the willingness of the firm to stand shutdowns. A union has control of the market if it is able to impose the rule on all competitors, thus putting none at a relative disadvantage. The willingness of a firm to take a shutdown depends on the costs involved, which themselves depend on whether the product is such that the business lost during the shutdown is largely a permanent loss that cannot be recovered later. If the product is of this

[36] J. Barbash, "The Impact of Technology on Labor-Management Relations," in G. Somers, E. Cushman, and N. Weinberg, *op. cit.*

[37] P. Weinstein, *Featherbedding and Technological Change*, Boston: D. C. Heath and Company, 1965.

type, as in entertainment, the water front, building construction, and transportation, there is a greater likelihood that make-work practices can be imposed. Although it is difficult to measure the importance of make-work rules at various points in time, there seems to be a feeling that they are less important now than in the period immediately after World War II. In part, this is due to the fact that such practices grew rapidly during 1937-1947. This period included several prewar years when firms, unfamiliar with the new unions, were learning to deal with them; the wartime years, when there was great pressure for uninterrupted production; and the first postwar years when there was a seller's market. After 1947, managements began to reform their rate structures and the classification of jobs. As one would expect, these changes did not occur without conflicts between management and labor.[38]

It should not be assumed, however, that make-work rules are entirely a product of unions. On the contrary, the roots of some of these rules are buried in the nineteenth century. Moreover, unorganized as well as organized workers engage in such practices. Several decades ago, Veblen claimed that the "conscientious withdrawal of efficiency" was common among all classes of society. He thought it unfortunate that the term "sabotage" was applied exclusively to the violent activities of organized workers, and did not include the "deliberate malingering, confusion, and misdirection of work" engaged in by employers and workers alike.[39]

There seems to be little interest in the direct use of public policy to outlaw featherbedding. In the last few years, the Supreme Court has held that a union's attempt to maintain jobs in the face of employer opposition is a "legitimate labor dispute" and therefore cannot be restricted by injunction. In the Taft-Hartley Act, Congress made it an unfair labor practice for a labor organization "to cause . . . an employer to pay . . . for services which are not performed"; but this proved abortive. One of the most important problems is the absence of a legally workable definition of featherbedding. A number of states have passed tougher laws on this subject, but when tested they have invariably proved unconstitutional. The primary grounds for the negation of these laws has been that they interfere too much with the rights of unions to bargain collectively.[40]

[38] S. Slichter, J. Healy, and R. Livernash, *op. cit.* All other things equal, the pressure for make-work rules—and their importance—is likely to be less during periods of relatively full employment.

[39] T. Veblen, *The Engineer and the Price System,* 1921. Also see S. Matthewson, *Restriction of Output Among Unorganized Workers,* New York: The Viking Press, Inc., 1931.

[40] See B. Aaron, "Governmental Restraints on Featherbedding," *Stanford Law Review,* 1953. Also see W. Gomberg, "The Work Rules and Work Practices Problem," *Labor Law Journal,* July 1961.

13. Conflict and Accommodation

Obviously, management wants to achieve greater efficiency through the adoption of new techniques, whereas the union wants job security for its members. The resulting clash between labor and management has been responsible for some important recent strikes. In many industries there is an elaborate set of work rules which reflects a host of factors, including differences among workers in status, a conscious choice by workers of leisure over greater productivity and higher wages, and, in some cases, featherbedding. Workers feel that they have a property right in existing work rules which cannot be ignored when changes in these rules are considered.[41] Given the desire by management to introduce new techniques, these work rules have often come under frontal attack. The West Coast longshoring industry provides an interesting illustration of one way in which this conflict has been resolved. Up to 1961, this industry had an extremely comprehensive set of work rules. Some rules required excessive manning. For example, in many ports four men would work while another four would serve as "witnesses." Other rules required the performance of unnecessary work. For example, some goods had to be unloaded from a trucker's pallet to the floor of the dock and then reloaded onto a longshoreman's pallet before they could be loaded on a ship.

The employers' association fought these rules for many years. During the late fifties, the union, convinced that the continuation of existing policies could be no more than delaying action, entered into a long series of negotiations with the employers. The result was a complete overhauling of work rules to allow the employers to "operate efficiently," "change methods of work," "utilize labor-saving devices," and "direct the work through Employer representatives while . . . avoiding speed up." Moreover, the union agreed to eliminate the hiring of unnecessary men. To obtain this agreement, the employers provided a fund, totaling $29 million over the five and one-half years of the agreement, to finance early retirement rights and an annual wage guarantee for the longshoremen. A man who retired voluntarily at sixty-two could get $220 per month until the normal retirement age of sixty-five, after which he would receive $115 per month and his regular social security benefit. If he worked until sixty-five, he would receive a lump sum of $7,920. Retirement might be compulsory at sixty-two, in which case the pension would be $320 per month until sixty-five. The wage guarantee is provided to protect against a shortage of work resulting from increases in efficiency. The parties contemplated a guarantee of thirty-five hours of work per week.[42]

[41] G. Taylor, "Union Policies and Technological Change," in J. Dunlop, *op. cit.*
[42] C. Killingsworth, "Cooperative Approaches to Problems of Technological Change," in G. Somers, E. Cushman, and N. Weinberg, *op. cit.*

Of course, many industries do not have such a comprehensive, deeply imbedded set of work rules. Autos and rubber are cases where there are few work rules which seriously limit management's powers with respect to work assignment, job combination, job elimination, or crew sizes. Steel is a case that falls between pre-1961 longshoring, on the one hand, and autos and rubber on the other. The 1959–1960 steel strike was intensified by managements' attempt to restore its authority in the area of work rules and the steelworkers' attempt to maintain safeguards that they regarded essential.[43] Also, industries differ in the strategy and tactics used by managements. Whereas the unions stress the effects of the adoption of new techniques on job security, managements stress the recapture of management rights. The methods used to obtain this objective vary considerably. Some managements attempt to overturn existing work rules and other restrictions in one concentrated attack; others try gradually to obtain the acquiescence of the workers and use various *quid pro quo*'s to induce them to cooperate. Examples of the latter managements are Armour, Kaiser, and the West Coast longshore industry.[44]

14. HOURS OF WORK

During the early sixties, organized labor urged the reduction of the regular workweek to thirty-five hours to provide more jobs for the unemployed. This spread-the-work doctrine is by no means new. In his annual report to the American Federation of Labor in 1887, Samuel Gompers said: "The displacement of labor by machinery in the past few years has exceeded that of any like period in our history . . . . The answer to all opponents to the reduction of the hours of labor could well be given in these words: That so long as there is one man who seeks employment and cannot obtain it, the hours of labor are too long." [45]

Labor leaders point out that there is nothing sacred about the forty-hour workweek. In 1850, the average workweek was seventy hours; in 1900, sixty hours; and in 1920, fifty hours (Figure 5.1). [46] Four broad classes of factors have been responsible for the movement toward shorter hours. First, rising real income has resulted in increasing demand for leisure. Second, there has been a change in the attitudes and mores inherited from a primarily agricultural pioneering community, long hours

[43] *Ibid.*
[44] J. Barbash, "The Impact of Technology on Labor-Management Relations," in G. Somers, E. Cushman, and N. Weinberg, *op. cit.*
[45] Quoted by C. Dankert, "Hours of Work," in W. Bowen, *Labor and the National Economy*, New York: W. W. Norton & Company, Inc., 1965. Also, see AFL–CIO, *Shorter Hours: Tool to Combat Unemployment*, Washington, D.C., 1963.
[46] The data in Figure 5.1 are based on number of hours paid for. When the growth of holidays and vacations is taken into account, it is clear that hours worked decreased after 1947 by more than is shown in Figure 5.1. See E. Jones, "New Estimates of Hours of Work, 1900–1957," *Review of Economics and Statistics*, November 1963.

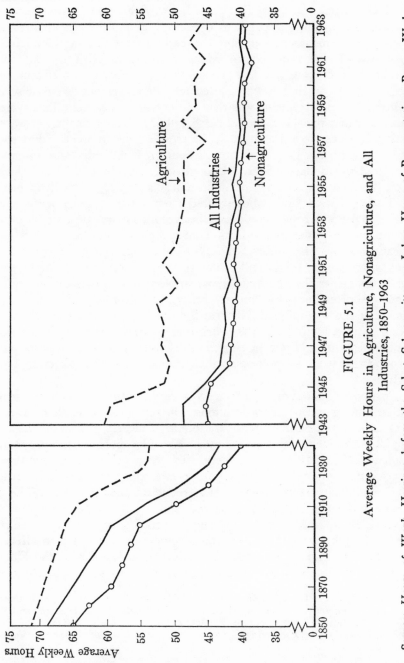

FIGURE 5.1

Average Weekly Hours in Agriculture, Nonagriculture, and All
Industries, 1850–1963

Source: Hours of Work, Hearings before the Select Subcommittee on Labor, House of Representatives, Part 1, Washington, D.C., 1963.

of work no longer being viewed as a blessing. Third, government legislation, like the NRA, Walsh-Healey, and Fair Labor Standards Acts, contributed substantially to the reduction of hours. Fourth, in some industries the increased bargaining strength of organized labor has been important.

Labor leaders maintained during the early sixties that a thirty-five-hour workweek was required to reduce unemployment. They did not claim that a forty-hour week was excessive in terms of its effects on health or safety or that it constituted an undue restriction of leisure time. Instead, their argument was that not enough forty-hour jobs were available and that the work should be spread. According to their view, a reduction to thirty-five hours would be troublesome in some industries, but it could generally be carried out without great difficulty and without a substantial inflationary effect. Although it is easy to understand their position, there are a number of important disadvantages to their proposal. To begin with, since labor wanted a reduction in hours without a reduction in pay, the result would have been higher wage rates, higher unit costs, and higher prices of products. Under these circumstances, it is by no means obvious that shorter hours would decrease unemployment. Moreover, employers might still prefer to work their present employees longer hours rather than hire additional employees, and employees might respond to shorter hours by "moonlighting," which would be to the disadvantage of the unemployed. Historically, there is no evidence that, over the long run, reductions in the workweek have resulted in decreased unemployment. In addition, a shorter workweek has been opposed on the ground that it would pull down the nation's potential production and growth rate.[47]

The proposed reduction of the workweek has not met with a warm reception among recent administrations. However, an increase in overtime rates received serious consideration in Congress and was recommended by President Johnson in 1964. The idea behind this proposal was somewhat similar to the reduction of the workweek. If overtime work were made more costly, it was felt that employers would rely on it less and would hire more workers, thus reducing unemployment. There are many difficulties in this proposal too, and it has not been adopted.[48] Finally, we should note that, although no general reduction has been made in the workweek, particular unions have sometimes succeeded in effecting a reduction. Perhaps the most dramatic case is Local 3 of the Electrical Workers Union, which forced an agreement in 1962 whereby the

[47] See C. Dankert, F. Mann, and H. Northrup, *Hours of Work*, New York: Harper & Row, Publishers, 1965; M. Joseph, "Hours of Work Issues," and J. Kreps and J. Spengler, "The Leisure Component of Economic Growth," both in *Report of the National Commission on Technology, Automation, and Economic Progress*, Washington, D.C., 1966.

[48] See T. Finegan, "Can a Case Be Made for Discouraging Overtime?," *Challenge*, April 1964.

standard workweek was set at twenty-five hours—five hours a day. This agreement resulted in considerable criticism, even in the labor movement. Many people in the union's national headquarters felt that Local 3 "had turned the campaign for shorter hours into a joke."[49] In evaluating the significance of this case, it should be noted that Local 3 had attained the six-hour day, thirty-hour week more than two decades before and that there was relatively little relation between the reduction in hours and protection against displacement, since there was a manpower shortage in the New York construction industry at that time.

15. SUMMARY

There is a longstanding fear of technological change among workers. In the fifties and early sixties, the fear of mass unemployment due to the adoption of new techniques was revived with great effect, the apparent menace being "automation." Automation, which refers to processes designed to mechanize the human cognitive, conceptual, and informational processes, consists primarily of automatic control mechanisms, computer technology, and transfer machines. The dangers of automation seem to have been exaggerated. If the government makes proper use of monetary and fiscal policy, there is no reason why rapid technological change must result in increased aggregate unemployment. The important thing is that the government increase aggregate demand at the proper rate. Of course, the job of choosing and carrying out appropriate fiscal and monetary policies is not easy, but the problems are by no means insoluble.

During the fifties and early sixties there was considerable concern that workers and jobs were becoming more and more mismatched. Statistical studies of the concentration of unemployment, as well as the course of events since the 1964 tax cut, provided little support for this view. Moreover, studies of the effects of the new methods and equipment adopted in recent years did not indicate any sharp or consistent increase in skill requirements. Although a substantial portion of all unemployment may exist because the workers available for employment do not possess the qualities that employers with unfilled vacancies require, there is little or no evidence that unemployment of this sort has increased greatly in recent years.

An adequate level of aggregate demand can go a long way toward assuring that aggregate unemployment will not exceed a socially acceptable minimum, but it cannot prevent labor from being displaced from particular occupations, regions, and industries, and being drawn to others. Nor would we want to eliminate such movements of labor, without which it would be impossible to adjust to changes in technology, popu-

[49] A. Raskin, "No 25-Hour Week for Him," *The New York Times Magazine*, March 18, 1962, p. 57.

lation, and consumer tastes. However, for the displaced worker, particularly if he is old, non-white, or unskilled, this adjustment process may mean great distress; and in recent times, society, which is, by and large, a beneficiary of such change, has recognized its obligation to minimize the losses and assist the readjustment of those who are hurt by it.

Although private policies cannot solve all of the problems associated with labor displacement, they can do a great deal. There is general agreement that, if possible, reductions in employment due to the adoption of new techniques (and other forms of change) should be carried out by attrition—retirements and voluntary quits. There is also quite general agreement that advance notice should be given by employers of the possibility or inevitability of major layoffs or plant shutdowns. Another line of attack is to combine job protection for more senior people with various types of limited income protection for less senior ones. In addition, it is often suggested that employers should help displaced workers to find alternative jobs or to obtain additional training or education. Two well-known experiments with plans to ease the problems of labor displacement have been carried out by Armour and Kaiser.

Beyond insuring an adequate level of aggregate demand, perhaps the most important way that the government can facilitate adjustment to the adoption of new techniques is by promoting the necessary adaptability of the labor force through education and training of the nation's youth. In addition, it is generally agreed that the government should help workers who are casualties of technological (and other) change to obtain the skills required to return to productive employment. The National Automation Commission has recommended bolder steps—the institution of a negative income tax, a program of public service employment, and considerable extension of educational opportunities. Thus far, these proposals have not received widespread support, but eventually their day may come.

Union policies toward management's adoption of new techniques can be classified into five types: willing acceptance, outright opposition, competition, encouragement, and adjustment. The policy adopted by a union depends primarily on the nature of the union, the nature of the industry, firm, or occupation, and the nature of the new technique. For example, a policy of opposition, when it occurs, is generally adopted by craft unions. Industrial unions usually find that the adverse effect of a new technique is limited to a small portion of their membership and that, whereas some members are hurt, others are better off. Consequently, industrial unions are more likely to follow a policy of adjustment.

When the adoption of a new technique reduces the number of workers that are needed, labor sometimes resists the employer's efforts to dispense with the unneeded employees. Make-work rules of various kinds are in existence; in some industries, like entertainment and railroad operation, they have been quite important. There seems to be little interest in the direct use of public policy to outlaw these rules, one of the important problems being the absence of a legally workable definition of feather-bedding. In recent years, there have been numerous clashes between management and labor over work rules. Management's attack on these rules has taken various forms, the West Coast longshore industry being an interesting case where management essentially bought out union restrictions.

The concern over automation's effect on employment led organized labor in the early sixties to urge the reduction of the regular workweek to thirty-five hours, the purpose being to spread the work and reduce the number of unemployed. There are important disadvantages to this proposal; for example, it is by no means obvious that shorter hours would decrease unemployment, since labor wants a reduction in hours without a reduction in pay. Although the proposal has not met with a warm reception among recent administrations, an increase in overtime rates—which is also designed to spread the work—was recommended by President Johnson in 1964. It too had important disadvantages and was not adopted.

CHAPTER VI

GOVERNMENT EXPENDITURES ON RESEARCH AND DEVELOPMENT

◇◇◇◇◇◇◇◇◇◇◇◇◇◇◇◇◇◇◇◇◇◇◇◇

1. EXPENDITURES BY FEDERAL DEPARTMENTS AND AGENCIES

The Federal government plays an extremely important role in the promotion of technological change and scientific advance in the United States. This chapter is concerned primarily with the magnitude, nature, rationale, and history of this role, some attention being devoted as well to university research and to research and development in other countries. We begin by looking at the amount spent by various Federal departments and agencies on research and development. What agencies account for most of the spending? What is the purpose of the R and D they support? How has the relative importance of various agencies shifted over time? Since the Federal government finances about two-thirds of the nation's research and development, these are very important questions, which must be answered in some detail.

In 1966, almost half of all Federal R and D expenditures were made by the Department of Defense (Table 6.1), the primary purpose being to provide new and improved weapons and techniques to promote the effectiveness of the armed forces. The largest expenditures were made by the Air Force; the smallest were made by the Army. Only about 25 percent was spent on research (rather than development), and this research was mainly in the physical and engineering sciences (Table 6.2).

TABLE 6.1

Federal Expenditures for Research and Development and R and D Plant, by Agency, Fiscal Years 1940–1966

DEPARTMENT OR AGENCY	1940	1948	1956	1964	1966ᵃ
	(MILLIONS OF DOLLARS)				
Agriculture	29.1	42.4	87.7	183.4	257.7
Commerce	3.3	8.2	20.4	84.5	93.0
Defense	26.4	592.2	2,639.0	7,517.0	6,880.7
Army ᵇ	3.8	116.4	702.4	1,413.6	1,452.1
Navy ᵇ	13.9	287.5	635.8	1,724.2	1,540.0
Air Force ᵇ	8.7	188.3	1,278.9	3,951.1	3,384.4
Defense agencies	——	——	——	406.9	464.5
Department-wide funds	——	——	21.9	21.1	39.7
Health, Education and Welfare ᶜ	2.8	22.8	86.2	793.4	963.9
Interior	7.9	31.4	35.7	102.0	138.7
Atomic Energy Commission	——	107.5	474.0	1,505.0	1,559.7
Federal Aviation Agency	——	——	——	74.0	73.4
National Aeronautics and Space Administration ᵈ	2.2	37.5	71.1	4,171.0	5,100.0
National Science Foundation	——	——	15.4	189.8	258.7
Office of Scientific Research and Development	——	0.9	——	——	——
Veterans Administration	——	——	6.1	34.1	45.9
All other agencies	2.4	11.8	10.4	39.7	66.1
Total	74.1	854.7	3,446.0	14,693.9	15,437.7

Source: Federal Funds for Science XIV (National Science Foundation, 1965), Table C-46. These figures are not entirely comparable with those in Chapter III, or those in subsequent tables. In this and other tables in this book, the totals may differ from those that are given because of rounding errors.

ᵃ Estimates based on requests in *The Budget, 1966*.

ᵇ Includes pay and allowances of military R and D personnel beginning in 1953 and support from procurement appropriations of development, test, and evaluation beginning in 1954.

ᶜ Federal Security Agency prior to 1952.

ᵈ National Advisory Committee on Aeronautics prior to 1958.

The second and third largest spenders on R and D in 1966 were the National Aeronautics and Space Administration and the Atomic Energy Commission, both of which are also intimately connected with the cold war. Together with the Defense Department, they accounted for almost 90 percent of the R and D expenditures of the Federal government. About one quarter of the R and D carried out by NASA and AEC was research, most of it in the physical and engineering sciences.

In contrast with the Big Three, the fourth, fifth, and sixth largest spenders were not concerned primarily with national defense and the space race. The bulk of the R and D expenditures of the Department of Health, Education and Welfare (HEW)—the fourth largest spender —was related to the work of the National Institutes of Health, the research arm of the Public Health Service. Consequently, most of the research expenditures of HEW were in the medical sciences. The fifth largest spender was the National Science Foundation (NSF), the general purposes of which are the encouragement and support of basic research and education in the sciences. Most of the NSF expenditures went for research in the physical and biological sciences. The sixth largest spender was the Department of Agriculture, where most of the R and D effort, which is coordinated with the research and educational activities of the land-grant colleges, was concerned with the production, utilization, and marketing of farm and forest products.

These six departments and agencies accounted for practically all of the Federal government's R and D expenditures in 1966. Table 6.1 shows the extent of the changes in the volume and pattern of Federal R and D spending in the past several decades. It is interesting to note that the Department of Agriculture spent more on R and D than did the Department of Defense in 1940. It is also important to note that the total amount of R and D financed by the Federal government in 1966 was over 200 times what it was in 1940 and over four times what it was in 1956. Much of this increase has been due to wartime and postwar increases in spending on defense and space. The Defense Department's expenditures on R and D rose greatly during World War II and continued to increase during the fifties.[1] In the early postwar period, the Atomic Energy Commission was established and its R and D expenditures grew rapidly. During the late fifties and early sixties, NASA's budget grew enormously. By the mid-sixties, Federal R and D spending had developed into the pattern shown in the last column of Table 6.1, there being a tremendous emphasis on defense and space technology.

---

[1] The leveling off of the Defense Department's R and D expenditures during the last few years covered in Table 6.1 was due mainly to the transition out of the development stage of the major ballistics missile programs such as the Atlas, Titan, and Minuteman.

TABLE 6.2

Characteristics of R and D Obligations of Federal Agencies, 1965 [a]

Department	Total R and D Obligations as Percent of Agency's Total Budget	Character of Work (percentage distribution)			Intramural R and D as a Percent of Total	Basic Research Obligations, by Field of Science (percentage distribution)						
		Basic Research	Applied Research	Development		Biological	Medical	Agricultural	Physical	Mathematical	Engineering	Social[b]
Agriculture	4	38	59	4	68	14	14	37	25	—	4	6
Commerce	9	38	33	28	70	—	—	—	78	1	11	10
Defense	14	4	22	73	24	3	9	—	53	11	18	4
Health, Education and Welfare	13	35	64	1	20	6	77	—	1	—	—	15
Interior	10	32	51	18	68	17	—	—	72	3	3	5
Atomic Energy Commission	48	20	6	74	2	14	8	1	70	2	6	—
Federal Aviation Agency	11	—	6	94	45	—	—	—	—	—	—	—
National Aeronautics and Space Administration	100	12	15	73	18	9	—	—	79	1	10	1
National Science Foundation	47	99	—	—	7	22	3	—	50	6	8	10

Source: Federal Funds for Science, XIV, National Science Foundation, 1965.
a Estimates for fiscal 1965, excluding agencies spending less than $50 millions.
b Includes psychology.

2. THE ROLE OF THE FEDERAL
GOVERNMENT PRIOR TO 1945

Although the statistics presented in the previous section are helpful in describing the nature and extent of Federal R and D expenditures, they provide an incomplete picture of the evolution of the Federal government's role in science and technology. The story goes back at least as far as George Washington, who recognized 180 years ago that the Federal government had a fundamental responsibility for promoting the acquisition and diffusion of new and useful knowledge. He, as well as Jefferson, Madison, and Adams, favored the establishment of a national university, which would be, among other things, a center of scientific research. Although Washington's national university never came into being, the Federal government did assume, prior to the Civil War, various responsibilities which required its entrance on a modest scale into scientific work. For example, the exploration and mapping of the frontier brought about the Coast and Geodetic surveys and the Lewis and Clark expedition.[2]

Between the Civil War and World War I, the government's role in science and technology expanded considerably. The Department of Agriculture, which received cabinet status in 1889, accumulated a number of bureaus concerned with research into botany, entomology, the eradication of diseases affecting animals and crops, and so on. The Hatch Act of 1887 led to Federal support for the agricultural experiment stations that were attached to the land-grant colleges promoted by the Morrill Act of 1862.[3] During World War I, the role of the government expanded further.[4] After considerable agitation by the National Academy of Sci-

[2] Another noteworthy development in this era was the Smithsonian Institution, created in 1846 as a consequence of James Smithson's will. The Smithsonian was a significant factor in American science during this period, particularly in its emphasis on basic research. It is also interesting to note that probably the first Federal grant for experimental research occurred in this era, the grant having been made to the University of Pennsylvania's Alexander Dallas Bache for an investigation in 1832 of the reasons for the explosion of steamboat boilers.

[3] We saw in section 1 that, prior to World War II, a large share of the Federal R and D budget (about 40 percent in 1940) went into the agricultural sciences. Government support in this field was no novelty, Parliament under the Puritan Commonwealth having granted funds for experimentation regarding the growth of indigo and other agricultural products in Georgia.

The Morrill Act established a system of grants of public lands to the states to create "land-grant" colleges for training in the agricultural and mechanical arts. The system afterward was expanded to include cash grants to the states to support experiment stations affiliated with the A. and M. colleges. Funds were divided among the stations in accord with a statutory formula rather than with administrative discretion.

[4] Three important scientific agencies were established between 1900 and our entrance into World War I—the National Bureau of Standards in 1901, the Public Health Service in 1912, and the National Advisory Committee for Aeronautics in 1915.

ences [5] (formed in 1863), President Wilson created the National Research Council [6] to help coordinate the work of scientists in and out of the government. Once it got started (in 1918), the NRC, with military and other civilian agencies (like the Bureau of Mines and the National Bureau of Standards [7]), carried out considerable work on gas warfare, optics, and other such subjects. A close partnership was established between industry, the universities, and the government. [8] After World War I, the government's research establishment was cut back to its prewar level, and the twenties saw little increase in the government's participation in science and technology. During the Depression of the thirties, there was renewed activity. A Presidential Science Advisory Board, created in 1933, investigated the use of science by government agencies and tried to deal with the unemployment problem among scientists. [9] In 1937, the National Resources Committee began a study of research in America, the results of which implied that further research might help to stimulate the economy. However, although the thirties witnessed some interesting developments in this area, they must realistically be viewed as a last steppingstone to World War II.

World War II resulted in enormous changes in the relationship between science and the Federal government. In 1940, President Roosevelt established the National Defense Research Committee to support and coordinate research regarding weapons. Headed by Vannevar Bush, President of the Carnegie Institution, the NDRC received generous sup-

[5] The idea of a National Academy goes back to the earlier discussions of a national university. The purposes of the Academy were to give the government help on technical problems and to provide honor to its members. It was a self-perpetuating group which set up an ad hoc committee to consider each government request for help. One early achievement was the report of its Committee on the Inauguration of a National Forest Policy, which pointed out that the nation was destroying its natural resources by wasteful development methods.

[6] The National Research Council is an operating subsidiary of the National Academy of Sciences. Unlike the Academy, it can include men on its committees who are not Academy members. During World War I, it supported research at universities, and when such work was ripe for development, the Army or Navy commissioned the scientists doing the work and they went into government laboratories.

[7] The National Bureau of Standards was established in the Treasury Department in 1901 to carry out the Federal responsibility for a national system of weights and measures. Transferred to the Department of Commerce, the Bureau became an agency of general service to American business. Working through an elaborate system of committees and trade associations, it contributed a great deal to the standardization of industrial products. Practically all of its work is carried out in in-house laboratories.

[8] World War I saw an unprecedented infusion of research into the economy, industrial research beginning in this period to rise to importance. See Chapter III, section 1.

[9] The board recommended government research grants to private institutions. This was not considered proper at the time by Ickes and others, and it was rejected.

For an excellent history of Federal scientific policies and activities to 1940, see A. Hunter Dupree, *Science in the Federal Government*, Cambridge, Mass.: Belknap Press, 1957.

port. It contained representatives of the Armed Forces, civilian government agencies, industry, universities, and other nonprofit organizations. Pooling their resources, they studied problems presented by the military, as well as projects of their own choosing. When it became apparent that development, as well as research, was needed, the Office of Scientific Research and Development was created in 1941 by executive order and attached to the Executive Office of the President. Besides acting as a clearinghouse for much of the R and D done by the Services, the National Advisory Committee for Aeronautics,[10] and the National Defense Research Committee, OSRD, headed by Bush, initiated its own projects and was a mobilization center for scientific manpower. For example, OSRD controlled the early work on the atomic bomb, passing it on to the Army's Manhattan Project in 1943.[11]

Besides carrying out work of this sort, OSRD also formulated and carried out important new policies relating to the performance of military R and D. For example, it decided that military R and D did not have to be carried out in military laboratories under military personnel, that a suitable mechanism for government financing of R and D carried out in private agencies was the research and development contract, and that close liaison had to be established between civilian scientists and military personnel at both the working and highest policy levels.[12] By virtue

[10] The National Advisory Committee on Aeronautics was established in 1915 to "supervise and direct the scientific study of the problems of flight, with a view to their practical solution, and to determine the problems which should be experimentally attacked, and to discuss their solution and their application to practical questions." Composed of twelve members, the committee carried out a program intended to serve the purposes of both military and civilian government agencies, as well as private industry.

[11] The total volume of OSRD's research and development work was less than that of either the Army or the Navy. But it brought the leading scientists into wartime work, and it established the new patterns. The OSRD was simply a holding company under which was operated the National Defense Research Committee, but its head was in a position of direct responsibility to the President. It brought entire scientific institutions into government service. See Don Price, *Government and Science*, New York: New York University Press, 1954; Irvin Stewart, *Organizing Scientific Research for War*, Boston: Little, Brown and Company, 1948; and J. P. Baxter, *Scientists Against Time*, Boston: Little, Brown and Company, 1946.

[12] Lee DuBridge has described these policies, which have affected the government's scientific program to this day, in the following terms:

First, military research and development need not be carried on exclusively in military laboratories directed by military personnel; it can also be done in civilian scientific laboratories directed by civilians, under the sponsorship of either a military or a civilian agency. After the war this policy was extended to non-military government research.

Second, a suitable mechanism for government financing of research in universities, industrial laboratories, and other private agencies is the research or development contract. This is a written agreement between the government and the private corporation to carry out investigations in a specified area, making the results available to the government. The government pays all of the costs incurred, both direct and indirect. The university or the company continues its

of Bush's position in the Executive Office of the President, science gained unprecedented access to the President. By the end of World War II, the Federal government had created a huge research establishment, the success of which had secured for scientists an important place in public policy formulation.

3. POSTWAR DEVELOPMENTS IN SCIENCE POLICY AND ORGANIZATION

Soon after the war ended, Vannevar Bush presented a report [13] to the President in which he recommended that a government agency be established to support basic research and the development of scientific manpower. In 1947, this recommendation was seconded in a report by the President's Scientific Research Board,[14] which urged that the government spend at least 1 percent of the gross national product on R and D. Bush's proposals were embodied in the Magnuson bill, which would have created a National Research Foundation governed by a nine-man board of eminent scientists operating without formal executive control. An alternative bill submitted by Senator Kilgore called for a foundation governed by a presidentially appointed administrator and advised by a large board. The Magnuson bill emphasized the freedom of science; the Kilgore bill reflected the opinion that public funds should not be distributed by an agency with such a diffuse channel of responsibility.[15] The scientific com-

---

normal salary and personnel policies and assumes responsibility for technical management within the scope of the contract. Civil Service rules and military "control" of scientists are thus both avoided.

Third, the military services must set up suitable mechanisms for close liaison between civilian scientists and responsible military authorities to ensure that scientific developments may be governed by practical military needs and requirements, and that military tactics, strategy, and training may be adapted to forthcoming new weapons. The liaison needs to be effected at the working level and the highest policy level. The nuclear-weapon problem is but one of many in which decisions had to be made by the Commander-in-Chief in consultation with top scientists.

See his "Policy and the Scientists," *Foreign Affairs*, 1963.

[13] V. Bush, *Science, the Endless Frontier*, Washington, 1945.

[14] The President's Scientific Research Board, *Science and Public Policy*, Washington, 1947. Apparently, this report was prompted partly by a feeling that Bush's report contained somewhat anti-democratic sentiments, that it dealt unfairly with government science, and that it magnified the importance of university science. See J. Penick, C. Pursell, M. Sherwood, and D. Swain, *The Politics of American Science*, Chicago: Rand McNally & Company, 1965.

[15] Also, Senator Kilgore feared the concentration of research funds in a few institutions and was willing to require that research grants be distributed according to a formula which would have aided the smaller colleges. The Magnuson bill allowed companies to patent the results of government-financed R and D, whereas the Kilgore bill prohibited such patents. The Bush group, which supported the Magnuson bill, opposed the inclusion of the social sciences, whereas the Urey-Shapley group, which supported the Kilgore bill, favored their inclusion.

munity was divided between the two bills. On the one hand, Bush, Isaiah Bowman (president of Johns Hopkins), and others closely associated with OSRD favored the Magnuson bill. On the other hand, Harold Urey and Harlow Shapley were the chief spokesmen of a more broadly based group which supported the Kilgore bill. In 1950, after considerable debate and the President's veto of one bill, a compromise was worked out. A National Science Foundation was established, which was to be governed by a Director appointed by the President and a National Science Board with limited power. Patents were allowed, and no specific provision was made for the social sciences.[16]

While the debate regarding the organization of the National Science Foundation was going on, another debate was raging concerning the organization of the proposed Atomic Energy Commission. The May-Johnson bill would have established a commission virtually independent of the President, except in international matters. Many scientists objected to the bill because, in their view, it would have put the commission under military control; other observers objected that the commission should be more fully responsible to the President. After hearings by a special senate committee, an alternative bill was prepared, and President Truman, who had earlier supported the May-Johnson bill, switched his support. As finally made law in 1946, the Atomic Energy Act called for a civilian commission fully responsible to the President, with one advisory committee composed of scientists and another composed of representatives of the Armed Services. During the early postwar years, the AEC was in many respects the predominant scientific agency in the Federal government.[17]

During the war, the Federal government poured large sums of money into medical investigations. When the war ended, although Bush recommended that the National Science Foundation undertake the support of medical research, the Public Health Service arranged for the National Institutes of Health (NIH) to continue the on-going investigations and to initiate a program of research grants and fellowships. NIH grew very rapidly after 1946, its expenditures increasing by about 25 percent a year. Congress was extremely generous in this field, appropriations often exceeding the President's budget allotment. In some quarters, there was serious question during the fifties (and in subsequent years) as to whether or not all of the money would be wisely spent.[18]

---

[16] Grants made by the National Science Foundation give the investigator great discretion, have few reporting agreements, and allow the grantee to keep the facilities purchased with the funds. According to J. Dupre and S. Lakoff, *Science and the Nation*, Englewood Cliffs, N.J.: Prentice-Hall, Inc., 1962, until 1957, NSF and NIH were the only agencies using grants to support basic research.

[17] See J. Newman and B. Miller, *The Control of Atomic Energy*, Whittlesey House, 1948, for the point of view of those drafting the MacMahon bill.

[18] For example, see J. Penick, C. Pursell, M. Sherwood, and D. Swain, *The Politics of American Science, op. cit.*

In the Defense Department, the early postwar years witnessed the establishment of the Office of Naval Research, which supported considerable basic research and performed many of the functions of the National Science Foundation before NSF came into being. There was also a series of attempts at unification of the organization of military research and development. When the Korean War began, each military service still retained a large degree of individuality, and nowhere was rivalry more acute than in the area of weapon development. There were bitter controversies over the relative worth of the aircraft carrier and the long-range bomber, the rocket and the pilotless aircraft, and one type of missile versus another. Concern was expressed about waste and excess expenditure through duplication in the R and D programs of the services; according to the Hoover Commission, the deficiencies resided primarily in the desire of each service to be self-sufficient.[19]

Between 1945 and 1957, while Federal expenditures on research and development increased phenomenally, there was a continual search for more efficient techniques of science administration. Difficult political and administrative problems had to be faced, regardless of whether very complete answers were at hand. Decisions had to be made regarding the extent of Federal support for science and technology, the allocation of this support between scientific fields and government functions, and the management of important scientific programs. The existing administrative and policy-making machinery sometimes seemed inadequate—and would soon be changed.[20]

4. SPUTNIK, THE SPACE RACE,
AND RECENT DEVELOPMENTS

In October 1957, Sputnik I was launched, causing an extensive revamping of the organization of science policy. President Eisenhower asked the President's Science Advisory Committee (PSAC), composed of eighteen distinguished scientists from outside the government who formerly had reported to the President through the Office of Defense Mobilization, to report to him directly. PSAC became the highest scientific advisory board in the government, and James Killian, its chairman, was appointed to a new and very important position as the President's Science Adviser (more formally, the President's Special Assistant for Science and Technology). For the first time, the President had a technically knowledgeable

[19] See U.S. Commission on Organization of the Executive Branch of the Government, *Research and Development in the Government*, Washington, D.C., May 1955.
[20] Two other noteworthy developments during the early fifties were the Oppenheimer case, involving questions of security, and the Astin case, involving the political control of scientific agencies.

assistant to complement the scientific advice received from the operating agencies. Soon afterwards, on the recommendation of the President's Science Adviser and PSAC, the Federal Council for Science and Technology was created to coordinate the programs of various agencies, the membership of the Council being the President's Science Adviser and high-level representatives of the government agencies responsible for appreciable expenditures on R and D.[21]

Out of the post-Sputnik ferment of Congressional hearings and national debate came the decision that the major responsibility for space exploration should be assigned to a single agency. There was considerable disagreement over whether the agency should be civilian or military, but President Eisenhower leaned toward the idea of a civilian agency. The National Aeronautics and Space Administration (NASA) was established, the National Advisory Committee for Aeronautics being the nucleus of the new agency. With the establishment of NASA, the United States was institutionally committed to manned space flight. In 1961, President Kennedy stated that we would attempt to be first to land a man on the moon. NASA's appropriations grew spectacularly, the growth of the space program being the subject of considerable debate. Many observers—and a significant portion of the scientific community—felt that too large a proportion of the nation's scientific talent was being devoted to a project where the benefits were so largely political. Viewing the situation from a different angle, the Air Force was unhappy because it would have liked to see the development of rockets directed toward Air Force ends. However, the growth in NASA's budget could hardly have been displeasing to the applied space scientists and to the Congressional committees that were the overseers of NASA and that took political credit for it.[22]

Another important change in the organization of Federal science policy-making occurred in 1962, when the Office of Science and Technology (OST) was established in the Executive Office of the President. This

[21] PSAC has attempted to develop broad perspectives on major national problems involving science and technology. Originally focusing primarily on the impact of technology on national security policy, its studies now extend to the impact of technology on questions of health, education, and welfare, and important aspects of Federal involvement in scientific activities. For discussions of PSAC and the role of scientific advisers, see Harvey Brooks, "The Scientific Adviser," and Robert Kreidler, "The President's Science Advisers and National Science Policy"; both in R. Gilpin and C. Wright, *Scientists and National Policy-Making*, New York: Columbia University Press, 1964.

Created by Executive Order in 1959, the Federal Council replaced the Interdepartmental Committee on Scientific Research and Development, which was set up in 1947. For further description of the Council's activities, see E. Wenk's testimony before the House Select Committee on Government Research, November 19, 1963.

[22] For some comments on the formation of NASA, see James Webb's testimony before the House Select Committee on Government Research, November 18, 1963. In the scientific community there has been considerable controversy over manned space flight. For example, some scientists argue that the major scientific data can be collected at less cost with instruments than with manned spacecraft.

office, headed by the President's Science Adviser, then Jerome Wiesner and now Donald Hornig, provides the President with a permanent staff to advise him on matters of national policy affected by or pertaining to science and technology. It also helps in the coordination of science and technology functions, and is authorized and directed to advise the Congress as well as the President on scientific policy matters. Possibly the most important result of providing a statutory basis for the scientific activities in the Executive Office of the President was that the head of OST may now appear before Congress to explain the government-wide views of programs and problems.[23]

The postwar period saw a tremendous surge in Federal support for science and technology. As Don Price has put it, science became "the major Establishment of the American political system . . . for which tax funds are appropriated almost on faith . . ." [24] In recent years, there is evidence that the relations between science and politics are becoming somewhat more strained, as members of Congress look for conflicts of interest between the scientific community and the nation as a whole. Moreover, the Federal science budget is leveling off. For the first time since the mid-fifties, when Federal science acquired the structure familiar today, the proposed budget for 1967 did not carry a request from the administration for an increase in funds for research and development. The primary reason was the military build-up in Southeast Asia. To pay for this war as well as for the education and welfare programs enacted in previous sessions of Congress, an attempt was made to hold the Federal science budget approximately constant. However, even without the Vietnam war, the growth in the Federal science budget seemed to be slowing down.[25]

[23] OST contains about twenty highly trained specialists in science and engineering who provide assistance in these areas. For discussions of the role of the President's Science Adviser and the Office of Science and Technology, see J. Wiesner's testimony before the House Subcommittee on Science, Research, and Development, October 16 and 24, 1963; his testimony before the Senate Select Committee on Small Business, June 6, 1963; his testimony before the House Select Committee on Government Research, November 20, 1963; and D. Hornig's testimony before the House Research and Technical Programs Subcommittee on January 7, 1966.

Two other postwar developments should be noted as well. First, all agencies with significant R and D expenditures now have scientists and engineers in high-level positions. Second, besides PSAC, many science advisory committees and panels (drawing on university and industrial scientists and engineers) have been established since World War II.

[24] D. Price, "The Scientific Establishment," *Proceedings of the American Philosophical Society*, June 1962, p. 235. Also, see his *The Scientific Estate*, Cambridge, Mass.: Belknap Press, 1965.

[25] During 1967, total Federal spending on research and development rose, but the increase was only 3 percent. A similar percentage increase was requested by the President for 1968. See *Science*, January 27, 1967. Note too that during the early sixties, Federal support for basic research increased much more rapidly than did Federal support for development. See the *Fifteenth Annual Report of the National Science Foundation*, Washington 1966.

5. THE DEPARTMENT OF DEFENSE

Since Federal expenditures on R and D are heavily concentrated in a small number of agencies, it is important that we look more closely at the kinds of research and development they support. In the following sections, we present a very brief description of their activities. First to be considered is the Department of Defense (DOD). The principal adviser to the Secretary of Defense on scientific and technical matters is the Director of Defense Research and Engineering, who supervises all research and engineering activities in the Department of Defense, directs the Advanced Research Projects Agency, and has administrative control over the Weapons Systems Evaluation Group. The director, with a staff of about 300, has the authority to approve, modify, or disapprove R and D projects and programs of the military departments and other defense agencies.[26] Most of the DOD's research and development expenditures go for the development of missiles, aircraft, military astronautics, and related equipment (Table 6.3). In the missile field, some of the major efforts in 1966 were to develop the advance-design Nike-X antimissile system, the Minuteman III, and the submarine-launched Poseidon missile.[27] In the airplane field, some of the major efforts were to develop the F-111 aircraft—General Dynamics' controversial TFX, which has variable sweep wings and comes in both Air Force and Navy versions; and the C5A cargo transport—

[26] When World War II ended, OSRD was dissolved, and in 1947 the Research and Development Board was created to integrate military R and D programs, to keep pace with scientific developments, to assign and coordinate R and D among the services, to advise the Joint Chiefs of Staff, and to act for the Secretary of Defense in all matters not involving major policy. The work of the board was done by a six-man council, fifteen technical committees, and over 100 (in 1953) panels. Unfortunately, the board was not very effective, among other reasons because the part-time civilian scientists were dominated by the military members, and the board lacked authority to finance projects independently of the services. See Price, *Government and Science, op. cit.*, p. 144 ff. In 1953, the board was abolished, and the office of Assistant Secretary of Defense for Research and Development was created to take over its duties. In 1956, the DOD created a Special Assistant to the Secretary of Defense for Guided Missiles to supplement the work of the assistant secretary. The Weapons Systems Evaluation Group was created in 1948 to provide operations research at the highest levels of the DOD. In 1958, the Advanced Research Projects Agency was established with funds to carry out projects independently of the services; and the position of Director of Defense Research and Engineering replaced that of Assistant Secretary of Defense for Research and Development. For further description of the director's responsibilities, see Harold Brown's testimony before the House Select Committee on Government Research, November 19, 1963.

[27] The Nike-X, an Army weapon with Bell Laboratories and Western Electric as prime contractors, uses advanced multifunction array radar and Sprint and Zeus missiles to defend against intercontinental ballistic missiles. The Poseidon, a Navy weapon with Lockheed as prime contractor, is designed to have twice the payload and accuracy of the Polaris. Boeing's Minuteman III will have a redesigned warhead to allow it to pierce a possible Soviet antimissile defense. *Missiles and Rockets*, July 26, 1965; and *Business Week*, March 12, 1966.

TABLE 6.3

Appropriations for Research, Development, Testing and Evaluation by the Department of Defense, 1965 and 1966

Type of Expenditure	1965 Actual	1966 Estimate
	(MILLIONS OF DOLLARS)	
Military sciences	621	608
Aircraft and related equipment	1,136	1,205
Missiles and related equipment	1,977	1,998
Military astronautics and related equipment	908	1,036
Ships, small craft, and related equipment	286	331
Ordnance, combat vehicles, and related equipment	361	393
Other equipment	785	893
Program-wide management and support	454	464
Emergency fund	——	19
Total	6,528	6,947

Source: *Budget of the U.S. Government for Fiscal Year 1967*, Appendix, p. 327.

Lockheed's huge airplane expected to weigh over 500,000 lbs.[28] In the military astronautics field, work proceeded on the manned orbiting laboratory, the Titan III, military communication satellites and improvements in satellite-tracking capabilities.[29]

The R and D program of the DOD includes over 1,000 projects ranging in size from a few thousand dollars to many millions, and covering a wide range of topics. The DOD divides these projects into six categories—research, exploratory development, advanced development, engineering development, operational-systems development, and management and support. Research and exploratory development, which together correspond to what the National Science Foundation calls "research," account for about one quarter of the total. Advanced development, which is directed toward the building of test and experimental hardware, accounts for another 10 percent. An example of this work is the X-15 rocket aircraft program, which has been conducted to explore various facets of hyper-

[28] For a description of the F-111, see *Electronics*, December 27, 1965. For a description of the C5A, see *Astronautics and Aeronautics*, August 1965.

[29] The manned orbiting laboratory, an Air Force project with Douglas Aircraft as prime contractor, is a two-man spacecraft designed to establish the military usefulness (including space reconnaissance) of man in space. The Titan III, an Air Force project with Aerospace Corporation providing systems engineering and Martin providing systems integration, is a space booster for quick-reaction military missions. See *Missiles and Rockets*, January 10, 1966 and January 17, 1966, p. 15.

sonic flight and relevant aspects of aircraft design.[30] Both engineering development and operational-systems development are directed toward the design and development of specific hardware for service use, the difference being that the latter, but not the former, have been approved for production and deployment. Together they account for about one half of the total expenditures. Important examples of these projects in 1963 were the programs to develop the improved Minuteman and the Polaris A-3 missile. Management and support, which include overhead and maintenance costs, as well as the funding of the Atlantic, Pacific, and White Sands Missile Ranges, account for about 15 percent.[31]

A large-scale weapons system program may result in the expenditure of several billions of dollars and may require five to ten years to bring the new system to full operational status. For example, more than $2.3 billion was spent on the development of Atlas, $2.5 billion on Polaris, and $2.6 billion on Titan. The activities preceding a decision to consider seriously the undertaking of a large program of this sort normally span several years, most of this time being devoted to the generation and evaluation of ideas and the formulation of tentative operational requirements and research and development objectives.

Once the decision has been made to examine the desirability of developing a new weapons system, some fairly well-defined phases follow over the next few years. First, there is the concept formulation phase, which is devoted to studies of the likelihood that the weapons system can be developed within the scheduled time and estimated costs, of the likelihood that the best technological approach has been selected, and of the probable cost and effectiveness of the proposed system. The primary purpose is to determine whether contract definition should be initiated. Second, there is the contract definition phase during which the participants prepare plans of the management and engineering approaches they hope to follow, and estimate the performance and cost of their proposed system as well as of the schedule. Third, negotiating around the contents of the proposals made in the contract definition phase, one or more definitive contracts are awarded and the design and development of the weapons system is begun. At this point, there is a tremendous buildup in the commitment of engineering manpower to the program. Finally, if it is decided to acquire production versions of the system, production normally overlaps development and test activities.[32]

---

[30] The X-15, which flies like an airplane in the atmosphere and is controlled by small reaction jets at the edge of space, has rocketed to the world record speed of 4104 m.p.h. for winged aircraft and attained a record altitude of more than sixty-seven miles. It has made contributions to airframe structure, aerodynamic heating, heat transfer, and other areas. It was built by North American Aviation for NASA and the Air Force.

[31] See H. Brown, *op. cit.*

[32] See R. Black and C. Foremen, "Transferability of Research and Development Skills in the Aerospace Industry," *Report of the National Commission on Technology,*

6. PROJECT HINDSIGHT

For several years, the Department of Defense has been carrying out a major study of the science and technology utilized in weapons systems. Project Hindsight, as this study is called, takes a number of weapons systems, tries to identify the contributions from post-1945 science and technology which were important in these systems, and tries to determine the individuals who were the principal contributors, the organizations with which they were working at the time, and the nature of the work that yielded these results. Fifteen systems have been studied to date, and 556 events, that is, discrete identified contributions, have been investigated.[33]

According to the results, a large number of these events is used in any of the larger systems, and it is the combined effect of these many events which is the primary source of the improved performance or reduced cost of the system. Without most of the other events, any single event—or any small number of them—would make little contribution. In cases where the systems had an identifiable predecessor, the great majority of the events did not exist at the time the predecessor system was committed to engineering development. The events generally began accumulating about twenty years before the engineering design date of the system. Their rate of occurrence increased steadily from that time on, reached a peak one or two years before the system design date, and then decreased gradually until it reached zero about six years after the design date. Over one third of the events occurred after the system was committed either to engineering design or production.

Turning to the source of these events, 41 percent were performed by government laboratories, 49 percent by industry, and 9 percent by universities. However, these proportions have changed over time, the share arising from Department of Defense laboratories having fallen from about 60 percent in the early forties to about 30 percent in the early sixties. During this period, industry's share has increased while the universities' share has remained approximately constant. These changes would be expected since the proportion of the Defense Department's R and D conducted in-house

Automation, and Economic Progress, February 1966. For some critical remarks concerning the R and D procurement process, see E. Roberts, "Questioning the Cost-Effectiveness of the R and D Procurement Process," in M. Yovits, D. Gilford, R. Wilcox, E. Staveley, and H. Lerner, *Research Program Effectiveness*, New York: Gordon and Breach Science Publishers, 1966.

[33] See C. Sherwin and R. Isenson, *First Interim Report on Project Hindsight*, Office of the Director of Defense Research and Engineering, Washington, D.C., October 13, 1966. More recent results are contained in C. Sherwin and R. Isenson, "Project Hindsight," *Science*, June 23, 1967. The figures in the text come from the earlier report.

has been decreasing and the proportion carried out by industry has been increasing. With respect to funding, the Department of Defense was by far the largest source, 87 percent of the events arising from work it funded directly. Moreover, another 9 percent were funded by the defense industry. On the basis of these figures, the Department of Defense concludes that, per dollar invested in scientific and technological work, the defense sector produces about sixteen times as many defense-utilized events as the non-defense sector.[34]

What was the objective of the work that produced an event? Sherwin and Isenson categorize all events as science events (the primary result being new knowledge) and technology events (the primary result being an improved technique, material, component, or subsystem). In the case of science events, which were 8 percent of the total, the great majority (7.7 percent of all events) arose from applied research, most of it directed toward a Defense Department need. In the case of technology events, which were 92 percent of the total, half arose in the advanced development stage of work on a system or system concept, about 20 percent arose in the engineering development phase, and about 25 percent arose from work aimed at a broad category of defense needs and not the requirements of a particular system or system concept. Of the technology events, the need for the particular contribution was first recognized by the performing research group in only 15 percent of the cases and by an external group in 85 percent of the cases. The nature of the technical solution was determined solely by the research group 76 percent of the time and was jointly determined with a systems group 24 percent of the time.

The principal theme of Project Hindsight is that the Defense Department's huge investment since 1945 in basic, or undirected, research has had relatively little direct consequence for advanced weaponry. On the other hand, applied, or directed, research, according to the study, has paid off well, the length of time to utilization of scientific findings being reduced when the scientist is working in areas related to the problems of his sponsor. These conclusions raise a great many questions, and are bound to be challenged by the spokesmen for basic research. For example, the latter are sure to point out that Project Hindsight fails to consider the countless results of research that contribute to the pool of general knowledge from which scientists and engineers draw ideas. Also, they are sure to remind the public that the contributions of only post-1945 science are included in the study—a point which the study's authors are careful to emphasize.

---

[34] Of course, it is not surprising that this ratio is quite high. The spillover from the non-defense sector into the defense sector would be expected to be less, per dollar of expenditure, than the results obtained directly from the defense sector's own research and development.

7. THE NATIONAL AERONAUTICS AND SPACE ADMINISTRATION AND THE ATOMIC ENERGY COMMISSION

The National Aeronautics and Space Administration directly operates a number of government laboratories or "centers," is responsible for the Jet Propulsion Laboratory at California Institute of Technology, co-operates with the Air Force in the operation of Cape Kennedy, and directs a large number of government contracts for the research, development, and fabrication of the equipment needed for space exploration. In 1965, about three fourths of NASA's expenditures went for the manned space flight program. Project Mercury, the first step in this program, helped to establish the basic feasibility of manned space flight. Project Gemini went on to provide two-man earth-orbital flights of longer duration and new techniques of rendezvous, docking, and steerable re-entry. In 1966, the bulk of NASA's expenditures on manned space flights were devoted to Project Apollo, whose goals are three-man earth-orbital flights, manned flight in the earth-moon region, and lunar landing and safe return (Table 6.4).

The Apollo program is divided by NASA into six parts—the procurement and testing of the spacecraft, the procurement and testing of the Saturn I, IB, and V launch vehicles, engine development, and mission support. In 1966, about three fourths of Apollo's expenditures were for the procurement and testing of the spacecraft and the Saturn V launch vehicles. A variety of major firms are involved in the Apollo program under the cognizance of the NASA Manned Space Flight Centers. Some of the most important are North American (contractor for the space-craft, the second stage of Saturn V and the H-1, F-1, and J-2 rocket engines), Boeing (contractor for the first stage of Saturn V), Chrysler (contractor for the first stage of the Saturn I and IB), Douglas (con-tractor for the second stage of the Saturn I and IB and for the third stage of Saturn V), and General Motors (guidance and navigation systems).[35]

In 1967, one of the major questions regarding NASA concerns the selection of new goals for the agency after it completes the Apollo pro-gram. Since years of planning, research, and building must precede any major new venture, it is not too soon to begin considering this question. In the post-Apollo period, NASA could emphasize weather prediction, communications, scientific research, and national security. Alternatively, it could emphasize planetary exploration, including fly-bys of Venus and

---

[35] See *1966 NASA Authorization,* Hearings before the Subcommittee on Manned Space Flight of the Committee on Science and Astronautics, U.S. House of Repre-sentatives, 89th Congress, 1st Session, March 3–17, 1965, Part 2.

TABLE 6.4

Research and Development Expenditures, National Aeronautics and
Space Administration, 1965 and 1966

TYPE OF EXPENDITURE	1965 ACTUAL	1966 ESTIMATE
	(MILLIONS OF DOLLARS)	
Manned space flight		
Gemini	308	227
Apollo	2,615	2,967
Advanced mission studies	26	10
Scientific investigations in space		
Physics and astronomy	176	189
Lunar and planetary exploration	267	327
Bioscience	31	46
Launch vehicle development	138	90
Space applications	70	84
Space technology	299	249
Aircraft technology	35	41
Supporting activities		
Tracking and data acquisition	253	231
Sustaining university program	46	46
Technology utilization	5	5
Total	4,271	4,512

Source: Budget of the U.S. Government for Fiscal Year 1967, Appendix, p. 867. Because of rounding errors, the totals may differ slightly from the sums of the figures.

Mars in the seventies and a manned Mars landing in the eighties. Or there
could be a sizable decrease of the national space effort and the assignment
of some of its resources to other purposes. It is difficult at present to evaluate some of these alternatives because man's fitness for long-duration
space flight has yet to be determined. A 1967 report of the President's
Science Advisory Committee provides explicit encouragement for a program directed ultimately at the exploration of the planets by man.[36]

The Atomic Energy Commission (AEC) was established to advance
nuclear science and technology for military application and public use.
It carries out a variety of production, research and development, and
supporting activities directed at its military and civilian responsibilities,
about 50 percent of its total 1966 budget going for research and development. In 1963, according to Glenn Seaborg, 48 percent of these R and D
expenditures were devoted to applied work with a military orientation.[37]

[36] For example, see Science, March 3, 1967, March 17, 1967, and September 9, 1966.
[37] See Glenn Seaborg's testimony before the House Select Committee on Government Research, November 18, 1963.

Thus, although the commission, which originated largely as a weaponeer for the military, has gradually assumed major R and D responsibility in a broad spectrum of civilian nuclear technology and science, it still spends almost half of its R and D funds for military purposes. Turning to non-military work, about 33 percent of the Commission's R and D expenditures went for applied research and development aimed at civilian nuclear power, peaceful uses of nuclear explosives, medical and industrial uses of radioisotopes, controlled thermonuclear power, nuclear rockets and nuclear power sources for our national space program, radioisotopic heat and power, and other such objectives. About 19 percent went for basic research, mainly in the physical and biomedical sciences. The physical sciences research program consists of research in high, medium, and low energy physics and in those aspects of chemistry, metallurgy, and mathematics of particular relevance to nuclear science and technology (Table 6.5).

The AEC does most of its research and development in government-owned, contractor-operated laboratories like Brookhaven National Laboratory (operated by Associated Universities, Inc.), Argonne National Laboratory (University of Chicago), Oak Ridge National Laboratory (Union Carbide), Lawrence Radiation Laboratory at Berkeley and Livermore (University of California), Los Alamos Scientific Laboratory (University of California), and Sandia Laboratory (Sandia Corporation, a subsidiary of Western Electric, Bell Telephone Laboratories, and American Telephone and Telegraph Co.). The three main weapons laboratories are Sandia, Livermore, and Los Alamos. Although they have great technical, political, and budgetary strength, these laboratories have experienced cycles of confidence and concern, their drive to improve weapons often running counter to government and international efforts to stabilize military technology. From 1961 to 1965, the proportion of total AEC expenditures devoted to military purposes declined from 75 percent to 50 percent. In principle, AEC laboratories are not to go, more than temporarily, beyond the fuzzy line that divides the development of new civilian technology from its systematic production. The multi-purpose laboratories have made some efforts to diversify their activities, even by carrying out nonnuclear work. Some observers believe that, in view of altered conditions and requirements, the role of these laboratories should be broadened considerably.

Until recently, two outstanding characteristics of AEC contract policy were concentration and continuity. More than half of its contract expenditures were for many years in the hands of seven contractors: Union Carbide, General Electric, Bendix, Sandia, DuPont, and the Universities of California and Chicago. Moreover, until 1964, changes were rarely made in the contractors managing major installations. In 1963, new criteria were announced whereby contractors at AEC installations were normally to be replaced by the solicitation of proposals "at the extension of the current contract term unless the Commission determines that replacement of the existing contractor would be greatly adverse to the best interests of the government." The new policy was partly a response to industry's contention that firms chosen to operate AEC facilities gained a competitive advantage in the growing private nuclear power industry. In accord with its new policy, the AEC announced in 1964 that its Hanford contract with General Electric would be segmented and transferred to a number of other contractors.[38]

8. The National Institutes
of Health and the
National Science Foundation

Finally, we look at the research programs of the National Institutes of Health [39] and the National Science Foundation. The mission of the National Institutes of Health, the first of which was established in the thirties, is to develop knowledge for the diagnosis, prevention, treatment, and cure of the diseases of man. From relatively modest beginnings, NIH has been enlarged, modified, and reorganized until it now encompasses nine

TABLE 6.5

Research and Development Expenditures, Atomic Energy
Commission, 1965 and 1966

Type of Expenditure	1965 Actual	1966 Estimate
	(millions of dollars)	
Special nuclear materials and weapons	527	514
Reactor development	577	563
Physical research	308	319
Biology and medicine	86	91
Other research and development	22	30
Total	1,520	1,517

Source: Special Analyses, Budget of the United States, Fiscal Year 1967, p. 122.

[38] See H. Orlans, Contracting for Atoms, Washington, D.C.: The Brookings Institution, 1967. For additional description of the R and D programs of the DOD, NASA, and AEC, see the Special Analyses, Budget of the United States, Fiscal Year 1967.

[39] As noted in section 1 above, the National Institutes of Health are responsible for the bulk of the R and D Expenditures of the Department of Health, Education and Welfare.

separate Institutes, supports 40 percent of all medical research in the United States, and has an important influence on biomedical science around the world. Except for the National Cancer Institute, all of the Institutes have come into existence since World War II. Expenditures in 1964 were largest in the Institute of Mental Health, the Cancer Institute, and the Heart Institute, which together accounted for about half of the total budget (Table 6.6).

The bulk of NIH's research is carried out extramurally, chiefly in colleges, universities, and hospitals. Each application to NIH for research support is reviewed on the basis of scientific merit by a panel of nongovernment scientists in the relevant field. Then it is reviewed by one of various advisory councils, composed of scientists, science administrators, and prominent lay citizens not employed by the Federal government. The councils recommend approval or disapproval of a project, and the law stipulates that grants can be made only with the councils' approval. However, if a council recommends a particular project, the Surgeon General is not obligated to approve that project, either in concept or in amount of money.[40]

The National Science Foundation plays an extremely important role in American science. Although it accounts for only about 15 percent of the total Federal support for basic research, it is the only agency that supports basic research across the board without relation to any specific operating mission. Moreover, it is the only scientific agency with a specific mandate for encouraging and strengthening education in the sciences. Like ONR and NIH, NSF relies heavily on the project system, whereby an institution, usually a university, requests support for one or more investigators in a particular area of research. Outside experts, as well as the foundation staff, review these proposals, the primary criterion for acceptance being scientific quality. Most of the foundation's grants go for work in the physical and biological sciences (Table 6.7).

Besides supporting basic research, NSF conducts important fellowship and research participation programs for undergraduates, graduate students, and postdoctoral scholars, supports institutes for science and mathematics teachers, and finances efforts to revise and modernize the scientific curricula in secondary schools and colleges. In addition, it supports national research programs like Project Mohole (which, before its termination by Congress in 1966, studied the earth's crust by deep drilling in the ocean bottom) and national research centers like the Kitt Peak National Observatory, as well as a program of institutional grants designed

---

[40] Descriptions of NIH's activities are contained in *Federal Research and Development Programs, Exhibit 2*, Hearings before the Select Committee on Government Research of the House of Representatives, 88th Congress, 1st Session, November 18–22, 1963, and in the NIH Study Committee's Report to the President, *Biomedical Science and its Administration*, February 1965.

TABLE 6.6

Appropriations for National Institutes of Health, 1964

OBLIGATION BY ACTIVITY	GENERAL MEDICAL	CHILD HEALTH	CANCER	MENTAL	HEART	DENTAL	ARTHRITIS	ALLERGY	NEUROLOGY	OTHER	TOTAL
				(MILLIONS OF DOLLARS)							
Grants											
Research	57	26	64	69	92	9	77	39	55	43	529
Fellowships	13	2	5	8	6	1	4	3	2	1	46
Training	36	4	12	65	15	5	13	8	14	—	173
State control	—	—	—	11	—	—	—	—	—	—	11
Direct Operations											
Research	—	—	17	11	11	3	11	11	7	—	71
Collaborative studies	—	ᵃ	42	4	1	—	1	5	4	—	58
International research	—	—	—	—	—	—	—	—	—	1	1
Biologics standards	—	—	—	—	—	—	—	—	—	5	5
Training activities	—	—	—	1	ᵃ	—	—	—	ᵃ	1	1
Professional assistance	—	—	—	4	—	—	—	—	—	4	4
Review and approval	2	ᵃ	2	3	2	1	1	1	2	1	15
Program direction	1	ᵃ	1	1	ᵃ	ᵃ	ᵃ	ᵃ	ᵃ	ᵃ	4
Total	108	34	143	176	127	19	108	67	84	51	918

Source: Hearings before the Select Committee on Government Research, House of Representatives, 88th Congress, 1st Session, Part 1, p. 701. Because of rounding errors, totals may differ slightly from the sums of the figures.
ᵃ Less than $500,000.

TABLE 6.7

Estimated Obligations of the National Science Foundation, 1965

PROGRAM	OBLIGATION
	(MILLIONS OF DOLLARS)
Basic research and supporting facilities	
Basic research project grants	
Biological and medical sciences	42
Mathematical and physical sciences	54
Social sciences	10
Engineering sciences	14
National research programs	
Antarctic research	7
Indian Ocean expedition	3
Project Mohole	25
Other	6
Specialized research facilities support	
Biological	5
Physical	16
Computing	5
Other	1
National research centers	
National Center for Atmospheric Research	8
Kitt Peak National Observatory	7
Other	5
Science education programs	
Course content improvement	14
Institutes	44
Fellowships	40
Other	16
Institutional science programs	75
Science information services	12
Other	16
	——
Total	424

Source: The National Science Foundation: A General Review of its First Fifteen Years, Report to the Subcommittee on Science, Research, and Development, House of Representatives, 89th Congress, 1st Session, pp. 38–39. Because of rounding errors, the total differs slightly from the sum of the figures.

to provide universities with funds uncommitted to particular research projects.[41]

9. The Rationale for the Major Federal Research and Development Programs

We have seen that the Federal government supports most of the nation's research and development. Why is this necessary? Can we not rely on free enterprise to allocate resources efficiently in the area of R and D? Without government support, would not the right sorts of R and D be carried out? To begin with, one must consider those activities where it is technically impossible or grossly inefficient to deny the benefits of the activity to a citizen who is unwilling to pay the price; examples are national defense and the space program. In these "collective consumption" activities, the Federal government is the sole or principal purchaser of the equipment used to perform the function. Since it has the primary responsibility for these activities, it must also take primary responsibility for the promotion of technological advance in relevant areas. Few people would deny that the Federal government has this responsibility; indeed, the most rock-ribbed conservatives insist that, in matters of national defense and national prestige, the Federal government insure that a proper rate of technological change is maintained. Of course, because the Federal government has the principal responsibility in these areas, it does not necessarily follow that it must support most of the relevant research and development. Heeding the example of some private firms, it might elect instead to encourage others to finance the R and D and to buy the fruits in the form of improved products. In fact, the Federal government follows this stategy in many areas of the public sector. But in the area of defense, such a strategy would be unthinkable because the risks would be so great, both to the nation and to firms supplying military equipment. Also, in the area of space exploration, this stategy has been rejected because of the size and riskiness of the space project.

Not all the major Federal R and D programs are designed to promote technological change in goods and services provided by the public sector of the economy. Some programs are designed to offset imperfections in the system that would otherwise lead to an under-investment in R and D. For example, the value of an improvement due to R and D may be less to the individual citizen than to the community as a whole. In part, this is the rationale for Federal support of health research: society

[41] See Leland Haworth's testimony before the House Select Committee on Government Research, November 18, 1963 and *The National Science Foundation: A General Review of its First 15 Years*, Report of Legislative Reference Service to the Subcommittee on Science, Research, and Development, U.S. House of Representatives, 89th Congress, 1st Session, 1965. For a discussion of the problems involved in defining basic research, see C. Kidd, "Basic Research—Definition," *Science*, February 13, 1959.

gains over and above the gains of the individual citizen as health standards rise, the most obvious case being the reduction of contagious diseases. Other programs designed, at least in part, to offset imperfections in the system are those of the National Science Foundation, the nonmilitary parts of the Atomic Energy Commission, and the Department of Agriculture. To justify these programs, economists often assert that there are considerable discrepancies between the private and social benefits (and costs) of R and D in these areas. They maintain that these discrepancies occur because the results of R and D can be appropriated only to a limited extent and because, in some cases, of the riskiness and costliness of the research and development.[42]

The case for Federal support of basic research seems reasonably strong. Industrial firms almost certainly will invest less than is socially optimal in basic research. This is because the results of such research are unpredictable and usually of little direct value to the firm supporting the research, although potentially of great value to society as a whole. With regard to agricultural research, Federal support could be defended originally on the grounds that the smallness of firms in farming would result in smaller R and D expenditures than would be socially desirable. As industries producing agricultural supplies and equipment grew, this argument was weakened. However, there remain certain aspects of farming that these companies do not touch. With regard to nonmilitary research on atomic energy, the expense of such research, as well as the dangers of monopoly, are often cited as reasons for Federal support. However, there has been considerable controversy over the role of the Federal government in the atomic energy programs.[43]

The choice of major research priorities is largely a political one. There are no simple cost-benefit criteria, for instance, which will decide whether health R and D expenditures should be increased at the expense of military R and D expenditures. The major choices are largely value judgments. Thus, the existing government R and D programs, like other government programs, are based only partly on purely economic criteria. Political pressures, the activities of special-interest groups, as well as historical accident, also play a role. It is difficult to see how this could be otherwise, since many variables that are of crucial economic importance cannot be measured very accurately. Ideally, one might like to base decisions on the marginal social rate of return from various types of research and development. Unfortunately, however, no one has found a way to measure these rates of return at all precisely.

[42] See K. Arrow, "Economic Welfare and the Allocation of Resources for Invention," *The Rate and Direction of Inventive Activity*, Princeton, N.J.: Princeton University Press, 1962; and R. Nelson, "The Simple Economics of Basic Scientific Research," *Journal of Political Economy*, June 1959.

[43] For example, see D. Price, *Government and Science*, op. cit., pp. 84–86; and D. Lilienthal's article in *International Science and Technology*, June 1963.

10. RELATIONS BETWEEN THE
PRIVATE AND PUBLIC SECTORS

Before World War II, the bulk of the research and development financed by the Federal government was done in government laboratories, relatively little being contracted out to industry or universities. For example, in the procurement of military aircraft, an open competition was held; the winning firm recovered its development costs in the form of profits on the sale of the airplanes, and the losing firms did not recoup their R and D investment. This situation changed radically during the war; and by the sixties, only about 20 percent of federally-financed R and D was carried out by government laboratories, the rest being contracted out to industry and universities. The agencies that rely most heavily on in-house laboratories are the Departments of Commerce, Agriculture, and Interior, all of which perform over two thirds of their R and D in such laboratories. In the Defense Department, the Army and Navy, with facilities like the Army Ballistics Research Laboratories, the Naval Ordnance Test Station, and the Fort Monmouth Signal Laboratory, depend more heavily on in-house laboratories than does the Air Force.[44]

The tremendous increase in Federal contracting has resulted in a blurring of the distinction between the private and public sectors. Some major contractors, particularly in the defense and space fields, do practically all of their business with the government. In many cases, their products —aircraft, missiles, and the like—have no civilian markets, much of their capital is provided by the government, and the government has agents involved in the managerial and operating structure of their organizations. Because of the great uncertainties involved in military R and D and the impossibility of competitive bidding for R and D contracts, the mechanism of the free market has been replaced largely by administrative procedure and negotiation. In a sense, as Don Price has pointed out, the government "has learned to socialize without assuming ownership." [45] Moreover, the need to maintain an industrial mobilization base, as well as political pressures, makes it likely that contracts will be awarded without strict attention to past performance.

Some observers are troubled by the government's tendency to contract out the management of vital national scientific programs, such as the ballistic missile program. In 1954, the Air Force placed full responsibility for systems engineering and technical direction in the hands of Space Technology Laboratories, a division of Ramo-Wooldridge Corporation.

[44] Almost two thirds of the Atomic Energy Commission's R and D is carried out in Federal contract research centers administered by industry and non-profit institutions (See section 7). These laboratories are not included as in-house in the NSF statistics.

[45] D. Price, *The Scientific Estate, op. cit.,* p. 43.

When Congressional criticism mounted, the Air Force transferred these functions to Aerospace Corporation, a nonprofit firm established to render advisory services to the government. In reviewing the program, the Comptroller General concluded, "By delegating the technical aspects of this program to a contractor, the Air Force has, to a significant degree, removed itself from the direct management of the program and, as a practical matter, has shifted a portion of its responsibility for the success of this crucial program to a contractor. We believe that a program of this importance should be conducted under the direct leadership and responsibility of the Government agency to which it is entrusted." [46]

Some people also question the propriety of the government's contracting out basic strategic studies. Nonprofit groups like the RAND Corporation, the Institute for Defense Analysis, and the Hudson Institute, have been created since World War II to provide research and advice for the armed services and the Secretary of Defense on questions of military strategy and tactics, as well as on related economic and political matters. In some respects, it may be unfortunate that such delicate questions have been placed in the hands of people who are only indirectly accountable to public scrutiny; but unless Congress is willing to increase the levels of compensation of Federal employees and to provide other inducements, it is difficult to see how the necessary expertise can be assembled in government agencies.[47]

During the fifties, there was evidence of a trend toward reduced competence of government laboratories. Contractors often were able to provide better salaries, better facilities, and better administrative support, with the result that government laboratories had more difficulty in attracting and holding first-class people. Moreover, it often seemed that contractors were given more significant and interesting assignments than the government laboratories. During the sixties, efforts were made to improve the work environment for scientists and technicians within the government. According to Adam Yarmolinsky, the "effects of the serious erosion of competence in our in-house laboratories which we faced in the Fifties have not yet been completely overcome. But the trend has been reversed."[48]

[46] Comptroller General of the United States, *Initial Report on Review of Administrative Management of the Ballistic Missile Program of the Air Force*, p. 2 of transmittal letter.

[47] For a description of RAND's work, see B. Smith, *The RAND Corporation*, Cambridge, Mass.: Harvard University Press, 1966; and E. Quade, *Analysis for Military Decisions*, RAND Corporation R–387–PR, November 1964.

[48] A. Yarmolinsky, "Science Policy and National Defense," *American Economic Review*, May 1966. However, in recent years, there has been some indication that some government laboratories have been slow to adjust to changing needs. For example, see Research and Technical Programs Subcommittee, House of Representatives, *A Case Study of Utilization of Federal Laboratory Resources*, U.S. Government Printing Office, 1966, and *Science*, December 23, 1966.

In 1962, the Bell Report,[49] produced by a top-level committee of Federal officials, was submitted to the President. This report stipulated that three criteria should be used to decide whether or not a particular R and D task should be contracted out. First, the top management and control of the Federal R and D effort must be firmly in the hands of full-time government officials.[50] Second, the basic rule should be to assign a job where it can be done most effectively and efficiently. Third, efforts should be made to avoid possible conflicts of interests, such as cases where a firm provides technological advice regarding a weapon system for which it later seeks a development or production contract. An important point made in the report was that, if the contract system is to work effectively, the government must be a sophisticated buyer. Efforts must be made by the government to maintain a staff of able and trained officials. The Bell Report received considerable attention and led to significant changes, but many observers believe that its full ramifications have yet to be felt.

11. GEOGRAPHICAL DISTRIBUTION OF FUNDS AND REGIONAL ECONOMIC GROWTH

In the mid-sixties, expenditures for research and development constituted about 15 percent of the Federal administrative budget. Thus, it is not surprising that Congress has been showing great interest in the geographical distribution of these expenditures. A subcommittee of the House Committee on Science and Astronautics has asserted that the geographical distribution of Federal R and D expenditures is too uneven, and recommended that Federal agencies attempt to reduce existing inequalities.[51] Much the same thing has been stated by a subcommittee of the House Committee on Government Operations.[52] It is important at this point for us to investigate the extent of the existing differentials and the reasons for their existence; some of the relevant public policy issues are discussed in the next chapter.

[49] Bureau of the Budget, *Report to the President on Government Contracting for Research and Development*, April 30, 1962. Also see D. Price, *The Scientific Estate*, *op cit.*, pp. 38–39.

[50] To maintain this control, the government obviously needs enough in-house R and D capability to help it judge the value of proposals from the private sector.

[51] See *Geographical Distribution of Federal Research and Development Funds*, Report of the Committee on Science and Astronautics, U.S. House of Representatives, 89th Congress, 1st Session, 1965. The concern in Congress over geographical concentration of R and D funds goes back to the forties and beyond. For example, Senator Kilgore wanted to insure the widest possible distribution of research support.

[52] See *Conflicts Between the Federal Research Programs and the Nation's Goals for Higher Education*, Eighteenth Report by the Committee on Government Operations, U.S. Government Printing Office, October 13, 1965.

The available data seem to indicate a considerable concentration of Federal R and D expenditures in a few states on the Eastern and Western seaboards. In 1963, over half of all prime contracts and grants went to California, New York, and Massachusetts (Table 6.8). Although

TABLE 6.8

Prime Contracts and Grants Awarded by Eight Major Federal Agencies, for Performance of Research and Development, by State, 1963

STATE	TOTAL	INDUSTRIAL FIRMS	UNIVERSITIES[a]	NON-PROFITS
		(PERCENT)		
California	39	41	29	33
New York	9	9	8	18
Massachusetts	5	3	12	15
Maryland and District of Columbia	5	4	6	7
Pennsylvania	4	3	3	5
Texas	3	4	2	1
Washington	3	4	1	b
New Jersey	3	3	2	1
Florida	3	3	1	b
Missouri	2	3	1	1
New Mexico	2	2	6	b
Colorado	2	3	1	1
Others	21	20	29	18
Total	100	100	100	100

Source: Geographical Distribution of Federal Research and Development Funds, Subcommittee on Science, Research and Development, Committee on Science and Astronautics, House of Representatives, February 1965, p. 7. Totals may not equal 100 due to rounding errors.

a Includes operation of contract research centers.
b Less than ½ of 1 percent.

these interstate differences are partly due to interstate differences in size and population, most of them cannot be explained in this way. According to the DOD, NASA, and AEC, they reflect the fact that engineering and scientific capabilities have for various reasons become concentrated in particular states, together with the tendency of these agencies to award R and D contracts on the basis of technological competence. Confining our attention to universities, there is a considerable concentration of Federal R and D funds in a relatively few institutions, fifty universities receiving about 75 percent of all research funds and ten receiving about 35 percent in 1963. In 1964, the top recipients (in order) were M.I.T., California, Johns Hopkins, University of Michigan, Stanford, Harvard,

University of Illinois, Columbia, University of Wisconsin, University of Chicago, University of Washington, and University of Pennsylvania. According to the House Committee on Science and Astronautics, there is less geographical concentration in federally supported university R and D than in all Federal R and D expenditures, but some tendency remains for funds to be concentrated on the East and West coasts.[53]

In recent years, there has been a tendency to stress the importance of research and development in promoting regional economic growth. It is frequently asserted that the firm that gets a Federal R and D contract has a great advantage in seeking the follow-on production contract, and that the region that gains a long head start in technology in a new and important field of government procurement is bound to enjoy a considerable advantage in the competition for government contracts. Various states have formed high-level scientific advisory committees to advise the state governments and to help the states obtain Federal R and D funds. Taking Boston's Route 128 as a model, a number of cities and states are trying to build science-based industrial complexes around existing universities; examples are Philadelphia's University City Science Center and North Carolina's Research Triangle. Although strong research and educational facilities undoubtedly are of great value to a region, very little is known about the extent of their influence on the regional rate of economic growth. Some areas seem to have been much more successful than others in linking their universities to the local economy and in exploiting their research resources.

State and local governments are beginning to support research and development, but the amounts they spend are still relatively small. For example, in 1964, California's state government, worried by the impact of possible reductions in defense spending on the state's economy, financed studies by aerospace firms of waste management, crime prevention, statewide information systems, and transportation. An important purpose of these studies was to indicate whether such firms could transfer their skills and experience to nondefense problems of this sort. In Pennsylvania, the state government financed a study by Westinghouse Air Brake of the feasibility and effects of a high-speed ground transportation system between Philadelphia and Pittsburgh.[54]

[53] See *Geographical Distribution of Federal Research and Development Funds, op. cit.*

[54] For some relevant discussion, see the testimony before the House Subcommittee on Science, Research, and Development, 1965; D. Allison, "The University and Regional Prosperity," *International Science and Technology*, April 1965; the April 1965 issue of *Industrial Research*; D. Price, *The Scientific Estate, op. cit.*, pp. 21-24; Black and Foreman, *op. cit.*; E. Roberts and H. Wainer, "Technology Transfer and Entrepreneurial Success," Conference on the Administration of Research, Miami, October 27, 1966; and H. Walt, "The Four Aerospace Contracts," *Report to the President of the National Commission on Technology, Automation, and Economic Progress*, February 1966.

12. UNIVERSITIES AND OTHER NONPROFIT INSTITUTIONS

We have referred at various points to the role of the universities in promoting science and technology. In contrast to industrial and government laboratories, the traditional responsibility of the universities has been to expand the frontiers of basic science, rather than to develop particular new products. Universities perform almost one half of the nation's basic research,[55] and have the unique responsibility of providing the scientists and engineers of the future. These two functions—basic research and graduate education—are closely related; in most cases PSAC's statement that "each is weakened when carried out without the other" [56] is quite correct.

Table 6.9 shows the source and distribution of research funds in ten major universities in 1965. The importance of federal funds is obvious. Taking the university sector as a whole, about three fourths of its research and development expenditures are financed by the Federal government, the chief supporters being the DOD (which obligated about $450 million of R and D funds to educational institutions in 1966), the Department of Health, Education and Welfare (about $550 million), the AEC (about $400 million), NASA (about $250 million), and NSF (about $200 million). However, much of this money does not go for purely academic research carried out within academic departments. Federal contract research centers—like California's Los Alamos Laboratory, Johns Hopkins' Applied Physics Laboratory, Caltech's Jet Propulsion Laboratory, and M.I.T.'s Lincoln Laboratory—account for 26 percent of the DOD's obligations, 83 percent of the AEC's and 49 percent of NASA's (but none of HEW's or NSF's). These facilities carry out applied and basic work focused on the needs of their government sponsors.[57]

During the postwar period, the universities have been called on to a greater and greater extent to help with pressing social, industrial, and military problems. Besides their management of Federal contract research centers, they provide research and expertise in areas ranging from chemistry to urban renewal. As government and industrial spending on R and

[55] This is probably an underestimate. Considerable basic research is carried out by university professors as normal parts of their teaching jobs and is not included in the official figures.

[56] President's Science Advisory Committee, *Scientific Progress, The Universities, and the Federal Government*, Washington, D.C., 1960, p. 5.

[57] See *Federal Funds for Research, Development, and other Scientific Activities*, National Science Foundation, 1965. These Federal contract research centers have sometimes resulted in considerable problems for the universities. For example, the secrecy of the work at the University of Chicago's Laboratory for Applied Sciences precipitated an intra-university dispute in 1963.

TABLE 6.9

Source and Distribution of Research Funds, Ten Major Universities, 1965

A. Research Volume and Distribution by Field

| University | Total Research (millions of dollars) | Basic Research (percent of total) | Field of Science (percent of total) | | | | | | Total |
			Physi-cal	Biologi-cal	Medi-cal	Engi-neering	Agricul-tural	Other	
Cornell	56	66	13	8	14	10	21	34	100
Illinois	42	85	17	5	14	33	20	11	100
M.I.T.[a]	42	95	36	10	—	46	—	9	100
University of Michigan	46	90	13	3	24	44	—	15	100
University of Pennsylvania	28	90	16	1	51	6	—	25	100
Princeton	30	85	78	7	—	12	—	3	100
Stanford	32	100	31	b	25	29	—	15	100
Wisconsin	35	90	26	5	17	5	28	20	100
Illinois Institute of Technology	28	n.a.	n.a.	n.a.	n.a.	n.a.	n.a.	n.a.	
Minnesota	23	95	19	4	43	13	12	7	100

B. Sources of Research Funds and Type of Performer

| University | Source of Funds (percent of total) | | | | | | Type of Performer (percent of total) | | | | |
	University	Federal	Industry	Foundation	Other	Total	Academic Department	Affiliated Laboratory	Experiment Station	Other	Total
Cornell	5	71	3	5	17	100	62	34	4	—	100
Illinois	22	63	3	1	11	100	100	—	—	—	100
M.I.T.[a]	2	90	4	—	3	100	100	—	—	—	100
University of Michigan	8	80	6	3	3	100	100	—	—	—	100
University of Pennsylvania	15	77	4	4	—	100	99	1	—	—	100
Princeton	6	90	1	3	—	100	57	—	—	43	100
Stanford	12	82	1	5	—	100	84	—	—	16	100
Wisconsin	22	61	4	9	4	100	100	—	—	—	100
Illinois Institute of Technology	[c]	50	50	—	—	100	4	96	—	—	100
Minnesota	10	77	2	6	5	100	92	—	8	—	100

Source: Industrial Research, April 1965, pp. 46–49.
[a] Although it is not stated explicitly in Industrial Research, these figures seem to exclude the Lincoln Laboratory and other Federal contract research centers.
[b] Included under medical sciences.
[c] Less than ½ of 1 percent.
n.a. Not available.

D has soared, top university professors in the sciences and social sciences have spent more and more of their time as consultants to government and industry. The result has been a marked change in the character of the major universities, both private and public; some public policy issues stemming from these developments are discussed in the next chapter.[58]

The universities themselves have become increasingly dependent on government funds. The arguments of the thirties about Federal support of science seem somewhat irrelevant at this point, since no major university could carry on its present research program without Federal money. Although dangers may be involved in this dependence, there is little evidence thus far that the government has interfered improperly in the direction of federally financed university research projects, the decentralized pattern of Federal support being one factor that has helped to protect the essential academic freedom of the universities. However, there is evidence, discussed in Chapter VII, that Federal grants for project research have made it difficult to preserve the desired balance between various departments and between research and teaching.

Nonprofit organizations other than colleges and universities perform only a small amount of the nation's R and D (about 3 percent in 1963), and they finance less than they perform. But if one considers only basic research, they are an important factor. In 1963, they performed about 11 percent of the nation's basic research and financed about 7 percent of it. Included in this category are the private foundations like the Ford Foundation, Rockefeller Foundation, and Carnegie Corporation of New York. These foundations support work in a wide variety of areas, such as the elimination of hookworm, yellow fever, and malaria in many parts of the world (Rockefeller), the development of the "new math" for U.S. schools (Carnegie), and the introduction of new contraceptive techniques to Indian villages (Ford and Rockefeller).[59] In 1957, there were about 5,000 such foundations (about 400 with R and D programs), twelve of which accounted for over half of their R and D expenditures, which totaled $72 million. About 84 percent of the R and D financed by the

[58] See Clark Kerr, *The Uses of the University*, Cambridge, Mass.: Harvard University Press, 1963; Harold Orlans, *The Effects of Federal Programs on Higher Education*, Washington, D.C.: The Brookings Institution, 1962; Charles Kidd, *American Universities and Federal Research*, Cambridge, Mass.: Belknap Press, 1959; and other publications cited in Chapter VII. For some interesting background reading, see J. Ben-David, "Scientific Productivity and Academic Organization in Nineteenth Century Medicine," *American Sociological Review*, December 1960; and "Universities and Academic Systems in Modern Societies," *European Journal of Sociology*, 1962.

[59] A few additional examples in other areas: The Rockefeller Foundation gave financial support to the National Research Council during World War I, to Fermi and Bohr in the 1920's, and built cyclotrons in the 1930's. The Ford Foundation has recently granted large sums to symphony orchestras and ballet companies, to educational television, to studies of international affairs, and to investigations of economic growth. See National Science Foundation, *Research and Other Activities of Private Foundations, 1960*, Washington, D.C., 1964, for a statistical summary of their activities.

major foundations in 1960 was bestowed as grants to other organizations —mostly universities—to carry out R and D projects, only 16 percent being performed by the foundations themselves. About 46 percent was in the life sciences.

Besides the foundations, there are a host of other nonprofit research organizations which differ in size, organizational form, and field of interest. There are the independent nonprofit research institutes like Battelle Memorial Institute, Mellon Institute (now part of Carnegie-Mellon University), Stanford Research Institute, and Midwest Research Institute. They do both applied and basic work, as well as technical consulting for industry and government.[60] Battelle has long been famous for its work in metallurgy, and Mellon is noted for its work in industrial chemistry. In addition, there are the voluntary health agencies, supported mainly by voluntary public donations, as well as certain organizations that do research primarily for the government, like the RAND Corporation. These organizations are of considerable importance; for example, we have noted already that RAND has carried out a series of very influential studies of national security problems.

13. Research and Development in Other Countries

The rate of technological change depends on the extent and nature of the research and development carried out abroad, as well as in the United States. Although there are no precise measures of the importance of foreign technology, it is obviously a significant factor. For example, cellophane came from France, DDT from Switzerland, and insulin from Canada. In 1953, one fifth of all patents granted in the United States were awarded to foreign residents, for inventions created abroad.[61] In view of the significance of foreign inventors, it is worthwhile taking a brief look at the pattern of R and D spending in other countries.

Although one must be cautious in interpreting the available data,[62] the following three points might be noted. First, the ratio of R and D expenditures to gross national product seems to have risen in all of the countries that could be included (Figure 6.1). Thus, the "research revolution" seems to have been going on abroad as well as in the United

[60] See V. Danilov, "The Not-For-Profit Institutes," *Industrial Research*, February 1966.
[61] Ministère de l'Industrie, Institut National Propriété Industrielle, Production des Inventions en France, Paris, 1960. I am indebted to R. Nelson for this reference. The latest data are for 1953. According to F. M. Scherer, the figure for more recent years is likely to be somewhat lower.
[62] For some of the difficulties, see *Science, Economic Growth, and Government Policy*, Organization for Economic Cooperation and Development, 1963.

States. Comparing one country with another at a given point in time, the ratio of R and D expenditures to GNP seems to be directly related to per capita GNP. Whereas advanced industrial nations generally spend more than 1 percent of GNP on R and D, the underdeveloped countries may spend less than ¼ percent.

Second, the ratio of R and D expenditures to GNP seems to be influenced by a nation's military needs and industrial structure. In the United States and the United Kingdom, the high ratios stem to a large degree from high levels of military expenditures. Including only civilian R and D, these two countries do not have exceptionally high ratios, considering their high GNP per capita. Also, some countries are much more dependent than others on agriculture, forestry, mining, and fisheries, all of

TABLE 6.10

Funds for Research and Development, by Source and by Performer
in Various Countries

COUNTRY	YEAR	GOVERNMENT	BUSINESS (MANUFACTURING IN PARENTHESES)	NONPROFIT SECTOR, INCLUDING HIGHER EDUCATION	TOTAL
			(PERCENT OF TOTAL)		
Performers of R and D					
Japan	1959	14	63 (56)	22	100
United States	1961	15	75 (73)	10	100
Netherlands	1959	20	64 (62)	15	100
United Kingdom	1961	28	63 (59)	9	100
France	1961	32	57 (51)	11	100
Canada	1959	48	39 (35)	13	100
Philippines	1959	65	35 (27)	—	100
Australia	1960	68	20 (n.a.)	12	100
Sources of Finance for R and D					
France	1961	78	22	—	100
United States	1961	66	32	2	100
Finland	1956	62	38	—	100
United Kingdom	1961	61	37	2	100
Canada	1959	61	31	8	100
Norway	1960	51	42	7	100
Japan	1959	36	64	—	100
Netherlands	1959	30	63	7	100

Source: *Science, Economic Growth and Government Policy,* Organization for Economic Cooperation and Development, 1963.

which support little R and D. Moreover, in Canada and Australia, much of the industry is foreign owned, and the relevant R and D is imported from the parent firms.

Third, the government provides a large portion of the funds for research and development in all of these countries (Table 6.10). The relatively large portions financed by government in France, the United Kingdom, and the United States are due partly to their military, space, and nuclear research programs. The proportion of R and D funds spent intramurally by the government varies widely from country to country. In Japan and the Netherlands, as in the United States, the government performs one fifth or less of the work. In Canada, Australia, and the Philippines, much more of the work is done within government research establishments.

In other countries, as well as the United States, the postwar period has witnessed important changes in the organization and management of research. In the U.S.S.R., the tremendous expansion of R and D during the fifties led to several major reorganizations of the Academy of Sciences, as well as other parts of the Russian science establishment. According to critics, the Academy did not pay sufficient attention to the application of new technology, and there was inadequate coordination of the work of the various research institutes and educational institutions. In Western Europe, more and more governments seemed to consider, or moved in the direction of formulating, explicit policies and plans with regard to science; and industry, which has sometimes been characterized as technologically less aggressive than its American counterpart, seemed to place more emphasis on the possibilities offered by the application of science.[63]

In recent years, Europeans have expressed considerable concern over the "technological gap" between the United States and Europe. They assert that superior know-how stemming from scientific and technical developments in the United States has allowed American companies to obtain large shares of European markets in areas like aircraft, space equipment, computers, and other electronic products. In 1966, Italian Foreign Minister Amintore Fanfani called for a technological "Marshall Plan" to speed the flow of United States know-how across the Atlantic. In trying to determine the extent and seriousness of this alleged gap, it is difficult to separate technical advantages from other competitive factors in explaining why American firms have left their European rivals far behind in some fields. Differences in educational levels and managerial skills, economies of scale, and other such factors may have been very important. Moreover, it is important to note that, while the United States is

[63] See N. DeWitt, *Education and Professional Employment in the U.S.S.R.*, National Science Foundation, 1961; "Reorganization of Science and Research in the U.S.S.R.," *Science*, June 23, 1961; A. King, "Science and Technology in the New Europe," *Daedalus*, Winter 1964; and A. Korol, *Soviet Research and Development*, Boston: M.I.T. Press, 1965.

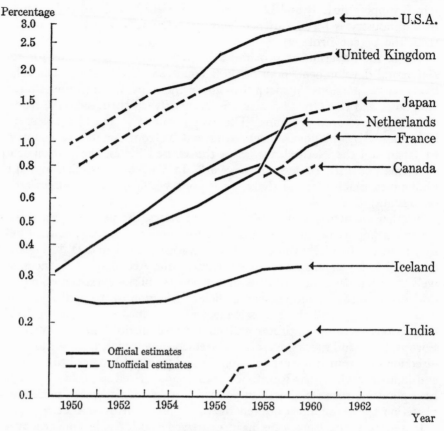

FIGURE 6.1

Gross National Expenditure on Research and Development as a
Percentage of Gross National Product (at market prices)

Source: Science, Economic Growth and Government Policy, Organization for
Economic Cooperation and Development, 1963.

the technological leader in some industries, it is not a technological leader
in many others. As of mid-1967, the United States official response to this
European concern has been in a spirit of willingness to cooperate, but
subject to further European initiative in development of specific programs of action compatible with mutual long-range political and economic
interests.[64]

[64] One of the biggest problems is that there is no clear definition of what people
mean by a technology gap. Many people seem to mean a difference in productivity
rather than in technology. According to some observers, if a gap exists, the problem
does not lie with European basic research, which has traditionally been strong; instead, it seems to lie in the movement of ideas out of the laboratory, into development, and on to the market. According to R. Morse, the problem is more a "manage-

Another problem that has received considerable attention in recent years is the migration of highly skilled individuals from the rest of the world to the United States. Countries throughout the world have awakened to the "brain drain," as is evidenced by many articles in the press and many speeches by politicians. It is clear that a considerable number of young scientists and engineers have come here to learn, and have stayed to work. Also, there have been a number of well-publicized cases where senior scientists have moved to this country. However, there is less agreement concerning the seriousness of the problem. There is no doubt that the emigration of highly skilled manpower is a loss in the view of nationalists. But if one thinks in terms of the welfare of a collection of individuals born in a particular country, regardless of where they ultimately reside, the problem is more complicated. The issue depends on the extent to which the emigration of highly skilled people decreases the welfare of the people remaining in the country of origin.[65]

The "technological" balance of payments, reflecting payments for technical know-how, patent royalties and the like, are an important element in our international balance of payments. According to the Organization for Economic Cooperation and Development, the United States received roughly ten times as much in technological payments from abroad in 1961 as went out in payments to other countries. Specifically, receipts were $577 million and payments were $63 million. The rate and direction of technological change in various countries also has major effects on the nature of imports and exports. For example, consider the plastics industry. After the development of a new plastic, there is a period of fifteen to twenty-five years when the innovating country has a decisive advantage, and is likely to be the leading country in per capita production and exports. It has a head start as well as the benefits of patents and commercial secrecy. Production may be licensed to other countries, but this usually occurs on a limited scale only after a number of years. Soon after the patents expire, a different phase begins. Imitation is easier, technical know-how spreads more readily, directly technical factors become less important, and other factors—such as materials costs—become much more important. Other countries are able to challenge the innovator in export markets, and sometimes in the innovator's home market as well,

---

ment gap" than a "technological gap." See E. Mansfield, *Defense, Science, and Public Policy*, W. W. Norton & Company, Inc., 1968.

In the area of fundamental science, as contrasted with applied technology, it is interesting to compare the number of Nobel Prizes in science and medicine won by various countries. Since 1949, the number of U.S. Nobel Prizes has increased sharply. The total number of prizes through 1967 is: United States, 74; United Kingdom, 47; Germany, 46; France, 20; Netherlands, 9; Soviet Union, 9; and Sweden, 9. See "Changed Nobel Concept," *The New York Times*, November 5, 1967.

[65] See H. Grubel, "The Brain Drain: A U.S. Dilemma," *Science*, December 16, 1966, and the papers by Humphrey and Johnson in E. Mansfield, *Defense, Science and Public Policy, ibid.*

although the innovator still benefits to some extent from his accumulated knowledge and experience and his ongoing research and development.[66]

14. SUMMARY

The Federal government plays an extremely important role in the promotion of science and technology in the United States, one measure of its importance being the fact that it finances about two thirds of the nation's research and development. In 1966, almost half of all Federal R and D expenditures were made by the Department of Defense, most of the DOD's R and D expenditures going for the development of missiles, aircraft, military astronautics, and related equipment. A large-scale weapons system program may result in the expenditure of several billions of dollars and may require five to ten years to bring the new system to full operational status. Research and exploratory development account for about one quarter of the DOD's R and D expenditures; advanced development, which is directed toward the building of test and experimental hardware, accounts for another 10 percent. In Project Hindsight the Department of Defense has attempted to study in a systematic way the sources of the science and technology utilized in recent weapons systems. According to the DOD, the results suggest that, in terms of direct consequences for advanced weaponry, post-1945 basic research has had a much lower payoff than applied research.

The next largest spenders on R and D are the National Aeronautics and Space Administration and the Atomic Energy Commission. In 1965, about three fourths of NASA's expenditures went for the manned space flight program. The space program has been the subject of considerable debate, many observers feeling that too large a proportion of the nation's scientific talent has been devoted to a project where the benefits are so largely political. As of 1967, one of the major questions regarding NASA concerns the selection of new goals for the agency after it completes the Apollo program. The Atomic Energy Commission was established in 1946 to advance nuclear science and technology for military application and public use. In 1963, about half of the AEC's R and D expenditures were devoted to applied work with a military orientation. The AEC does most of its research and development in government-owned, contractor-operated laboratories like Brookhaven and Oak Ridge, most of which are operated by educational institutions. Like the DOD

---

[66] For some studies of technology transfer and international trade, see C. Freeman, "Research and Development in Electronic Capital Goods," *National Institute Economic Review, November* 1965; "The Plastics Industry: A Comparative Study of Research and Innovation," *National Institute Economic Review,* November 1963; M. Posner, "International Trade and Technical Change," *Oxford Economic Papers,* October 1961; and R. Vernon, "International Investment and International Trade in the Product Cycle," *Quarterly Journal of Economics,* May 1966.

and NASA, about 75 percent of the AEC's R and D expenditures are for development, not research.

The fourth and fifth largest spenders are the Department of Health, Education and Welfare and the National Science Foundation. The bulk of HEW's expenditures are made by the National Institutes of Health; the Mental Health, Cancer, and Heart Institutes account for about half of the NIH total. Congress has been extremely generous in this field, appropriations often exceeding the President's budget allotment. NIH's expenditures have increased about 25 percent a year since 1946. The National Science Foundation was established in 1950 to encourage and support basic research and education in the sciences; it represented a compromise between the Magnuson bill, which emphasized the freedom of science, and the Kilgore bill, which reflected the opinion that public funds should not be distributed by an agency with an extremely diffuse channel of responsibility. Although NSF accounts for only about 15 percent of the total Federal support for basic research, it plays an extremely important role since, unlike other agencies, it has no operating mission. Like NIH, it relies heavily on the project system.

Although the role of the Federal government in science and technology expanded steadily during the period preceding 1940, it was World War II that resulted in the enormous Federal involvement in research and development. During the war, a close partnership was established by the government, industry, and universities, this partnership being built around the use of contracts to finance government research carried out by private firms and nonprofit institutions. After the war Federal R and D expenditures rose dramatically, and two great science-oriented agencies, AEC and NSF, were created. In 1957, after the launching of Sputnik I, the organization of national science policy was extensively revamped and another important new scientific agency, NASA, was created. The President's Science Advisory Committee and the President's Science Adviser, the Federal Council for Science and Technology, and more recently, the Office of Science and Technology became extremely important elements in policy formation. In very recent years, there is evidence that the relations between science and politics are becoming somewhat more strained as the Federal R and D budget tends to level off.

The reasons advanced for Federal R and D programs vary from case to case. In the areas of national defense and such national-prestige-associated ventures as the space program, the Federal government clearly has primary responsibility for the promotion of technological change; and because of the difficulties involved in allowing others to finance the R and D and buying the fruits in the forms of improved products, the Federal government must finance most of the R and D itself. With regard to basic research, health research, agricultural R and D, and nonmilitary atomic R and D, Federal programs are often defended on the grounds that too little will be spent by private industry because of the external economies from R and D, the peculiar properties of information as an economic good,[67] and the riskiness of R and D. Obviously, existing government R and D programs are based only partly on purely economic criteria. Only about one fifth of the research and development financed by the Federal government is actually done in government laboratories. The tremendous increase in Federal contracting has resulted in a blurring of the distinction between the private and public sectors. Some observers are troubled by the government's tendency to contract out the management of vital national R and D programs. There is also considerable interest, inside Congress and out, in the geographical distribution of Federal R and D contracts and grants.

The universities play a very important role in the promotion of science and technology, their traditional functions being basic research and the training of scientists. During the post war period, they have also been called on to a greater and greater extent to help with pressing social, industrial, and military problems. They perform almost one half of the nation's basic research, three fourths of it being supported by the Federal government. The arguments of the thirties about Federal support of science seem somewhat irrelevant at this point, since no major university could carry on its present research program without Federal funds. There is little evidence that the government has interfered improperly in the direction of federally financed university research projects, the decentralized pattern of Federal support being one factor that has helped to protect the essential academic freedom of the universities. Other nonprofit organizations—the private foundations like Ford, Rockefeller, and Carnegie, the independent research institutes like Battelle and Stanford, government-sponsored organizations like RAND, and many others—also contribute significantly to the nation's research efforts.

The rate of technological change depends on foreign, as well as domestic, research and development. In 1953, one fifth of all patents granted in the United States were awarded to foreign residents for inventions created abroad. For all countries for which data are available, the ratio of R and D expenditures to gross national product has been rising. International differences in this ratio seem to be related to differences in per capita gross national product, military needs, and industrial structures. In all of these countries, the government finances a large portion of the nation's R and D, but the proportion spent intramurally by the government varies widely. In other countries, as well as the United States, the postwar period

[67] Some of its peculiarities are as follows: A given piece of information is an indivisible commodity. The cost of transmitting a given body of information is frequently very low. In the absence of legal protection, the owner of a piece of information cannot simply sell it on the open market, since any one purchaser can destroy the monopoly by reproducing the information at little or no cost. The value of a piece of information to a potential purchaser is not known until he has the information—but then he has acquired it without cost.

has witnessed important changes in the organization and management of research. For example, in the U.S.S.R., the tremendous expansion of R and D in the fifties led to several major reorganizations of the Academy of Sciences. In Western Europe, there has been considerable concern over the "technological gap" between the United States and Europe in areas like aircraft and computers. In many countries there has also been concern over the "brain drain"—the migration of highly skilled individuals from the rest of the world to the United States.

CHAPTER VII

PUBLIC POLICY AND TECHNOLOGICAL CHANGE

◇◇◇◇◇◇◇◇◇◇◇◇◇◇◇◇◇◇◇◇◇◇◇

1. A TIME OF INQUIRY AND APPRAISAL

The past few years have witnessed a significant increase in the amount of attention devoted to public policies concerning technological change. In Congress, at least four subcommittees have launched investigations to determine the proper role of the Federal government in the support and management of research and development.[1] The President has established a commission which has studied the patent system and recommended ways in which it should be reformed. The National Academy of Sciences has been asked to evaluate the state of basic science in the United States and the techniques currently used by the government to select scientific

[1] These subcommittees are cited in sections 10 to 17 of this chapter. There are a number of reasons for these investigations. Federal R and D expenditures, about 15 percent of the Federal administrative budget in the mid-sixties, are large enough to be politically visible. The rapid expansion of the Federal science budget seems to be coming to an end, thus making it harder than in the past to "avoid" problems of choice. More than half of the nation's scientists and engineers are supported, directly or indirectly, by Federal R and D expenditures. In addition, of course, there is a growing recognition of the importance of science and technology, the public stake in them, and the increasing interdependence of the whole structure of science and technology.

programs. Many of the state governments have formed scientific advisory committees to help in the formulation of relevant state policies. In this chapter, we discuss some of the important policy issues that emerge from these and other investigations. First, we look at various questions regarding the patent system, as well as relevant aspects of our antitrust policies. Second, we discuss military development policies and Federal support for civilian technology. Third, we consider a number of issues relating to basic research, higher education, and the supply of engineers and scientists. Finally, we discuss various issues regarding the Federal decision making process concerning research and development programs.[2]

2. THE PATENT SYSTEM

One of the major instruments of national policy regarding technology is the patent system. The United States patent laws grant the inventor exclusive control over the use of his invention for seventeen years, in exchange for his making the invention public knowledge. Not all new knowledge is patentable. A patentable invention "is not a revelation of something which existed and was unknown, but the creation of something which did not exist before." [3] "There can be no patent upon an abstract philosophical principle." [4] A patentable invention must have as its subject matter a physical result or a physical means of attaining some result, not a purely human means of attaining it. Moreover, it must contain a certain minimum degree of novelty. " 'Improvement' and 'invention' are not convertible terms . . . [W]here the most favorable construction that can be given . . . is that the article constitutes an improvement over prior inventions, but it embodies no new principle or mode of operation not utilized before by other inventors, there is no invention." [5]

[2] The discussion of public policy issues is not confined to this chapter. For a discussion of issues concerning labor displacement and adjustment to new techniques, see Chapter V. For a discussion of some issues regarding the management of Federal R and D programs, see Chapter VI.

[3] Pyrene Mfg. Co. v. Boyce, C.C.A.N.J., 292 F. 480.

[4] Boyd v. Cherry, 50F. 279, 282.

[5] William Schwarzwaelder and Co. v. City of Detroit, 77F. 886, 891.

What proportion of patented inventions are used commercially, and how great are the private returns from them? The Patent, Copyright, and Trademark Foundation of George Washington University selected a 2 percent random sample of patents granted in 1938, 1948, and 1952, and determined (by interviews or correspondence with the inventor or assignee) the utilization status of the inventions sampled. According to the results, 51 percent of the patents assigned at date of issue to large companies were used commercially, 71 percent of those assigned at date of issue to small companies were used commercially, and 49 percent of the patents unassigned at date of issue were used commercially. For mechanical inventions, 57 percent were used commercially; whereas for electrical and chemical inventions, 44 percent were used commercially.

Not all of the patents in commercial use are profitable to their owners. The Patent, Copyright, and Trademark Foundation obtained information on profitability from assignees on 127 of 292 inventions reported in past or current use. Two thirds of those

Since Congress passed the original patent act in 1790, the arguments used to justify the existence of the patent laws have not changed very much. First, these laws are regarded as an important incentive to induce the inventor to put in the work required to produce an invention. Particularly in the case of the individual inventor, it is claimed that patent protection is a strong incentive. Second, patents are regarded as a necessary incentive to induce firms to carry out the further work and make the necessary investment in pilot plants and other items that are required to bring the invention to commercial use. If an invention became public property when made, why should a firm incur the costs and risks involved in experimenting with a new process or product? Another firm could watch, take no risks, and duplicate the process or product if it were successful. Third, it is argued that, because of the patent laws, inventions are disclosed earlier than otherwise, the consequence being that other inventions are facilitated by the earlier dissemination of the information. The resulting situation is often contrasted with the intense secrecy with regard to processes which characterized the medieval guilds and which undoubtedly retarded technological progress and economic growth.[6]

Not all economists agree that the patent system is beneficial. A patent represents a monopoly right, although as many inventors can testify, it may represent a very weak one. Critics of the patent system stress the social costs arising from the monopoly. After a new process or product has been discovered, it costs little or nothing for other persons who could make use of this knowledge to acquire it. The patent gives the inventor the right to charge a price for the use of the information, the result being that the knowledge is used less widely than is socially optimal.[7] Critics

---

used in the past (for which there were data) were profitable; one third showed losses. Nine tenths of those currently in use (for which there were data) were profitable; one tenth showed losses. Dollar estimates of profits and losses were provided by assignees for 93 patents in current or past use. For the results, see B. Sanders, "Patterns of Commercial Exploitation of Patended Inventions by Large and Small Companies," *Patent, Copyright, and Trademark Journal*, Spring 1964.

[6] See V. Bush, *Proposals for Improving the Patent System*, Study 1 of the Senate Subcommittee on Patents, Trademarks, and Copyrights, 1956; G. Frost, *The Patent System and the Modern Economy*, Study 2 of the Senate Subcommittee on Patents, Trademarks, and Copyrights, 1957; and F. Machlup, *An Economic Review of the Patent System*, Study 15 of the Senate Subcommittee on Patents, Trademarks, and Copyrights, 1958.

[7] Since the use of knowledge by one individual does not reduce the ability of another individual to use it, it would be socially desirable in a static sense for existing knowledge to be available for use wherever it is of social value. However, if there were no financial reward for the knowledge producer, there would be less incentive to produce new knowledge. To promote optimal use while preserving this incentive, it has been suggested that society would be better off if the profits obtained by the patent holder could be awarded to him as a lump sum and if there were unrestricted use of the information. Unfortunately, this proposal suffers from important practical difficulties. See E. Mansfield, "Economics, Public Policy and the Patent System," *Journal of the Patent Office Society*, May 1965; and "National Science Policy," *American Economic Review*, May 1966, as well as section 3 below.

also point out that patents have been used to create monopoly positions which were sustained by other means after the original patents had expired; they cite as examples the aluminum, shoe machinery, and plate glass industries.[8] In addition, the cross licensing of patents often has been used by firms as a vehicle for joint monopolistic exploitation of their market.

Critics also question the extent of the social gains arising from the system. They point out that the patent system was designed for the individual inventor, but that over the years most research and development has become institutionalized. They assert that patents are not really important as incentives to the large corporation, since it cannot afford to fall behind in the technological race, regardless of whether or not it receives a patent. They point out that, because of long lead times, most of the innovative profits from some types of innovations can be captured before imitators have a chance to enter the market. Moreover, they claim that firms keep secret what inventions they can, and patent those that they cannot.[9]

Surveys of business firms provide mixed answers about the importance of patents in encouraging R and D and innovation. Some firms feel that patents are extremely important and that their research and innovative activities could not be sustained without them; others feel that patents make little difference in their search for, and introduction of, new products and processes. The electronics, chemicals, and drug industries make extensive use of patents; the automobile, paper, and rubber industries do not. Patents are much more important for independent inventors and small firms than for large firms, which are better able to carry out their inventive and innovative activities without the protection of the patent system. They are much more important for major product inventions than for process inventions (which can often be kept secret for a considerable period of time) or for minor product inventions.[10]

Do the benefits derived from the patent system outweigh its costs? Like many broad issues of public policy, the facts are too incomplete and too contaminated by value judgments to permit a clear-cut, quantitative estimate of the effects of the patent system. Nonetheless, with or without such an estimate, it is impossible to avoid the relevant policy issue, and when confronted with it, there are few leading economists, if any, who favor abolition of the patent system. Even those who publish their agnosticism with respect to the system's effects admit that it would be irresponsible, on the basis of our present knowledge, to recommend abolishing it.

[8] See A. Kahn, "The Role of the Patents," in J. Miller, *Competition, Cartels, and Their Regulation*, Amsterdam: North Holland Publishing Company, 1962.

[9] See C. Edwards, *Maintaining Competition: Requisites of a Government Policy*, New York: McGraw-Hill, Inc., 1949; A. Plant, "The Economic Theory Concerning Patents for Inventions," *Economica*, February 1934; and F. Machlup, *op. cit.*

[10] See A. Kahn, *op. cit.*; F. Scherer *et al.*, *Patents and the Corporation*, Boston: Harvard Business School, 1959; and the National Academy of Sciences-National Research Council, *The Role of Patents in Research*, Washington, D.C., 1962.

Nonetheless, many economists seem to be interested in altering some of its features—which is hardly surprising in view of the fact that the patent system has continued for over a century without major change.

3. Proposed Changes
in the Patent System

Over the years, there have been many proposals for reforming the U.S. patent system. Some have proposed that the length of the patent be varied in accord with the importance of the invention or the cost of making it. This proposal seems reasonable, since it is highly improbable that a single inflexible system can apply optimally both to major technological break-throughs and to more routine, incremental changes. However, there are administrative difficulties arising from the problem of deciding the relative importance of inventions. Others have proposed that patent holders be required to pay an annual registration fee, the penalty for nonpayment being the premature termination of the patent. The purpose of this proposal, which has been put in effect in several countries (including the United Kingdom), is to weed out worthless patents.[11]

Turning to more radical proposals, a system of general compulsory licensing has sometimes been suggested, which would permit everyone to obtain licenses under any patent. Under this system, patentees could no longer hope for attractive monopoly profits, but only for royalties from their licenses and cost advantages over their royalty-paying competitors. This proposal has been resisted almost everywhere because of the difficulties of determining "reasonable royalties" and because of a fear that inventive and innovative activity would be unduly discouraged.[12] Another proposal, put forth by Michael Polanyi, would "supplement licenses of right by government rewards to patentees on a level ample enough to give general satisfaction to inventors."[13] Every inventor would have the right to claim a public reward, and all other persons could use the invention

[11] See F. Machlup, *op. cit.*; and P. Federico, *Renewal Fees and Other Patent Fees in Foreign Countries*, Study 17 of the Senate Subcommittee on Patents, Trademarks, and Copyrights, 1958.

[12] An important facet of the controversy over compulsory licensing is the charge of suppression of patents which has been persistently repeated and angrily rejected. See Floyd Vaughn, *The United States Patent System*, Norman, Okla.: University of Oklahoma Press, 1956; Corwin Edwards, *op. cit.*; and M. Polanyi, "Patent Reform," *Review of Economic Studies*, Summer 1944. Also, see C. Corry, *Compulsory Licensing of Patents—A Legislative History*, Study 12 of the Senate Subcommittee on Patents, Trademarks, and Copyrights, 1958.

[13] M. Polanyi, *ibid.* Proposals for systems of prizes and bonuses to inventors, rather than patents, are very old. For example, Alexander Hamilton suggested that the Federal government award prizes for important inventions. However, the problem of selecting inventors and inventions has limited the attention accorded this sort of scheme.

freely. Because of the difficulty in setting individual awards, this proposal has received only a limited amount of attention.

It seems unlikely that fundamental changes of this sort will be made. If changes come about, they are likely to be less sweeping. For example, there has been some interest in a "delayed examination" system, like that adopted in 1964 by the Dutch. Under the present system in the United States, the Patent Office examines all patent applications in order of their filing date as to formalities, and sees whether the three essential statutory requirements of novelty, utility, and non-obviousness of the subject matter over the prior art are met.[14] Under a delayed examination system, an application is first examined only as to formal matters. If the application is in order, it is published as a "provisional" patent; and a full examination is made as to novelty and invention only if certain fees are paid by an interested party within a certain period of time. If full examination is not requested within this period, the patent will lapse.

The delayed examination system has some important advantages. Since the invention is published more quickly than under the present system, the technological information embodied in the patent will be disseminated more rapidly. This is socially desirable, though not always beneficial to the inventor. In addition, the provisional patent should be enough for patent applications filed chiefly for defensive purposes, that is, out of fear that if a patent is not obtained, someone else may obtain a patent on the same thing and use it against the original inventor. Thus, the delayed examination system should relieve the Patent Office of the burden of giving these applications a full examination, and this in turn should help to solve one of the Patent Office's oldest and most important problems—the long delay in issuing patents. In recent years, the average patent is issued after 3.5 years before the Patent Office.

There is also a question regarding the desirability of our interference procedure, which has long been criticized as overly time consuming and complex. The United States and Canada are the only countries where the question of priority among claimants of a single invention is adjudicated within the Patent Office. In most countries, the first applicant is granted the patent, and later applicants can go to court to have the question of priority determined. In addition, there is a question as to whether or not we in the United States are correct in allowing employee-inventors to assign away all their rights in patents relating to the business of the employer or resulting from work done for the employer, in consideration of employment. In West Germany, for example, the employed inventor receives under certain circumstances an extra compensation for his invention. Very little is known about the effects of such schemes on the

---

[14] By "formalities" is meant compliance with various rules of application. "Novelty," with some exceptions, means being the first to invent. "Invention" is a contribution above the exercise of ordinary skill.

performance of the employee-inventor or on the employer's incentives to carry out research and development. In the United States, there is little indication that existing practices will be altered in the forseeable future.[15]

In 1966, the President's Commission on the Patent System recommended a number of changes in the legal superstructure of the system, the purpose being to speed patent approval, tighten the standards of patentability, and reduce the cost of challenging and defending patent rights. It recommended that, when two or more persons separately apply for a patent on the same invention, the patent should issue to the one who was first to file his application. Moreover, applicants should be responsible for knowing all prior inventions and developments anywhere in the world. One consequence of these proposals, if adopted, would be the abolition of interference proceedings. In addition, the commission recommended that the existence of supposedly new technology should be publicized by automatically printing patent applications within two years from the filing date. An inventor or firm could keep the invention secret only by withdrawing an application or not filing one in the first place.

The Commission also recommended that standby statutory authority be provided for an optional delayed examination system whereby the examination is deferred at the option of the applicant. Any outside party would be allowed to challenge any patent application by paying a fee for Patent Office experts to look into claims to prior development. Also, losers in a patent challenge would be required to pay the entire cost of the litigation, treble damages would be allowed in some infringement suits, and a district court ruling on the validity of a patent would apply everywhere in the country. (The last recommendation prevents a patent owner who loses a claim in one court from harassing an opponent by filing suit in another jurisdiction. At present, this can be done.) The period of patent protection would be changed to twenty years from date of first application, and computer languages and programs would not be patentable. Legislation will be required before these changes can be made.[16]

4. GOVERNMENT PATENT POLICY

Under what circumstances should title to patents arising from government-financed R and D remain with the contractor, the Federal government taking no more than a royalty-free license? During the last several years, this question has been considered at length in Congress, the executive branches of the government, and the pages of economic, legal, and

[15] For example, see F. Neumeyer, *The Law of Employed Inventors in Europe*, Study 30 of the Senate Subcommittee on Patents, Trademarks, and Copyrights, 1963.
[16] *To Promote the Progress of the Useful Arts in an Age of Exploding Technology*, Report of the President's Commission on the Patent System, Washington, D.C., 1966. For a discussion of some of the adverse reaction to the proposed changes, see "Criticism of Patents Bill Is Expected," *New York Times*, April 16, 1967.

business journals.[17] It is not surprising that the question has arisen. There has been an enormous increase in the amount and proportion of research and development work conducted at public expense, and the agencies that account for most of these expenditures—the DOD, NASA, and the AEC —have adopted different policies with respect to patents.

Opponents of the license policy, where title to the patents remains with the contractor, describe it as a great giveaway.[18] They argue that since the government pays for the R and D, it is entitled to all of its fruits, including patented inventions. If an invention of overwhelming social importance arises from publicly financed research, it is obvious, according to their view, that the invention should not remain in the hands of a private person who could exploit it to his own profit-seeking advantage. Moreover, they believe that new techniques will be used more quickly and more widely if they can be made freely available to all. On the other hand, those who favor the license policy contend that inventions will be used more quickly and more widely under such a policy, because what is free to all has limited value to any. In addition, they assert that government R and D will be performed more efficiently and by more highly qualified contractors than under a title policy, where title to the patents remains with the government.[19]

The President's Patent Commission avoided any recommendation in this area since "this question is being considered actively elsewhere in the Executive Branch and by Committees of Congress." [20] The present Federal policy, expressed by the President's Memorandum of October 1963 on Government Patent Policy, recognizes that neither a license nor a title policy is appropriate in all cases. This memorandum states that there are situations where the principal or exclusive rights should be taken by the government; for example, if agencies contract for the development of products specifically intended for use by the public, if use of the product will be required by government regulation, or if products are directly related to the public health. On the other hand, where the contractor is expected to build upon existing knowledge in a field where he has an established technical competence and a nongovernmental commercial posi-

[17] For example, see W. Leontief, "On Assignment of Patent Rights on Inventions Made Under Government Research Contracts," *Harvard Law Review*, January 1964; L. Preston, "Patent Rights Under Federal R and D Contracts," *Harvard Business Review*, October 1963; D. Watson, A. Bright, and A. Burns, "Federal Patent Policies in Contracts for Research and Development," *The Patent, Trademark, and Copyright Journal*, 1960; and M. Holman, "The Utilization of Government-Owned Patented Inventions," *The Patent, Trademark, and Copyright Journal*, 1963.

[18] Senator Long of Louisiana is one of the most vehement critics of this policy. The Department of Defense and the Department of Commerce have been the most important agencies that usually follow a license policy.

[19] Of course, there are several possible variants of the license and title policies. For example, the government can retain title and grant exclusive licenses.

[20] *To Promote the Progress of the Useful Arts in an Age of Exploding Technology, op. cit.*, p. 53.

tion, the memorandum stipulates that the rights should normally remain with the contractor. However, if the contractor has not used the invention or made it available in three years, the government can require the contractor to grant nonexclusive royalty-free licenses.[21]

5. ANTITRUST POLICY

The antitrust laws are designed to promote competition and to control monopoly. For example, the Sherman Act of 1890, the first major federal legislation directed against monopoly, outlaws conspiracies or combinations in restraint of trade and forbids the monopolizing of trade or commerce.[22] The courts have had the difficult job of deciding what business conditions are actually forbidden by these acts. At the time of the U.S. Steel decision in 1920, the Supreme Court interpreted monopolization to mean market conduct which tends to coerce rivals, and held that "the law does not make mere size an offense or the existence of unexerted power an offense." This interpretation stood for two decades, but was altered in the Alcoa case of 1945, when the Court said that control by a firm of a large proportion of the market could by itself constitute a violation of the Sherman Act.

There are at least two fairly distinct approaches to antitrust policy. The first approach is concerned primarily with market performance—the industry's rate of technological change, efficiency, and profits, the conduct of individual firms, and so on. Advocates of this approach argue that, in deciding antitrust cases, one should review in detail the performance of the firms in question to see how well they have served the economy. This test, as it is usually advocated, relies heavily on evaluation of the technological "progressiveness" and "dynamism" of the firms in question. Unfortunately, it is difficult to know how such an evaluation is to be carried out, since there is no way of telling at present whether the rate of technological change in a particular industry represents "good" or "bad" performance. In view of the vagueness of the criteria and the practical realities of the antitrust environment, the adoption of this test would probably be an invitation to nonenforcement.[23]

The second approach emphasizes the importance of an industry's market structure—the number and size distribution of buyers and sellers in the

[21] See the *Patent Advisory Panel Progress Report to the Federal Council for Science and Technology*, Washington, June 1964. In weighing the arguments discussed in this section, it should be noted that the rate of utilization of privately owned patented inventions originating in Federally financed R and D is substantially less than that of all privately owned patented inventions.

[22] See E. Mansfield, *Monopoly Power and Economic Performance*, New York: W. W. Norton & Company, Inc., 1964, for a collection of papers describing and evaluating the antitrust laws.

[23] See E. Mason's preface to C. Kaysen and D. Turner, *Antitrust Policy*, Cambridge, Mass.: Harvard University Press, 1959.

market, the ease with which new firms can enter, and the extent of product differentiation. According to this approach, one should look to market structure for evidence of undesirable monopolistic characteristics. Although many economists favor this approach, others claim that a vigorous antitrust policy based on this test would be a mistake; for example, as pointed out in previous chapters, Schumpeter and Galbraith assert that large firm size and a high level of concentration are conducive to rapid technological change and rapid utilization of new techniques.[24] If true, this is an extremely important point. But is it true? Does the evidence indicate that an industry dominated by a few giant firms is generally more progressive than one composed of a larger number of smaller firms? Some of the relevant findings have been presented in several previous chapters. Although the evidence is extremely limited, it should be brought together at this point and examined.

6. Firm Size, Market Structure, Technological Change, and the Utilization of New Techniques

To prevent confusion, it is advisable to distinguish among several related issues. First, what is the effect of an industry's market structure on the amount it spends on R and D? Suppose that, for a market of given size, we could replace the largest firms by a larger number of somewhat smaller firms—and thus decrease concentration. If the largest firms in this industry were giants, like Standard Oil of New Jersey or U.S. Steel, the available evidence, which is extremely tentative, does not suggest that total R and D expenditures are likely to decrease considerably. On the contrary, there is usually no tendency for the ratio of R and D expenditures to sales to be higher among the giants than among their somewhat smaller competitors. However, if the largest firms in the industry were considerably smaller than this or if concentration were reduced greatly, one might expect a decrease in R and D expenditures, because firm size often must exceed a certain minimum for R and D to be profitable.[25]

Second, to what extent would such a change in market structure be harmful because of economies of scale in R and D? Obviously, the answer to this question varies with the type of research or development being considered. In research, the optimal size of group may be fairly small in many areas; for example, the transistor, the maser, the laser, and radio

---

[24] As Galbraith puts it, "The foreign visitor, brought to the United States by the Economic Cooperative Administration, visits the same firms as do attorneys of the Department of Justice in their search for monopoly." J. K. Galbraith, *American Capitalism*, Boston: Houghton Mifflin Company, 1952, p. 96.

[25] See Chapter III, and F. Scherer, Testimony before Senate Subcommittee on Antitrust and Monopoly, May 18 and 25, 1965.

command guidance were conceived by an individual or groups of not more than a dozen persons. In development, the optimal size of effort tends to be larger, particularly in the aircraft and missile industries where tremendous sums are spent on individual projects.[26] However, in most industries, the limited data that are available do not seem to indicate that only the largest firms can support effective R and D programs; there is generally no indication that the largest programs have any marked advantage over somewhat smaller ones.[27]

Third, is there any evidence that R and D programs of given scale are carried out more productively in large firms than in small ones? The data are extremely limited, but they seem to indicate that, in most industries for which we have information, the answer is no. In most of these industries, when the size of R and D expenditures is held constant, increases in size of firm are associated with decreases in inventive output. The reasons for this are by no means obvious. Some observers claim it is because the average capabilities of technical people are higher in the smaller firms, R and D people in smaller firms are more cost conscious than those in larger firms, and the problems of communication and coordination tend to be less acute in smaller firms.[28]

Fourth, what is the effect of an industry's market structure on how rapidly new processes and products, both those developed by the industry and those developed by others, are introduced commercially? The answer seems to depend heavily on the types of innovations that happen to occur. If they require very large amounts of capital, it appears that the substitution of fewer large firms for more smaller ones may lead to more rapid introduction; if they require small amounts of capital, this may not be the case. Another important factor is the ease with which new firms can enter the industry. If increased concentration results in increased barriers to entry, it may also result in slower application of new techniques, since innovations often are made by new firms. Indeed, many new firms are started for the specific purpose of carrying out innovations.[29]

Fifth, what is the effect of an industry's market structure on how rapidly innovations, once they are introduced, spread through an industry? The

[26] Development costs are sometimes very high in other industries too. For example, DuPont spent $25 million to develop Corfam, and $50 million for Delrin. (However, these figures may be increased somewhat by the cost of pilot plants, some of whose output is sold commercially.) See D. Stillerman's and F. Scherer's testimony before the Senate Subcommittee on Antitrust and Monopoly, May 18, 1965.

[27] See E. Mansfield, *Industrial Research and Technological Innovation*, New York: W. W. Norton & Company, Inc., 1968, Chapter II; and J. Jewkes, D. Sawers, and R. Stillerman, *The Sources of Invention*, New York: St. Martin's Press, Inc., 1959.

[28] E. Mansfield, *ibid.*, and A. Cooper, "R and D Is More Efficient in Small Companies," *Harvard Business Review*, June 1964.

[29] See E. Mansfield, *ibid.*, Chapter VI; R. Schlaifer's testimony before the Senate Subcommittee on Antitrust and Monopoly, May 25, 1965; and G. Brown, "Characteristics of New Enterprises," *New England Business Review*, June–July, 1957.

fact that large firms tend to be quicker than small firms to introduce a new technique does not imply that increased concentration results in a faster rate of diffusion. On the contrary, the very small amount of evidence in Chapter IV bearing on this question seems to suggest that greater concentration in an industry may be associated with a slower rate of diffusion. However, the observed relationship is weak and could well be due to chance.[30]

Contrary to the allegations of Galbraith, Schumpeter, and others, there is little evidence that industrial giants are needed in all or even most industries to insure rapid technological change and rapid utilization of new techniques. Moreover, there is no statistically significant relationship between the extent of concentration in an industry and the industry's rate of technological change, as measured by the methods described in Chapter II.[31] Of course, this does not mean that industries composed only of small firms would necessarily be optimal for the promotion and diffusion of new techniques. On the contrary, there seem to be considerable advantages in a diversity of firm sizes, no single firm size being optimal in this respect. Moreover, the optimal average size is likely to be directly related to the costliness and scope of the inventions that arise. However, in general, these factors do not make giantism necessary. To repeat, there is little evidence that industrial giants are needed in all or even most industries to promote rapid technological change and rapid utilization of new techniques.

7. ANTITRUST POLICY AND THE PATENT SYSTEM

The patent system, if left unchecked by a vigorous antitrust policy, can be made an effective device for the spread of monopoly power. In 1790, when the first patent law was enacted, invention was a matter of individual tinkering, and the inventor's limited talents, energy, and financial resources made it very unlikely that he could monopolize an industry. However, during the next century, these safeguards were substantially weakened. By the first decade of this century, "the patent system had become a special sanctuary for trusts, pools, and trade confederacies," in the judgment of two leading students of the problem.[32]

Over the past thirty years, there has been a discernible trend toward resolving conflicts between the patent system and antitrust policy in favor

[30] E. Mansfield, *ibid.*, Chapter VII.

[31] E. Mansfield, *ibid.*, Chapter IV; and N. Terleckyj, *Sources of Productivity Advance*, Ph.D. Thesis, Columbia University, 1960.

[32] G. Stocking and M. Watkins, *Monopoly and Free Enterprise*, New York: The Twentieth Century Fund, 1951, p. 454.

of the latter. The mortality rate for patents before the courts has increased substantially, and the mortality rate has varied directly with the rank of the court. From 1948 to 1954, the district courts ruled on 664 patents in reported cases and found 355 invalid and 108 not infringed; during the same period, the Supreme Court threw out five of the seven patents that came before it.[33] Moreover, Congress has also set higher standards for patentability. In the early statutes, the test was whether the invention was "new and useful." In the Patent Act of 1952, a patent may not be obtained "if the subject matter as a whole would have been obvious at the time the invention was made to a person having ordinary skill in the art to which said subject matter pertains."

In addition, the courts have curtailed the extension of the effects of the patent beyond the invention described in the patent claim. In the forties, the Supreme Court established the doctrine that the license could not fix the prices of unpatented products produced by patented processes. Also, it ruled against a patent provision based on the sale of an unpatented as well as a patented commodity. Unless they result in industry price fixing, price restrictions established by the patentee on the licensee are generally held to be legal, but in recent years there has been considerable effort to reverse this doctrine. The courts have also shown a tendency to deny the patentee exclusive use in cases where it results in substantial monopoly power. Between 1941 and 1957, over 100 judgments provided for compulsory licensing or outright dedication. The rationale for these decisions is illustrated by the statement of Judge Forman in the General Electric case: "In view of the fact that General Electric achieved its dominant position in the industry and maintained it in great measure by its extension of patent control the requirement that it contribute its existing patents to the public is only a justified dilution of that control made necessary in the interest of free competition in the industry." [34]

8. THE ACQUISITION OF NEW WEAPONS

Since the Department of Defense accounts for almost half of the Federal R and D budget, its policies regarding the utilization of R and D resources are obviously of great importance. As noted in Chapter III, one of the most important characteristics of the weapons acquisition process is its

[33] D. Dewey, *Monopoly in Economics and Law*, Chicago: Rand McNally & Company, 1959, p. 175.
[34] 115 F. Supp. 835 (D.N.J. 1953). This section relies heavily on J. Markham, "Inventive Activity: Government Controls and the Legal Environment," in *The Rate and Direction of Inventive Activity*, National Bureau of Economic Research, 1962. Note that the tax laws can also influence the rate of technological change. For example, research and development was encouraged by the 1954 changes in the tax laws which permitted R and D expenditures to be deducted as a current expense rather than being treated as a capital investment.

uncertainty. A weapons system as it is initially conceived is generally quite different from the weapons system which actually emerges from development. For example, a study of six fighter plane development projects shows that four of the six ended up with engines that differed from the original plans, three had different electronic systems, five had to be modified extensively and three came out of development essentially different airplanes. Changes of this sort occur because engineers try to squeeze the last ounce of performance out of their systems, because the experts' consensus can be quite wide of the mark, because unanticipated technical problems arise, and sometimes because of poor planning. Besides these uncertainties which originate largely in the technological character of weapons development, there are other uncertainties regarding the demand for a particular weapons system. Because of unexpected changes in the rate of progress of related technologies and unexpected changes in the nature of opposing forces, a weapons system may be much less valuable than originally estimated. The importance of these uncertainties is magnified, of course, by the vast size and extended duration of major weapons programs.

Because of these uncertainties, the market system, in anything like its customary form, has not been applied to the acquisition of new weaponry. Instead, the government has exercised control over sellers through the auditing of costs and through the intimate involvement of its agents in the managerial and operating structure of the sellers. Moreover, there is extensive government ownership of the sellers' facilities, the government decides what weapons are to be created through its program decisions, and payments to the sellers are frequently based on costs incurred (although, as we shall see, simple cost-plus pricing has become much less important than it used to be). Clearly, "competition" in this environment does not mean what it does in the market system. Another important difference between the weapons acquisition process and the development process in most other areas of the economy is the extent of the technological advance that is attempted. The attempt in military development for rapid and major advances on a broad front have little counterpart in the normal activities of commercial industries.

Several other characteristics of the nation's weapons contractors should also be noted. First, the market position of a particular contractor is rather insecure. Product lines change rapidly to meet changing requirements of new technology, and it has been relatively easy for newcomers to join the ranks. One problem that has sometimes occurred is that firms have directed their efforts in such a way as to enhance their capability for new projects at the expense of good work on current projects. Second, the critical resources of a weapons contractor are scientific and engineering talent rather than the more conventional inputs noted in Chapter II. Third, performance on past programs has not always been given sufficient weight in the selection of contractors. In part, of course, this is because opinions may vary on the quality of past performance and because good performance in the past does not necessarily mean good performance in the future. In addition, however, source selection involves multiple objectives and other economic and political considerations may play an important role.

How well have our weapons programs been carried out? Studies made in the early sixties suggest that, although technical performance, reliability, and development time have been at least reasonably satisfactory, there has been a notable failure to hold development and production costs to reasonable levels. In part, this has been due to inadequate attention being given to the efficient use of technical and other manpower and to the development of increments of technical performance and other features that are not worth their cost ("gold-plating"). More fundamentally, it has been due to the greater emphasis that the services have placed on time and quality considerations than on cost reduction, the result being that contractors recognized that a record of meeting schedules with good products was much more important in getting new business than a reputation for low costs. Moreover, cost-plus contracts provided little incentive to reduce costs. During the sixties, efforts have been made by Secretary of Defense McNamara to emphasize cost reduction to a much greater extent than was formerly the case.[35]

9. MILITARY DEVELOPMENT POLICY

Based on a long series of studies of military development projects, economists at the RAND Corporation, led by Burton Klein, have made a number of suggestions regarding military development policy. In their view,[36] it is important that the government devote a very significant proportion of its military R and D expenditures to activities falling outside the major weapons systems programs, that is, to basic research, exploratory development, and advanced development. By developing in this way a large menu of technology, we can hope to buy at a relatively low price the capability to adapt our weapons programs to the actual strategic situ-

[35] See B. Klein, "The Decision Making Problem in Development," *The Rate and Direction of Inventive Activity*, Princeton, N.J.: Princeton University Press, 1962; C. Kaysen, "Improving the Efficiency of Military Research and Development," *Public Policy*, 1963; P. Cherington, "Kaysen on Military Research and Development: A Comment," *Public Policy*, 1963; C. Hitch, "Character of Research and Development in a Competitive Economy," *Proceedings of Conference on Research and Development*, National Science Foundation, 1958; P. Cherington, "The Interaction of Government and Contractor Organizations in Weapons Acquisitions," *The Economics of Research and Development*, Columbus, Ohio: Ohio State University, 1965; T. Glennan, "Issues in the Choice of Development Policies," *RAND Corporation P–3153*, June 1965; B. Klein, "Policy Issues Involved in the Conduct of Military Development Programs," *The Economics of Research and Development*, Columbus, Ohio: Ohio State University, 1965; and M. Peck and F. Scherer, *The Weapons Acquisition Process*, Boston: Harvard University Press, 1962.

[36] Klein, *ibid.*

ation in a short period of time. According to Glennan,[37] there is a particular need for more advanced development, which is the first point in the evolution of a system where military needs are confronted with available and potential technology. The prototype hardware of various kinds that are constructed in advanced development are possible building blocks in the development of operational systems. Apparently, an underinvestment of this sort occurs because of the nature of existing procedures and the preferences of program managers.

In carrying out weapons systems programs, Klein[38] suggests that a frankly experimental approach be adopted. Requirements for systems should be stated initially in broad terms, flexibility should be maintained, and decisions on the best set of compromises should be postponed until there is a reasonable basis for making them. Components should be tested as soon as possible, and the integration of the system should be postponed until the major uncertainties have been reduced substantially. Since he believes that the uncertainties involved are very great initially but that they diminish substantially as a project proceeds, he argues that the optimal strategy to overcome difficult technological problems often is to run in parallel several approaches designed to serve the same end. This is in contrast to the type of development strategy which emphasizes the integration, to the maximum extent possible, of the total process of development and production, the entire process being viewed as a single planning problem to be dealt with as a whole from the beginning. In the past, the latter strategy has been important in the acquisition of new weapons.

One of the important conclusions of the RAND studies is that, in planning military development, there has been a tendency to underestimate and suppress uncertainty. For example, the services have tended to specify their requirements for advanced weapons systems too early, too optimistically, and in too great detail. Also, there has been evidence in some programs of a commitment to production tooling at too early a stage of the development. In addition, problems of other kinds have been cited, some stemming from the way in which contractors are selected and

[37] T. Glennan, "Research and Development," in S. Enke, *Defense Management*, Englewood Cliffs, N.J.: Prentice-Hall, Inc., 1967.

[38] Klein, *op. cit.* For some criticism of Klein's ideas, see Peck and Scherer, *op. cit.* Note that, particularly in the period immediately after Sputnik, it was urged in many quarters that military R and D should be centralized under a "science czar" and that interservice rivalry should be reduced or abolished. The argument for parallel R and D efforts (see Chapter III) can be used to justify competition, rather than centralized control of R and D. However, it is important to add that, if there is no weeding out of inferior projects, this argument does not hold. See K. Arrow, "Comment," *The Rate and Direction of Inventive Activity*, Princeton, N.J.: Princeton University Press, 1962, p. 356; C. Hitch, "Character of Research and Development in a Competitive Economy," *Conference on Research and Development*, National Science Foundation, 1958.

rewarded. In contrast to earlier days when there was competition among prototypes, competition now occurs at the design stage, because the development of more than one model is considered too expensive. Unfortunately, there are great uncertainties at the design stage and companies have a natural tendency to be optimistic, the result being that it is difficult to make a wise selection. Moreover, once the decision has been made, there is no more competition (although there may be considerable rivalry among alternative systems). The services are locked to a sole source, which ordinarily carries out production as well as development.[39]

Secretary McNamara and (former) Comptroller Hitch have attempted to improve the situation through the institution of a number of changes in procedures and organization, two of the most important innovations being the program definition phase and incentive contracts. During the program definition phase, now known as contract definition, competing contractors pursue alternative paths toward defining the development effort to be carried out and identifying the design specifications for the end product. At the end of this phase, they submit bids containing cost estimates for development and procurement. The point of the program definition phase is to postpone commitment to procurement of a specific item until the major uncertainties that can be resolved have been resolved. Hopefully, it will be possible to avoid cases like the ill-fated B-70 program where about $1.5 billion was spent on technology, a substantial fraction being wasted effort devoted to coordinating subsystem development, integrating logistics and training considerations into the design, and laying out a production capability. Moreover, the program definition phase allows the rival claims of competing contractors to be tested more rigorously than by an examination of their sales presentations. Obviously, however, the program definition phase is not—and was not meant to be—a cure-all.[40]

Changes have also been made in the types of contractual arrangements used in military research and development. Until the sixties, these contracts were typically cost-plus-fixed-fee (CPFF), this kind of contract being defended on the ground that the "product" was so unpredictable that the risks to the seller would require a very high fixed price if it were feasible at all. Recognizing that there is little incentive to reduce costs in CPFF contracts, the Department of Defense began to switch to incentive contracts during the early sixties. Since they reward cost reduction by

[39] See C. Hitch and R. McKean, *The Economics of Defense in the Nuclear Age,* Cambridge, Mass.: Harvard University Press, 1965; C. Hitch, "Comment," in *The Rate and Direction of Inventive Activity,* Princeton, N.J.: Princeton University Press, 1962; and the references in note 35.

[40] See Chapter VI, section 5 and A. Yarmolinsky, "Science Policy and National Defense," *American Economic Review,* May 1966. For some criticism of the program definition phase, see H. Baldwin, "Slow-Down in the Pentagon," *Foreign Affairs,* January 1965. For further discussion, see E. Mansfield, *Defense, Science, and Public Policy,* New York: W. W. Norton & Company, Inc., forthcoming.

giving the firm a certain percentage of the difference between its actual costs and the negotiated target costs, incentive contracts are likely to lead to greater efficiency than CPFF contracts, if the target costs are the same. However, many observers challenge the assumption that the target costs are the same, pointing out that the contractor, with considerable advantages in the negotiation of target costs, has more incentive to increase these costs under incentive contracts.[41]

A more drastic proposal has been made by Carl Kaysen,[42] who argues that, to a greater extent, military research *and* development should be divorced from production, and performed in nonprofit research institutes and government laboratories, which in his view are better suited than business firms to carry out this task. If development could be separated from production, it would be possible to reap the benefits from competition at the development stage and from a freer choice of suppliers and contract instruments at the production stage. A fundamental consideration in judging this proposal is the cost involved in separating development from production. It is sometimes argued that these costs are high, because there is considerable overlap and similarity between these two functions and because learning is transferred between them. We need much better estimates of these costs, as well as the possible benefits. In its present form, this scheme may be so at odds with political reality as to be of limited practical significance, but it raises a number of interesting questions.

Finally, there has been considerable concern over the concentration of military R and D expenditures in a relatively few firms. In 1964, three firms—North American, General Dynamics, and Lockheed—received 23 percent of the Defense Department's R and D money; and ten firms received 53 percent. This tendency is not confined to the DOD; for example, in 1963, three firms received 37 percent of NASA's R and D money, and ten firms received 61 percent. Critics assert that this concentration of R and D funds promotes undue concentration of production and employment because the firm that receives an R and D contract generally receives the follow-on production contract and because the research

---

[41] The Secretary of Defense has claimed that at least 10 cents is saved for each dollar shifted from CPFF to incentive contracts. (See DOD Cost Reduction Program —Second Annual Progress Report.) For discussions of incentive contracts, see O. Williamson, "The Economics of Defense Contracting," Universities-National Bureau of Economic Research Conference on Defense Economics, 1966; and F. Scherer, *The Weapons Aquisition Process: Economic Incentives*, Cambridge, Mass.: Harvard University Press, 1964. Note in passing that the use of CPFF contracts tended to encourage the stockpiling of engineers and scientists. Also, incentive contracts may include performance and delivery date criteria. See F. Moore, "Incentive Contracts" in S. Enke, *Defense Management*, Englewood Cliffs, N.J.: Prentice-Hall, Inc., 1967.

[42] See Kaysen, *op. cit.*, Cherington, "Kaysen on Military Research and Development," *op. cit.*, and Mansfield, "National Science Policy," *op. cit.* Of course, the argument concerning the separation of development from production can be separated from the argument concerning the role of non-profit and government laboratories.

will sometimes be of benefit to the commercial work of the performing firm. Also, and this is a somewhat different point, some observers feel that military R and D should be split up into a larger number of smaller pieces, particularly at the research phase, where there is less likelihood of important economies of scale.[43]

10. Contribution of Military and Space Research and Development to Civilian Technology

During the sixties, there has been a great deal of interest in the extent of the benefits to civilian technology—the "spillover" or "fallout"—from military and space R and D. NASA has been particularly interested in the extent of the spillover, because if large, it would be an additional argument, besides the political and perhaps military ones, for its program. Numerous groups within the Administration, for example, the White House Panel on Civilian Technology,[44] have been interested in the extent of this spillover, because of its implications regarding the extent to which civilian technology was really being drained of scientists and engineers by the military and space programs. What is the value of the spillover from military and space R and D into the civilian economy? One definition of its value is the difference between the value of the goods and services produced in the civilian economy and the value of such production if no results from military and space R and D could have been used there. But this difference cannot be measured with any accuracy. Because of the many indirect benefits, because one would have to estimate when the same results would have been obtained without military or space R and D, because the civilian research effort might well have proceeded in entirely different directions, the task seems impossible.

But is it possible to make a very rough appraisal of the past importance of this spillover? Perhaps a crude lower bound can be obtained by taking various important inventions in the civilian economy that resulted from military and space R and D, estimating roughly how long it would have taken without such R and D to have obtained these inventions, and estimating the value of the extra product due to their having been available that much sooner. An important difficulty in this procedure is that it

[43] For example, see R. Barber, *The Politics of Research*, Washington: Public Affairs Press, 1966; and O. Williamson, *op. cit.*

[44] The White House Panel on Civilian Technology was formed in the summer of 1961 and was dissolved in late 1962. Its membership consisted of university and business scientists and engineers, and representatives from the Department of Commerce and the Executive Office of the President. The Panel was concerned with the question of whether or not too little R and D was being carried out in particular industries, notably textiles, housing, and urban transportation, as well as with the identification of obstacles to the use of existing technology.

assumes that the course of technological change would have been the same in the civilian economy if the results of military and space R and D had not been available as it would have been otherwise. Nevertheless, if this very crude method were applied, it seems likely that the estimated value of the spillover that occurred in the past would prove to be substantial. The electronic computer, numerical control, integrated circuits, atomic energy, synthetic rubber, these and many other significant inventions stemmed at least partly from military R and D. Moreover, there is undoubtedly considerable opportunity for such spillover from current military and space R and D. For example, the space program may have important effects on civilian communication, weather prediction, and medical instrumentation. (See Table 7.1 for some areas of technology where, according to the Denver Research Institute, the space program has made contributions which have, or may have, commercial application.)

Nonetheless, there seems to be a widespread feeling that the spillover per dollar of military-space R and D is unlikely to be as great as in the past, because the capabilities that are being developed and the environment that is being probed are less intimately connected with civilian activities than formerly. The devices needed to send a man to the moon may have relatively little applicability in the civilian economy because they "over-satisfy" civilian requirements and few people or firms are willing to pay for them. Perhaps, however, the spillover is more likely to occur in the form of general technology, rather than the direct transfer of specific devices. The Denver Research Institute, after a detailed study, concluded in 1963 "that more subtle forms of technological transfer have had, and will continue to have, the greatest impact—not the direct product type of transfer which is most often publicized." [45]

Attempts have been made by some government agencies to increase spillover, but the extent of their success is by no means clear. An important example of such a program is NASA's attempt to "match up" inventions occurring as byproducts of its work with civilian industry. For example, the Midwest Research Institute receives information on technological developments that have been used in the space program, evaluates them in terms of industrial applicability, and then holds industrial briefings to communicate the results to industry. The Aerospace Research Applications Center at Indiana University stores all technological reports of the Space Agency in a computer facility, and provides these data to the thirty industrial firms participating in its program. Members of the Center's staff learn what a participant's technological needs are by having

[45] Denver Research Institute, *The Commercial Application of Missile-Space Technology*, Denver, Colo., 1963, p. 5. Another study of technology transfer carried out more recently by the Denver Research Institute is J. Gilmore, *The Channels of Technology Acquisition in Commercial Firms, and the NASA Dissemination Program*, Denver Research Institute, 1967.

TABLE 7.1

Tabulation by Type and Degree of Identified Missile/Space Contribution

Area of Technology (1)	Stimulation of Research (2)	Dominant Types of Identified Contribution				Apparent Degree of Contribution		
		Development of New Processes and Techniques (3)	Improvement of Existing Products (4)	Development of New Products (5)	Cost Reduction (6)	Strong (7)	Moderate (8)	Slight (9)
Instrumentation								
Resistance strain gages	X		X	X			X	
Infrared instrumentation					X		X	
Pressure measuring equipment	X		X	X			X	
Temperature measuring equipment			X	X			X	
Instrumentation amplifiers								X
Electronic components								
Semiconductors	X		X	X			X	
Microsystems electronics	X				X	X		
Thermoelectric refrigeration			X		X			X
Connectors, cables, and printed circuits			X				X	
Display systems				X			X	
Control systems								
Inertial guidance	X					X		
Electronic computer systems	X		X	X			X	

(1)	(2)	(3)	(4)	(5)	(6)	(7)	(8)	(9)
Power sources								
Solar cells	X				X			
Energy conversion	X					X	X	
Fuel cells	X					X	X	
Magnetohydrodynamics	X							
Propulsion								
Cryogenics	X				X		X	
Fluid transfer systems			X		X		X	
Fabrication								
Filament winding	X	X				X		
Chemical milling	X	X				X		
High energy forming	X	X				X		
Solid state bonding	X	X				X		
Materials								
Refractory metals	X					X		
Maraging steels	X							X
Physical metallurgy	X							
Superalloys	X							X
Epoxy resins				X				X
Medical technology	X	X		X				X
Telemetry and communications	X		X			X	X	
Management control systems		X						

Source: Denver Research Institute, *The Commercial Application of Missile-Space Technology*, Denver, Colo., 1963, Part I, p. 14.

him provide a "profile of technical interests," then attempting to retrieve pertinent information. Also, the University of Maryland sends a description of promising innovations resulting from the space program to a relatively large number of companies in the relevant field.[46]

Whether or not the spillover from defense-space R and D is smaller now than in the past, it is clear that such R and D should not be justified on the basis of spillover alone. There can be little doubt that we could have obtained these benefits at lower cost and with greater certainty if comparable resources had been devoted directly to civilian purposes. This is a very important point—and one that is sometimes lost sight of.

11. FEDERAL SUPPORT FOR RESEARCH AND DEVELOPMENT IN TRANSPORTATION, HOUSING, AND POLLUTION CONTROL

Turning from the military and space efforts, we find a widespread feeling that as a nation the United States is underinvesting in certain types of research and development. For example, Nelson has stated that "aside from the fields of defense and space, peacetime atomic energy, and perhaps public health, it is likely that we are relying too much on private incentives as stimulated by the market to generate R and D relevant to the public sector . . . [Also,] aside from the fields of defense and space, there probably is too little research and experimentation aimed at exploring radically new techniques and ways of meeting needs . . . Surely we can do better than to rely so heavily on 'spillover' from defense and space to open up the really new possibilities in materials, energy sources, etc." [47]

Three areas often cited as needing more research and development are transportation, housing, and pollution of air and water. With regard to transportation, our cities suffer from congestion, commuting to work is often difficult and time-consuming, the accident toll is considerable, and delays in terminals are high. According to the critics, new transportation technologies point toward the solution of many of these problems, but

[46] For various opinions regarding the spillover question, see D. Allison, "The Civilian Technology Lag," *International Science and Technology*, December 1963; E. Mansfield, "The Economics of Research and Development," in W. Alderson, V. Terpstra, and S. Shapiro, *Patents and Progress*, Homewood, Ill.: Richard D. Irwin, Inc., 1965; R. Solo, "Gearing Military R and D to Economic Growth," *Harvard Business Review*, December 1962; R. Lesher and G. Howick, "Background, Guidelines and Recommendations for Assessing Effective Means of Channeling New Technologies in Promising Directions," *Report of the National Commission on Technology, Automation, and Economic Progress*, February 1966; and the Denver Research Institute, *ibid*.

In Great Britain, the National Research Development Corporation was established in 1948 to help achieve commercial utilization of government R and D. The NRDC also supports the development of ideas submitted to it by private sources.

[47] R. Nelson, "Technological Advance, Economic Growth, and Public Policy," *RAND Corporation P–2835*, December 1963, p. 17.

their potential benefits are not being realized, because of unresolved organizational, administrative, and financial problems; because of the failure to take a more integrated look at transportation as a whole; and because the resources devoted to far-reaching R and D in this area are meager.[48]

With regard to housing, there is a feeling in many quarters that the industry is backward technologically and that more advanced technologies should be explored in an effort to reduce housing costs. The impediments to the development and use of new techniques are numerous, the typical construction firm being too small to carry out its own R and D, and the industry being fragmented into various types of trades and subcontractors. Moreover, outmoded building codes bar many types of innovation, the codes being protected by various special interest groups and the fragmented character of local governments.[49]

There is considerable public concern regarding increases in air and water pollution. The growth of urban populations has concentrated the discharge of wastes into a small sector of the atmosphere, and resulted in increased contamination. A similar pollution of water resources has taken place. "We have been unbelievably irresponsible in contaminating our water resources to the point where we are now faced with a problem of limited supply. . . . As our population density has increased, the natural cleansing ability of streams has been exceeded." [50] To combat air and water pollution, the President's Science Advisory Committee and the National Commission on Automation have recommended that an enlarged research program be carried out.[51]

[48] See *The Federal Research and Development Programs: The Decision Making Process*, Hearings before a Subcommittee of the House Committee on Government Operations, January 7, 10, and 11, 1966. Note that Congress has passed two important bills in this area in recent years, the 1964 Urban Mass Transportation Act and the 1965 High-Speed Ground Transportation Act, both of which provide funds for research and development. Also see E. Hassell, "The Role of Technological Change in Transportation Policy," *Report of the National Commission on Technology, Automation, and Economic Progress*, February 1966.

It is interesting to note that in another, quite different part of the transportation industry, critics charge that too much money is being spent to develop a supersonic transport, the estimated cost of which will reach $4.5 billion before the first production model appears in 1974. One of the major problems is, of course, the sonic boom. See *Science*, September 8, 1967.

[49] See *Conversion of Defense Resources with Emphasis on Expanded Programs of Urban Development, Mass Transportation, and Water Resource Development*, Ithaca, N.Y: Cornell University Press, 1966; and H. Schechter and B. Horne, "Technology, Automation, and Economic Progress in Housing and Urban Environment," *Report of the National Commission on Technology, Automation, and Economic Progress*, February 1966.

[50] National Commission on Technology, Automation, and Economic Progress, *Technology and the American Economy*, Washington, D.C., 1966.

[51] See *The Federal Research and Development Programs: The Decision Making Process, op. cit.; Conversion of Defense Resources with Emphasis on Expanded Programs of Urban Development, Mass Transportation, and Water Resource Development, op. cit.; Restoring the Quality of Our Environment*, Report of the Environmental Pollution Panel of the President's Science Advisory Committee, The White

Two things should be noted regarding the alleged deficiency in R and D expenditures in these areas. First, one cannot make any estimate of the adequacy or inadequacy of R and D expenditures in a given field by looking simply at society's evaluation of the importance of the activity. In addition, one must consider the probability and cost of achieving a significant improvement in the activity through research and development. No matter how important a particular goal may be, if more research and development are unlikely to help us achieve it, there is no reason to increase our R and D expenditures in this area.[52] Second, there is a feeling in some quarters that a lack of promising, well-developed research ideas and of receptivity to change in these areas is responsible for the low level of R and D spending. According to the President's Science Adviser, "what we lack in many of the civilian problem areas . . . is not a consensus on their importance. Rather, it is a lack of solid R and D program proposals. . . . We cannot buy and create progress in a field which is not ready to progress."[53] Also, there is a feeling that the need is for use of techniques already available, rather than for more R and D. For example, Capron "would place federally supported R and D fairly low on the list of things we need in the fields of urban housing and urban transportation. . . . Our problems in these areas are much more institutional and organizational."[54]

12. Federal Support for Civilian Technology

Transportation, housing, and pollution control are not the only areas considered to suffer from an underinvestment in research and development. According to the Council of Economic Advisers, "in a number of industries the amount of organized private research undertaken is insignificant, and the technology of many of these low-research industries has notably failed to keep pace with advances elsewhere in the economy."[55] Freeman, Poignant, and Svennilson conclude that, "in spite of the great increase in research and development activity, there are good reasons for believing

---

House, Washington, D.C., 1965; National Commission on Technology, Automation, and Economic Progress, op. cit.; National Academy of Sciences, Waste Management and Control, Washington, D.C., 1966; Public Health Service, "Technological Change as it Relates to Air Pollution"; Federal Water Pollution Control Administration, "Water Pollution Control"; and Public Health Service, "Report on the Solid Waste Problem"; all in Report of the National Commission on Technology, Automation, and Economic Progress, February 1966.

[52] For an effective statement of this point, see W. Capron's testimony in The Federal Research and Development Programs: The Decision Making Process, op. cit.

[53] Testimony of D. Hornig in The Federal Research and Development Programs: The Decision Making Process, op. cit., p. 6.

[54] W. Capron, op. cit., p. 19.

[55] Council of Economic Advisers, Annual Report, 1964, p. 105.

that in many cases this activity is still below the level desirable for efficient and sustained economic growth." [56]

In 1963, the Department of Commerce proposed a Civilian Industrial Technology program to encourage and support additional R and D in industries that it regarded as lagging. It proposed that support be given to important industries, from the point of view of employment, foreign trade, and so forth, which have "limited or dispersed technological resources." Examples cited by the department included textiles, building and construction, machine tools and metal fabrication, lumber, foundries and castings. The proposal met with little success on Capitol Hill. Industrial groups opposed the bill because they feared that government sponsorship of industrial R and D could upset existing competitive relationships.[57] More recently, Nelson, Peck, and Kalachek [58] have suggested that a National Institute of Technology be established to provide grants for research and development aimed at placing the technology of various industries on a stronger scientific footing and to test the feasibility and attributes of advanced designs. In their view, work of this sort, which falls between basic research and product development, is likely to be in need of additional support. In cases where a broad-scale systems view is required but is deterred by the smallness of existing firms and the fragmentation of market interest, the institute would also support work through the middle and later stages of development.

Unfortunately, there is little evidence to support or deny the belief that the areas in question suffer from an underinvestment in R and D. Since we cannot estimate the social returns from additional R and D of various sorts at all accurately, it is difficult to make a strong case one way or the other. The proponents of additional government support for civilian technology rely heavily on the argument that R and D generates significant external economies and that, under these circumstances, private initiative is unlikely to support work to the extent that is socially optimal. However, this argument only suggests that the government or some other organization not motivated by profit should support some R and D in these areas; it does not tell us whether such support is currently too large or too small.

Under these circumstances, perhaps the most sensible strategy, both in connection with the proposed Institute of Technology and some of the other programs discussed above, is to view the relevant policy issues in the context of the theory of sequential decision making under uncertainty. To the extent possible, R & D programs should be begun on a small scale and

[56] C. Freeman, M. Poignant, and S. Svennilson, *Science, Economic Growth, and Government Policy*, Organization for Economic Cooperation and Development, 1963, p. 42.

[57] See U.S. Department of Commerce, *The Civilian Industrial Technology Program*, Washington, D.C., 1963; and D. Allison, *op. cit.*

[58] R. Nelson, M. Peck, and E. Kalachek, *Technological Advance, Economic Growth, and Public Policy*, Washington, D.C.: The Brookings Institution, 1966.

organized so as to provide data regarding the returns from a larger program. On the basis of the data that result, a more informed judgment can be made regarding the desirability of increased—or in some cases, decreased—programs of Federal support. A strategy of this sort has been suggested by Nelson, Peck, and Kalachek, as well as the present author. If this approach is adopted, it is important that proper attention be given to devising methods by which the results of the small-scale program are to be measured. Without such measures, the sequential approach will obviously be of little use.[59]

13. THE INDUSTRIAL EXTENSION SERVICE AND PERFORMANCE-BASED FEDERAL PROCUREMENT

In 1965, the State Technical Services Act was passed by Congress. It authorizes for industry a program somewhat analogous to the agricultural extension service—universities and technical schools throughout the country distributing technological information to local firms and serving as economic planning centers for their areas. The program, under the direction of the Department of Commerce (which proposed a similar plan in its Civilian Industrial Technology program), was expected to include about thirty states in its first year. The major purpose of this industrial extension service is to increase the rate of diffusion of new technology. Some firms, particularly small ones, are slow to adopt new techniques because they are unable to comprehend and evaluate technical information. The industrial extension service provides demonstrations, short courses, and conferences, as well as referral to specialized consultants and experts. In this way, it hopes to narrow the gap between average and best practice.

The industrial extension service faces problems that were absent in the case of the agricultural extension service. Whereas the latter could deal with a relatively homogeneous group of clients, the former cannot; whereas it was possible in earlier days for an agricultural extension agent to be familiar with most relevant aspects of agricultural technology, it is impossible now for anyone to be familiar with most aspects of industrial technology; whereas individual farmers seldom view each other as competitors, in manufacturing, one firm's gain in productivity and sales may be partly at the expense of another. In addition, it is more difficult in the case of the industrial extension service to delineate the set of appropriate clients. The firms that are most eager to use the service and those that are easiest to persuade to adopt new techniques are not necessarily those for whom the service can do the most good.

[59] See E. Mansfield, "National Science Policy," *op. cit.*; and R. Nelson, "Aggregate Production Functions and Economic Growth Policy," *The Theory and Empirical Analysis of Production*, National Bureau of Economic Research, 1967.

According to the provisions of the Technical Services Act, each state has considerable latitude in drawing up its own program. The effectiveness of a program will depend on how well it can identify fields and types of firms where there is a technical lag and on how well it can get its message across. It will also depend on the extent to which it becomes a passive reference service, rather than a more active force in promoting new technology, as well as on the costliness of providing information of the right sort to the firms in need of it—and in such a manner that they will be persuaded to use it. Within five years after the approval of the Act, a public committee appointed by the Secretary of Commerce, will evaluate the impact and significance of the program.[60]

Turning to another proposal to stimulate the use of new technology, it has been suggested that performance criteria, which specify the desired end result without limiting the design to existing products, be substituted where possible for product specifications in Federal procurement. Performance criteria of this sort have the obvious advantage of stating directly what the customer wants. For example, rather than specifying the chemical composition of paint, the government might specify how long it should last. Proponents of performance-based Federal procurement claim that it will free industry to innovate, limited only by the requirement that it perform certain specified functions; encourage cost reduction for the government; and encourage the government to serve as a pilot customer for technical innovations in areas where it represents a big enough market or a market sufficiently free from local restrictions, codes, and so forth to make it worth industry's while to innovate. Respecting its role as a pilot customer, one important consideration is to stimulate state and local governments to apply new technologies by demonstrating their successful application in Federal programs. There is a feeling in some quarters that the diffusion of new technology in state and local programs is unnecessarily impeded by the desire of local officials to buy locally, the influence of labor unions on building codes, lack of information by local officials, fragmentation of local government, and the tendency to look for "product" rather than "functional" needs.

In evaluating this proposal, it should be noted that Federal procurement is an important factor in many civilian markets; for example, the Federal government accounted in 1964 for almost 15 percent of all building and construction and 7 to 9 percent of the sales of fuel and lubricants, construction equipment, and photographic services. Performance criteria are already being devised in a number of nondefense areas, such as roofing

---

[60] See R. Nelson, M. Peck, and E. Kalachek, *op. cit.; State Technical Service Act of 1965,* Hearings before the Subcommittee on Commerce and Finance of the House Committee on Interstate and Foreign Commerce, June 1, 2, and 3, 1965; *State Technical Services Act,* Hearings before the Senate Committee on Commerce, June 8, 9, and 10, 1965; and *Science,* September 24, 1965.

materials and data processing systems, the work being carried out by the National Bureau of Standards. Many observers believe that performance criteria should be used more extensively, although they recognize that several problems stand in the way. First, the various aspects and dimensions of a product's performance are often difficult to observe directly, the consequence being that performance criteria are relatively expensive to develop. Second, performance criteria are relatively expensive to administer. Whereas simple inspection may show that physical specifications are met, it may cost thousands of dollars to establish whether performance criteria are met. Third, to the extent that government purchasing is pushed in the direction of new products, political problems are likely to be encountered.[61]

14. BASIC RESEARCH AND HIGHER EDUCATION

It is generally agreed that the government should support basic research, but there is considerable uncertainty in Congress and elsewhere regarding the optimal amount of this support and the optimal allocation among scientific fields. These are perhaps the most difficult science-policy problems. Formally, the government should push its expenditures to the point where the marginal social benefits from various kinds of basic research equal the marginal social benefits from the relevant resources in alternative uses. However, this rule, which is hard enough to apply in the case of applied research and development,[62] is practically useless in the case of basic research, because its benefits are so difficult to predict. Faced with this enormously complex problem, the House Committee on Science and Astronautics in 1963 asked the advice of a distinguished panel of the National Academy of Sciences. As one would expect, the panel's recommendations generally are based on criteria, like scientific merit, that are no more quantifiable than marginal social benefits. For example, many panel members recommend that every "qualified" scientist be given "adequate" support. Some argue that a 15 percent annual increase in total expendi-

---

[61] See R. Nelson, M. Peck, and E. Kalachek, *op. cit;* National Bureau of Standards, *Improving the National Climate for Innovation,* Washington, D.C., 1965; A. Barber, "Some Thoughts on Diversification," Speech at Ann Arbor, Mich., January 26, 1965; G. Ackley, "American Economic Policies—The Goals and Priorities," Speech before the New England Conference on Opportunities and Problems of Defense Conversion, September 21, 1964; M. Myerson *et al., Housing, People, and Cities,* New York: McGraw-Hill, Inc., 1962; M. Michaelis, "Obstacles to Innovation," *International Science and Technology,* November 1964.

[62] For an interesting attempt to measure the social rate of return from agricultural research, see Z. Griliches, "Research Costs and Social Returns: Hybrid Corn and Related Innovations," *Journal of Political Economy,* 1958.

tures on basic research will meet national needs, but their argument seems to be based largely on arbitrary educational targets.[63]

Recent years have also seen a clearer recognition that the size and composition of Federal R and D expenditures, as well as other policies of Federal agencies, influence the allocation of scientific and engineering effort between teaching, on the one hand, and applied research and development, on the other.[64] Machlup and others have pointed out that applied programs, like NASA's, compete with teaching for scarce scientific and engineering talent, and that increases in these applied programs can be dangerous if, by curtailing the supply of teachers, they reduce excessively the rate of increase of the supply of scientists and engineers. Studies have been made of the distribution of scientists and engineers between teaching and other work, and simple models have been used to derive "optimal" allocation rules. Unfortunately, as their authors are aware, these studies suffer from the fact that applied work and teaching may require somewhat different sorts of talents, that the available data completely overlook the crucial differences in quality among scientists and engineers, and that the models oversimplify the relationships between teaching and R and D.[65] Nonetheless, the basic point—that applied research and development compete with basic research and teaching for scarce talent—is worth making.

There has also been considerable interest in the effects of Federal research grants to universities on the quality of undergraduate education. For example, the House Subcommittee on Research and Technical Programs claims that Federal research programs "have harmed scientific higher education by excessively diverting scientific manpower from

[63] See National Academy of Science, *Basic Research and National Goals,* Report to the House Committee on Science and Astronautics, 1965, particularly the papers by Brooks, Johnson, Kaysen, Kistiakowsky, and Weinberg. This volume, which reflects the thinking of some of the country's most distinguished scientists, contains a great deal of useful material. However, the assignment is close to an impossible one. (Note that the panel is careful to distinguish between "little science" and "big science," the arguments in the text pertaining mostly to the former.) Also, see R. Gilpin and C. Wright, *Scientists and National Policy Making,* New York: Columbia University Press, 1964; D. Price, *The Scientific Estate,* Cambridge, Mass.: Harvard University Press, 1965; B. Smith, "The Concept of Scientific Choice," *RAND Corporation* P-3156, June 1965; and A. Weinberg, "Criteria for Scientific Choice," *Minerva,* 1963 and 1964.

[64] For simplicity, I lump together basic research and teaching. Of course, there is a strong complimentarity between them, the importance of which is pointed out by F. Machlup, *The Production and Distribution of Knowledge,* Princeton, N.J.: Princeton University Press, 1962, and by the President's Science Advisory Committee, *Scientific Progress, the Universities, and the Federal Government,* Washington, D.C., 1960.

[65] For one thing, the quality of teaching depends on the extent and quality of previous research; for another, there are important complimentarities between teaching and research. For a recent study, see M. Intrilligator and B. Smith, "Some Aspects of the Allocation of Scientific Efforts Between Teaching and Research," *American Economic Review,* May 1966.

teaching, and by overemphasizing research to the detriment of teaching. . . ." [66] (It claims too that an important imbalance has developed between the natural sciences, on the one hand, and the social sciences and humanities, on the other.) [67] Because it is so difficult to measure the quality of undergraduate education, it is difficult to know how seriously to take these criticisms. Although the subcommittee seems to think that the adverse effects of government research programs are borne out by the published testimony of university professors and administrators, a close examination of this testimony shows that a great many of the respondents do not agree with this conclusion. The subcommittee report seems to oversimplify the situation.[68] Undergraduate education, particularly in the four-year college, is faced with many problems, but it is not clear that government research grants and contracts have, on balance, done more harm than good.

Another set of policy issues that has attracted considerable attention concerns the distribution of Federal R and D spending. There are substantial disparities among regions and among universities in the volume of these expenditures, the differences being due largely to regional and institutional concentration of scientific strength. During the past few years, there has been growing pressure in Congress and elsewhere for an equalization of these expenditures; and in September 1965, the President issued a major policy directive asking Federal agencies to be more responsive to

[66] *Conflicts Between the Federal Research Programs and the Nation's Goals for Higher Education*, U.S. House Committee on Government Operations, 1965, p. 6.

[67] The National Foundation on the Arts and Humanities was established in 1965 to help remedy the situation. See *Science*, October 1, 1965. There has been considerable talk in Congress and elsewhere about establishing a National Social Science Foundation. See *Science*, October 28, 1966, and F. Harris, "The Case for a National Social Science Foundation," *Science*, August 4, 1967.

[68] Judging from the June 1965 report, *Responses from the Academic and other Interested Communities to an Inquiry by the Research and Technical Programs Subcommittee of the Committee on Government Operations*, about 40 percent of the respondents did not feel that Federal research programs have had a deleterious effect.

For some other discussions of the effects of government research grants and contracts on higher education, see the National Acadamy of Sciences, *Federal Support of Basic Research in Institutions of Higher Learning*, Washington, D.C., 1964; H. Orlans, *The Effect of Federal Programs on Higher Education*, Washington, D.C.: The Brookings Institution, 1962; C. Kidd, *American Universities and Federal Research*, Cambridge, Mass.: Harvard University Press, 1959, and C. Kerr, *The Uses of the University*, Cambridge, Mass.: Harvard University Press, 1963. Of course, one important consideration in this area has been fear of Federal control of education.

We should also note that there has been considerable discussion of the adequacy of the allowances for indirect costs arising from government research grants to universities. For example, see *Government and Science*, Study No. 5, U.S. House Committees on Science and Astronautics, 1965, as well as the corresponding hearings before the committee, and P. Handler, "Some Major Issues Concerning the Support of Fundamental Research," *Science*, 1967. Also, problems in government-university relationships have sometimes arisen because of loyalty requirements, security measures, and classified research on campus. Recently, there has been considerable criticism of the use of "effort reporting."

the have-nots in the competition for Federal funds.[69] He also altered the composition of the President's Science Advisory Committee and the National Science Board, fewer members being drawn from the major East and West Coast universities. In view of these developments, the relevant question seems to be how, rather than whether, this equalization process should be carried out. In the case of universities, some of the proposed methods have important disadvantages. For example, it would be unwise to allocate research funds according to a quota system based on regional student enrollment (or something similar), or to spread most of the available funds over a large number of minor universities, or to move from a system emphasizing project grants to one emphasizing institutional development grants.[70] Contrary to the expectations of some, it simply is impossible in the short-run to establish fifty or one hundred universities that are first-rate in most major scientific fields, and there is a danger that in trying to do so, the relatively few that at present are strong in the sciences may be seriously weakened. The others should be encouraged to attempt to excel in only a few areas and to broaden their scope gradually.[71]

15. THE SUPPLY OF SCIENTISTS
AND ENGINEERS

At various times during the past decade, there has been considerable concern over the adequacy of our supply of scientific and engineering manpower. The tremendous increase in R and D expenditures has resulted, particularly in the post-Sputnik era, in many assertions that there is, or soon will be, a shortage. For example the President's Science Advisory

[69] See U.S. House Committee on Science and Astronautics, *Government and Science*, 1965; U.S. House Select Committee on Government Research, *Studies I-X*, 1964; U.S. House Committee on Government Operations, *Conflicts Between the Federal Research Programs and the Nation's Goals for Higher Education*, 1965; the President's Science Advisory Committee, *Scientific Progress, the Universities, and the Federal Government*, Washington, 1960; and *Science*, September 24, 1965, pp. 1483-5.

It has become customary for people interested in science policy to distinguish between "big science", where research is very expensive because of high equipment costs, and "little science", where support is given individual investigators and does not involve large capital costs. The political attention focused on the location of "big science" facilities is evidenced by the tremendous competition among states and cities for the 200 BEV Accelerator.

[70] See D. Hornig, "Universities and Federal Science Policies," *Science*, November 12, 1965; and House Subcommittee on Science, Research and Development, *Higher Education in the United States*, 1965; and L. Haworth's statement in the *Fourteenth Annual Report* of the National Science Foundation, 1965.

[71] See D. Wolfe, "Diversity of Institutional Goals," *Science*, November 19, 1965; and G. Stigler, *The Intellectual and the Market Place*, New York: The Free Press of Glencoe, 1963; and the references in note 70. Greater interinstitutional cooperation and sharing of facilities and faculties might also be a useful development. In addition, more cooperation might be worked out between educational institutions and Federal contract research centers (and some in-house government laboratories).

Committee concluded in 1962 that impending shortages of scientists and engineers threatened the successful fulfillment of important national commitments, and urged that we increase the number of doctor's degrees awarded annually in engineering, mathematics, and physical science to 7,500 in 1970. In 1966, this goal was still regarded as reasonable by many leading scientists and government officials.[72]

Unfortunately, there is considerable uncertainty as to whether or not a shortage exists. As Jerome Weisner, former Science Adviser to the President put it,

This is a question about which it is hard to get good facts. The government has tried, over the last half dozen years, to come to grips with this question. While I worked here, I oscillated violently between believing that we were creating terrible manpower shortages and feeling that we were running a danger of creating an oversupply. Every time we got some new data, we oscillated between these two extremes. It is because the labor market is so flexible; that is, when you create more jobs by starting scientific activities, you attract people who have been doing other things.[73]

Another reason why people reach different conclusions is that they use different definitions of a shortage. A shortage may be defined (1) as a situation where more scientists and engineers are demanded at going salaries than are supplied;[74] (2) as a situation where such a discrepancy between demand and supply occurs temporarily because salary adjustments lag behind a rising demand; (3) as a situation where wages rise, relative to other occupations, with the result that some activities performed by scientists and engineers must be performed by other workers; (4) as a situation where fewer scientists and engineers are available and employed than should be, according to some standard of what is best for society.

According to Alchian, Arrow, and Capron,[75] there is little evidence that a shortage in the first sense existed during the late fifties, although the government may have used its massive buying power to depress salaries somewhat; but there is considerable evidence of a shortage in the second sense at that time. Blank and Stigler, who use the third definition, con-

---

[72] President's Science Advisory Committee, *Meeting Manpower Needs in Science and Technology*, Washington, D.C., 1962. For more recent views see *The National Science Foundation: Its Present and Future*, report of the House Committee on Science and Astronautics, 1966.

[73] *The National Science Foundation: Its Present and Future, ibid.*, p. 70.

[74] Of course, for such a situation to prevail more than temporarily, salary controls would be required.

[75] A. Alchian, K. Arrow, and W. Capron, *An Economic Analysis of the Market for Scientists and Engineers*, RAND Corporation, 1958; D. Blank and G. Stigler, *The Demand and Supply of Scientific Personnel*, National Bureau of Economic Research, 1957; W. Hansen, "The 'Shortage' of Engineers and Scientists," *Review of Economics and Statistics*, 1961.

clude that there is little evidence of a shortage of this sort up to the mid-fifties, but Hansen suggests that more recent data indicate its existence in later years. Turning to the last definition, which obviously is the most important, the answer depends on how one defines the standard of what is best for society. Comparisons are sometimes made with the Soviet Union, but it is by no means clear that the United States should use its resources in the same way as the Soviet Union. Another procedure is to project into the future, the relationship between output and the number of people employed in these professions. For example, the Bureau of Labor Statistics has estimated that in 1970 the United States will require about 550,000 scientists and 1,485,000 engineers, which means that the number of scientists and engineers must increase by about 90 percent over 1959 levels. But there is no reason to believe that this would be the optimal number, since the assumptions underlying these projections have no convincing theoretical basis. The truth is that the optimal number of scientists and engineers, when optimal is defined in this way, depends on one's value judgments; and the answer must be expected to vary accordingly.[76]

16. PROPOSED CHANGES IN THE NATIONAL SCIENCE FOUNDATION

In 1966, the House Subcommittee on Science, Research, and Development proposed a number of important changes in the operations and functions of the National Science Foundation. The subcommittee's basic criticism is that

. . . the Foundation has functioned, and still does, in a manner that is largely passive. It has not itself put a sustained effort into developing substance, form, and direction of the programs it supports. Once granted its annual budget, NSF has to a large extent followed a practice of waiting for talented outsiders to suggest appropriate projects on which to spend it. . . . The Foundation's input toward the evolution of national science policy, never strong, seems to have weakened further in recent years.[77]

To improve the situation, the subcommittee recommends the following three changes: First, the foundation's position within the executive branch should be upgraded. It should be held responsible for the nation's science

---

[76] See National Science Foundation, *The Long-Range Demand for Scientific and Technical Personnel*, Washington, D.C., 1956. The fact that quality is as important as quantity of scientific personnel also complicates the picture.

There is also considerable concern over whether or not our supply of scientists and engineers is allocated optimally. Particularly since the advent of the space program, there has been a feeling in many quarters that too little of our talent was being allocated to civilian needs. Although this question is closely tied up with the larger question of national goals, it also involves the efficiency with which the DOD and NASA use the engineers and scientists that they currently hire, directly or indirectly. These subjects have been touched on in previous sections.

[77] *The National Science Foundation: Its Present and Future, op. cit.,* pp. xiv–xv.

resources, freeing the Office of Science and Technology and the President's Science Advisory Committee from their detailed oversight in this area. In particular, it should evaluate the state of the various scientific disciplines; evaluate the condition of our scientific resources; and direct some research, basic or applied, to help bring into being new technology required in the public interest. Moreover, the social sciences should be explicitly included. Second, the character of the National Science Board should be altered. Its functions should be streamlined to relieve it of routine administrative tasks, and both Congress and the Executive Office of the President should be encouraged to use the board as a source of advice and independent viewpoint. Third, the authority of the foundation's director should be extended to allow him to pass on all proposals for NSF support, subject only to board restraint in exceptional cases. His pay grade should be elevated and additional high-level managerial talent should be made available to him. His prestige and influence in the executive branch should be enhanced.

If the changes are adopted, the foundation will become more clearly a part of the central machinery of government directed toward the achievement of national objectives. Besides evaluating projects submitted to it, it will actively select areas of research to be emphasized. Decisions will become more the responsibility of the director, and he will become more clearly accountable to the Congress and the President. These changes have much to recommend them. The most important dangers are that the foundation's political vulnerability will increase, and that applied research may be increased at the expense of basic research.

This proposal is by no means the only one in this area emanating from Congress. On the contrary, Congress is becoming increasingly important in initiating changes in science policy. This is different from the earlier postwar years when, except for atomic energy affairs, government science policy was generally initiated within the executive branch. Another proposal of the House Subcommittee on Science, Research, and Development stems from its concern over the dangerous side effects which applied technology is creating or is likely to create. For example, chemicals developed to reduce the insect population have polluted the soil, and human beings now have measurable quantities of these pesticides in their tissues. The subcommittee has proposed an early warning system which might be established by the Federal government "to keep tab on the potential dangers, as well as the benefits, inherent in new technology."[78] Other groups, such as a committee of the American Association for the Advancement of Science, have expressed similar concern. One problem in the subcommittee's suggestion is the difficulty in predicting the consequences of new technology. However, the subcommittee is undoubtedly right

[78] *Review and Forecast*, Second Progress Report of the House Subcommittee on Science, Research, and Development, Washington, D.C., 1966.

in believing that more attention should be directed at the external diseconomies generated by technological change.

17. DUPLICATION AND COORDINATION

During the sixties, Congress has begun to look more closely at the management of Federal R and D programs, there being the concern on Capitol Hill that these programs involve needless duplication and waste. For example, according to Congressman Carl Elliot of Alabama, "A suspicion that there may be unjustifiable duplication of effort arises from the fact that 11 agencies and departments perform research in health and medicine; 5 agencies perform space research, exclusive of aircraft technology; 7 are doing work in oceanography, 8 in water research and 16 in meteorology. Multiple-agency interest is also apparent in such broad categories as defense, environmental health, natural resources, nuclear energy, and the like." [79] Partly in response to Congressional pressure, more attention is being given to the coordination of R and D that cuts across agency lines. For example, in the case of oceanography, the President's Science Advisory Committee recommended in 1966 that a new mission-oriented agency be established to encompass a great portion of the non-Navy oceanographic programs that are now scattered through the government. At that time, an Interagency Committee on Oceanography was charged with planning and coordinating the overall program. Also, the Environmental Science Services Administration was created in 1965 to provide a single national focus for a number of allied scientific disciplines, like meteorology, that are concerned with the weather and the physical environment.[80]

In the mid-sixties, there has been considerable pressure from many sources to repeat the pattern of AEC and NASA and to create separate agencies to deal with specific technologies, like oceanography. According to the proponents of this approach, a new and emerging technology does not receive adequate attention unless the existing capabilities are assembled in one agency. Moreover, in the case of some technologies, like space technology, they are so complex and expensive that one cannot afford to develop them separately for each mission. The main argument against the creation of new agencies for new technologies is that the promotion of the technology tends to become an end in itself apart from the social goals which it serves. Thus, it is sometimes charged that atomic energy has been pushed more enthusiastically than it would have been if the decisions had been made on the basis of the advice of scientists with more general in-

[79] *Federal Research and Development Programs,* Hearings before the Select Committee on Government Research, November 18, 1963, p. 3.
[80] See President's Science Advisory Committee, *Effective Use of the Sea,* Washington, D.C., 1966; and *The Federal Research and Development Programs: The Decision Making Process, op. cit.*

terests and in accord with the priorities of administrators and politicians who looked more closely at the contribution of a particular technological development to the ends of public policy.

Problems of coordination are bound to occur in any large enterprise. Unquestionably, they occur in the Federal R and D establishment, and the critics are right to press for improvements. Nonetheless, there is sometimes a tendency to overestimate the problem of duplication of effort. In basic research, there is little unnecessary, conscious duplication because the results are freely published and the rewards for duplicating someone else's work are generally quite small. Where conscious duplication occurs, it is likely to be required to confirm previous experimental findings. This, of course, is a valuable activity. In development, it sometimes seems that there is unnecessary duplication of effort. However, in some of these cases, parallel efforts are deliberately mounted in order to assure the quick attainment of an important objective. As we saw in Chapter III, this can be the cheapest way to proceed. Besides duplication, there is considerable concern that Federal R and D programs are inefficient, one apparent indication of this being the fact that so few programs produce useful results. In the Department of Defense, for example, it has been estimated that, for every twenty ideas which are explored, only five are carried to advanced development, only one or two are carried through the engineering for service use, and "zero or perhaps one of them . . . [are] deployed for service use." [81] Estimates of this sort can be quite misleading. Although there may have been considerable inefficiency, the mere fact that many projects do not succeed is no proof of such waste since, even if there were no inefficiences, many projects would fail, because of the inherent uncertainties in research and development.

18. FEDERAL ALLOCATION OF RESEARCH AND DEVELOPMENT RESOURCES

Congress has also been concerned about other aspects of the management of Federal R and D programs. In 1966, Congressman Henry Reuss of Wisconsin pointed out that the allocation of Federal R and D expenditures is a fragmented process, no one really having responsibility for the adequacy of the over-all allocation. He expressed concern "that in the great bulk of R and D manpower expenditures, there is no central authority which takes a look at them, before they are launched, to determine whether there is an adequate supply of scientists to do the job—or whether you would not be robbing Peter to pay Paul if you do start a given new program." [82]

[81] H. Brown's Testimony in *Federal Research and Development Programs, op. cit.,* p. 177.
[82] *The Federal Research and Development Programs: The Decision Making Process, op. cit.,* p. 57.

According to the current organizational and budgetary procedure, research and development is considered an aspect of each Federal activity. Judgments are made about the relative importance of various Federal programs (defense, agriculture, and so forth), and decisions are made regarding the total amount that should be spent on each one. Then many of the basic decisions regarding the level and allocation of R and D spending are made in the individual agencies and departments where R and D needs and opportunities are evaluated in a mission context. This is different from the procedure favored by Reuss and others, whereby the executive branch and Congress would focus attention directly on the R and D components of all agencies' expenditures and attempt to reach an optimal allocation.

With regard to the present system, it is important to add that the existence of large programs which are science-oriented and devoted to means rather than ends, makes the tradeoff between R and D and other activities within some agencies rather artificial. It is also important to note that the sorts of tradeoffs within R and D proposed by Reuss are being made to some extent within the executive branch, particularly by the interaction of OST with the Bureau of the Budget. Although these tradeoffs within R and D may have little influence in any single budgetary year, their cumulative impact over many budget years can be significant. However, it is true, of course, that Congress continues to be much more oriented toward the agency tradeoffs than the tradeoffs within R and D.

Although it is generally acknowledged that somewhat more coordination would be a good thing, Reuss's proposal has not stirred up a great deal of enthusiasm, most observers being impressed with the difficulties involved in direct allocation of R and D resources. The customary cost-effectiveness techniques are of limited use, because there is no good way of measuring the relative importance of various Federal objectives and because the outcome of R and D projects is so uncertain. Also, the problem is complicated by the fact that R and D resources are by no means homogeneous. Nonetheless, these problems cannot be avoided simply by keeping the present system. Whether or not they are made explicit, judgments of this sort are imbedded in any decision that is reached, regardless of how the budgetary and decision making procedures are organized. Despite the enormous difficulties, it seems likely that more attempt will be made in the future to compare the costs and benefits of various kinds of research and development. However, it does not seem likely, or desirable, that the government will attempt to program science and technology on the basis of a totally integrated science and technology budget.[83]

During the late fifties, as well as in more recent years, there have been

[83] See the testimony of Hornig, Staats, and Capron in *The Federal Research and Development Programs: The Decision Making Process, op. cit.;* and H. Brooks, "Science and the Allocation of Resources," *American Psychologist*, March 1967.

proposals of a cabinet-level Department of Science, which would include the AEC, NASA, NSF, the basic research activities of the DOD, the National Bureau of Standards, the Office of Technical Services, the Patent Office, and part of the Smithsonian Institution. Advocates of a Department of Science, led by then-Senator Hubert Humphrey, advanced the following arguments in its favor. First, the secretary of such a department, because of his cabinet rank, would assure greater status for science. Second, the department would help to eliminate useless duplication and to promote a better allocation of scientific manpower. Third, it would constitute a policy link between Congress and the President.[84] The proposal has been opposed by the scientific community, for what seem to be good reasons. The 1958 Parliament of Science (and numerous scientists who testified) opposed the proposal because they feared further centralization and because it seemed administratively and politically unwise. Since the agencies that would be merged have great status and importance, the department might well be torn by intramural dissension. Moreover, the merger of agencies with practical missions with NSF might well result in the neglect of basic research programs. Finally, since the new department could not hope to include all government scientific activities (because Defense, Agriculture, and so on would have to maintain research establishments), the new department would have to compete with existing departments and could not act as a coordinator of all scientific activities.[85]

19. SUMMARY

One of the principal instruments of public policy designed to promote technological change is the patent system. Proponents of the patent system argue that these laws are an important incentive for invention, innovation, and early disclosure of new technology. Critics of the patent system stress the social costs arising from monopoly and question the importance of patents as an incentive in the modern economy. Despite its faults, it is difficult to find any realistic substitute for the patent system. Fundamental changes involving compulsory licensing, systems of government awards, and variable lengths of patents have been proposed, but there is little chance that they will be accepted. More modest proposals, such as delayed examination, are more likely to succeed. In recent years, there has been a prolonged controversy over the treatment of patents arising from government research, some favoring a license policy, others favoring a title policy.

Economists have long been interested in the relation between an industry's market structure and the rate at which it creates, accepts, and utilizes

[84] For example, see Hubert Humphrey, "The Need for a Department of Science," *Annals of the American Academy of Political and Social Science,* 1960.
[85] See D. Price, *The Scientific Estate, op. cit.*

new technology. According to Galbraith, Schumpeter, and others, a vigorous antitrust policy may thwart rapid technological change and rapid utilization of new techniques, since industries dominated by a few giant firms tend to be more progressive technologically than ones composed of a larger number of smaller firms. The available evidence does not seem to support this hypothesis. In most industries for which data are available, there is no indication that total R and D expenditures would decrease if the largest firms were replaced by somewhat smaller ones; there is no indication that the R and D expenditures carried out by the largest firms are more productive than those carried out by somewhat smaller firms; and there is no indication that greater concentration results in a higher rate of diffusion of innovations. If innovations require a large amount of capital, there is evidence that the substitution of fewer large firms for more smaller ones may lead to quicker commercial introduction. However, there is no statistically significant relationship between an industry's concentration and its estimated rate of technological change.

Since the Department of Defense accounts for almost half of the Federal R and D budget, its policies regarding the utilization of R and D resources are obviously of great importance. Studies carried out in the early sixties suggested that, although technical performance and development time were reasonably satisfactory, the cost of major military development programs was exceedingly high. The Department of Defense has attempted to improve the situation through a number of changes in procedures and organization. Economists have made a number of suggestions regarding military development policy. There has also been considerable discussion of the effects of various contractual arrangements used in military R and D, as well as of the concentration of military R and D expenditures in a relatively few firms. There has also been considerable controversy over the extent of the "spillover" from military and space R and D to civilian technology. In view of the concentration of the nation's scientific resources in military and space work, it is important that ways be established to promote such spillover, so long as the benefits of the extra spillover exceed the costs of these programs.

Relative to our well-supported military and space programs, there is a feeling in many quarters that the United States as a nation is underinvesting in other kinds of research and development. Three areas frequently cited as needing more R and D are transportation, housing, and pollution control. In 1963, the Department of Commerce proposed a civilian technology program to encourage and support additional R and D in industries that it regarded as lagging, but met with little success on Capitol Hill. In 1965, one element of the program, the State Technical Services Act, was passed by Congress. Since we cannot estimate the social returns from additional R and D at all accurately, it seems sensible to view the relevant policy issues in the context of the theory of sequential decision making under uncertainty. To the extent possible, programs designed to change the amount of R and D in particular parts of the public or private sectors should be begun on a small scale and organized so as to provide data regarding the returns from a larger program.

It is generally agreed that the Federal government should support basic research, but there is considerable uncertainty in Congress and elsewhere regarding the optimal amount of this support and its allocation among scientific fields. Thus far, no promising technique has been found to deal with this range of problems. A related set of issues is concerned with the effects of Federal R and D expenditures on higher education, some observers claiming that too many scientists have been taken away from teaching and that undergraduate education has been hurt. Unfortunately, little solid evidence exists in this area either. In 1965, the President announced a policy of equalizing Federal R and D expenditures among universities. In carrying out this policy, it is important that regional quotas and other such rigid allocation schemes be avoided and that pork-barrel procedures be resisted.

In recent years Congress has begun to look more closely at the management of Federal R and D programs, some members fearing that there is considerable duplication and waste. To a considerable extent, it is true that the decision-making process with regard to the allocation of R and D funds is fragmented, no one really having responsibility for the adequacy of the overall allocation. However, in evaluating this criticism, the difficulties in direct allocation of R and D funds should be faced realistically. There have been proposals of a cabinet-level Department of Science, but they have been opposed by the scientific community, for what seem to be good reasons. There have also been proposed changes in the National Science Foundation. If these changes are adopted, the foundation will play a more active role in the formulation of a national science policy.

Index

The Author

Edwin Mansfield is Professor of Economics at the Wharton School, University of Pennsylvania. In addition to his teaching duties, Professor Mansfield serves as a consultant to the RAND Corporation, the Federal Power Commission, and the U.S. Army, and is a member of both the Ford Foundation Committee on Technical Change and the Governor's Science Advisory Committee. He has been a consultant to the National Commission on Technology, Automation, and Economic Progress, and other public and private agencies concerned with the economics of technical change. Before joining the Wharton faculty, Professor Mansfield taught at the Carnegie Institute of Technology, Yale University, and Harvard University. During 1967–68, he was on leave at the California Institute of Technology and the RAND Corporation.

A graduate of Dartmouth College, Professor Mansfield received his M.A. and Ph.D. from Duke University in 1955. He has been awarded Fulbright and Ford Faculty Research Fellowships, and holds the Diploma of the Royal Statistical Society. An Associate Editor of the *Journal of the American Statistical Association*, Professor Mansfield has published over forty articles and books on problems in economics, statistics, and operations research, including, in addition to this volume, *Monopoly Power and Economic Performance; Managerial Economics and Operations Research;* and *Industrial Research and Technological Innovation*, all published by W. W. Norton & Company, Inc.

DATE DUE

JAN 11 '83			
JAN 4 1983			
GAYLORD			PRINTED IN U.S.A.